TEACHER'S PLANNING GUIDE

Project-Based Inquiry Science™

PLANETARY FORECASTER

IT's ABOUT TIME®
HERFF JONES EDUCATION DIVISION

IT's ABOUT TIME®

HERFF JONES EDUCATION DIVISION

84 Business Park Drive, Armonk, NY 10504
Phone (914) 273-2233 Fax (914) 273-2227
www.its-about-time.com

Program Components

Student Edition	Durable Equipment Kit
Teacher's Planning Guide	Consumable Equipment Kit
Teacher's Resources Guide	Multimedia
	— My World Software

ISBN 978-1-58591-607-8
1 2 3 4 5 CRS 12 11 10 09 08

This project was supported, in part, by the **National Science Foundation** under grant nos. 0137807, 0527341, and 0639978. Opinions expressed are those of the authors and not necessarily those of the National Science Foundation.

Principal Investigators

 **Janet L. Kolodner** is a Regents' Professor in the School of Interactive Computing in the Georgia Institute of Technology's College of Computing. Since 1978, her research has focused on learning from experience, both in computers and in people. She pioneered the Artificial Intelligence method called *case-based reasoning*, providing a way for computers to solve new problems based on their past experiences. Her book, *Case-Based Reasoning*, synthesizes work across the case-based reasoning research community from its inception to 1993.

Since 1994, Dr. Kolodner has focused on the applications and implications of case-based reasoning for education. In her approach to science education, called Learning by Design™ (LBD), students learn science while pursuing design challenges. Dr. Kolodner has investigated how to create a culture of collaboration and rigorous science talk in classrooms, how to use a project challenge to promote focus on science content, and how students learn and develop when classrooms function as learning communities. Currently, Dr. Kolodner is investigating how to help young people come to think of themselves as scientific reasoners. Dr. Kolodner's research results have been widely published, including in *Cognitive Science, Design Studies,* and the *Journal of the Learning Sciences.*

Dr. Kolodner was founding Director of Georgia Tech's EduTech Institute, served as coordinator of Georgia Tech's Cognitive Science program for many years, and is founding Editor in Chief of the *Journal of the Learning Sciences*. She is a founder of the International Society for the Learning Sciences, and she served as its first Executive Officer. She is a fellow of the American Association of Artificial Intelligence.

 **Joseph S. Krajcik** is a Professor of Science Education and Associate Dean for Research in the School of Education at the University of Michigan. He works with teachers in science classrooms to bring about sustained change by creating classroom environments in which students find solutions to important intellectual questions that subsume essential curriculum standards and use learning technologies as productivity tools. He seeks to discover what students learn in such environments, as well as to explore and find solutions to challenges that teachers face in enacting such complex instruction.

Dr. Krajcik has authored and co-authored over 100 manuscripts and makes frequent presentations at international, national, and regional conferences that focus on his research, as well as presentations that translate research findings into classroom practice. He is a fellow of the American Association for the Advancement of Science and served as president of the National Association for Research in Science Teaching. Dr. Krajcik co-directs the Center for Highly Interactive Classrooms, Curriculum and Computing in Education at the University of Michigan and is a co-principal investigator in the Center for Curriculum Materials in Science and The National Center for Learning and Teaching Nanoscale Science and Engineering. In 2002, Dr. Krajcik was honored to receive a Guest Professorship from Beijing Normal University in Beijing, China. In winter 2005, he was the Weston Visiting Professor of Science Education at the Weizmann Institute of Science in Rehovot, Israel.

Daniel C. Edelson is Vice President for Education and Children's Programs at the National Geographic Society. Previously, he was the director of the Geographic Data in Education (GEODE) Initiative at Northwestern University, where he led the development of Planetary Forecaster and Earth Systems and Processes. Since 1992, Dr. Edelson has directed a series of projects exploring the use of technology as a catalyst for reform in science education and has led the development of a number of software environments for education. These include My World GIS, a geographic information system for inquiry-based learning, and WorldWatcher, a data visualization and analysis system for gridded geographic data. Dr. Edelson is the author of the high school environmental science text, *Investigations in Environmental Science: A Case-Based Approach to the Study of Environmental Systems*. His research has been widely published, including in the *Journal of the Learning Sciences*, the *Journal of Research on Science Teaching*, *Science Educator*, and *Science Teacher*.

Brian J. Reiser is a Professor of Learning Sciences in the School of Education and Social Policy at Northwestern University. Professor Reiser served as chair of Northwestern's Learning Sciences Ph.D. program from 1993, shortly after its inception, until 2001. His research focuses on the design and enactment of learning environments that support students' inquiry in science, including both science curriculum materials and scaffolded software tools. His research investigates the design of learning environments that scaffold scientific practices, including investigation, argumentation, and explanation; design principles for technology-infused curricula that engage students in inquiry projects; and the teaching practices that support student inquiry. Professor Reiser also directed BGuILE (Biology Guided Inquiry Learning Environments) to develop software tools for supporting middle school and high school students in analyzing data and constructing explanations with biological data. Reiser is a co-principal investigator in the NSF Center for Curriculum Materials in Science. He served as a member of the NRC panel authoring the report Taking Science to School.

Mary L. Starr is a Research Specialist in Science Education in the School of Education at the University of Michigan. She collaborates with teachers and students in elementary and middle school science classrooms around the United States who are implementing *Project-Based Inquiry Science*. Before joining the PBIS team, Dr. Starr created professional learning experiences in science, math, and technology, designed to assist teachers in successfully changing their classroom practices to promote student learning from coherent inquiry experiences. She has developed instructional materials in several STEM areas, including nanoscale science education, has presented at national and regional teacher education and educational research meetings, and has served in a leadership role in the Michigan Science Education Leadership Association. Dr. Starr has authored articles and book chapters, and has worked to improve elementary science teacher preparation through teaching science courses for pre-service teachers and acting as a consultant in elementary science teacher preparation. As part of the PBIS team, Dr. Starr has played a lead role in making units cohere as a curriculum, in developing the framework for PBIS Teacher's Planning Guides, and in developing teacher professional development experiences and materials.

Acknowledgements

Three research teams contributed to the development of *Project-Based Inquiry Science* (PBIS): a team at the Georgia Institute of Technology headed by Janet L. Kolodner, a team at Northwestern University headed by Daniel Edelson and Brian Reiser, and a team at the University of Michigan headed by Joseph Krajcik and Ron Marx. Each of the PBIS units was originally developed by one of these teams and then later revised and edited to be a part of the full three-year middle-school curriculum that became PBIS.

PBIS has its roots in two educational approaches, Project-Based Science and Learning by Design™. Project-Based Science suggests that students should learn science through engaging in the same kinds of inquiry practices scientists use, in the context of scientific problems relevant to their lives and using tools authentic to science. Project-Based Science was originally conceived in the hi-ce Center at the University of Michigan, with funding from the National Science Foundation. Learning by Design™ derives from Problem-Based Learning and suggests sequencing, social practices, and reflective activities for promoting learning. It engages students in design practices, including the use of iteration and deliberate reflection. LBD was conceived at the Georgia Institute of Technology, with funding from the National Science Foundation, DARPA, and the McDonnell Foundation.

The development of the integrated PBIS curriculum was supported by the National Science Foundation under grants no. 0137807, 0527341, and 0639978. Any opinions, findings and conclusions, or recommendations expressed in this material are those of the authors and do not necessarily reflect the views of the National Science Foundation.

PBIS Team

Principal Investigator
Janet L. Kolodner

Co-Principal Investigators
Daniel C. Edelson
Joseph S. Krajcik
Brian J. Reiser

NSF Program Officer
Gerhard Salinger

Curriculum Developers
Michael T. Ryan
Mary L. Starr

Teacher's Planning Guide Developers
Rebecca M. Schneider
Mary L. Starr

Literacy Specialist
LeeAnn M. Sutherland

NSF Program Reviewer
Arthur Eisenkraft

Project Coordinator
Juliana Lancaster

External Evaluators
The Learning Partnership
Steven M. McGee
Jennifer Witers

The Georgia Institute of Technology Team

Project Director:
Janet L. Kolodner

Development of PBIS units at the Georgia Institute of Technology was conducted in conjunction with the Learning by Design™ Research group (LBD), Janet L. Kolodner, PI.

Lead Developers, Physical Science:
David Crismond
Michael T. Ryan

Lead Developer, Earth Science:
Paul J. Camp

Assessment and Evaluation:
Barbara Fasse
Daniel Hickey
Jackie Gray
Laura Vandewiele
Jennifer Holbrook

Project Pioneers:
JoAnne Collins
David Crismond
Joanna Fox
Alice Gertzman
Mark Guzdial
Cindy Hmelo-Silver
Douglas Holton
Roland Hubscher
N. Hari Narayanan
Wendy Newstetter
Valery Petrushin
Kathy Politis
Sadhana Puntambekar
David Rector
Janice Young

The Northwestern University Team

Project Directors:
Daniel Edelson
Brian Reiser

Lead Developer, Biology:
David Kanter

Lead Developers, Earth Science:
Jennifer Mundt Leimberer
Darlene Slusher

Development of PBIS units at Northwestern was conducted in conjunction with:

The Center for Learning Technologies in Urban Schools (LeTUS) at Northwestern, and the Chicago Public Schools
Louis Gomez, PI;
Clifton Burgess, PI
for Chicago Public Schools.

The BioQ Collaborative
David Kanter, PI.

The Biology Guided Inquiry Learning Environments (BGuILE) Project
Brian Reiser, PI.

The Geographic Data in Education (GEODE) Initiative
Daniel Edelson, Director

The Center for Curriculum Materials in Science at Northwestern
Brian Reiser,
Daniel Edelson,
Bruce Sherin, PIs.

The University of Michigan Team

Project Directors:
Joseph Krajcik
Ron Marx

Literacy Specialist:
LeeAnn M. Sutherland

Project Coordinator:
Mary L. Starr

Development of PBIS units at the University of Michigan was conducted in conjunction with:

The Center for Learning Technologies in Urban Schools (LeTUS)
Ron Marx, Phyllis Blumenfeld,
Barry Fishman,
Joseph Krajcik,
Elliot Soloway, PIs.

The Detroit Public Schools
Juanita Clay-Chambers
Deborah Peek-Brown

The Center for Highly Interactive Computing in Education (hi-ce)
Ron Marx,
Phyllis Blumenfeld,
Barry Fishman,
Joseph Krajcik,
Elliot Soloway,
Elizabeth Moje,
LeeAnn Sutherland, PIs.

Field-Test Teachers

National Field Test

Tamica Andrew
Leslie Baker
Jeanne Bayer
Gretchen Bryant
Boris Consuegra
Daun D'Aversa
Candi DiMauro
Kristie L. Divinski
Donna M. Dowd
Jason Fiorito
Lara Fish
Christine Gleason
Christine Hallerman
Terri L. Hart-Parker
Jennifer Hunn
Rhonda K. Hunter
Jessica Jones
Dawn Kuppersmith
Anthony F. Lawrence
Ann Novak
Rise Orsini
Tracy E. Parham
Cheryl Sgro-Ellis
Debra Tenenbaum
Sarah B. Topper
Becky Watts
Debra A. Williams
Ingrid M. Woolfolk
Ping-Jade Yang

New York City Field Test

Several sequences of PBIS units have been field- tested in New York City under the leadership of Whitney Lukens, Staff Developer for Region 9, and Greg Borman, Science Instructional Specialist, New York City Department of Education

6th Grade

Norman Agard
Tazinmudin Ali
Heather Guthartz Aniba
Asher Arzonane
Asli Aydin
Shareese Blakely
John J. Blaylock
Joshua Blum
Tsedey Bogale
Filomena Borrero

Zachary Brachio
Thelma Brown
Alicia Browne-Jones
Scott Bullis
Maximo Cabral
Lionel Callender
Matthew Carpenter
Ana Maria Castro
Diane Castro
Anne Chan
Ligia Chiorean
Boris Consuegra
Careen Halton Cooper
Cinnamon Czarnecki
Kristin Decker
Nancy Dejean
Gina DiCicco
Donna Dowd
Lizanne Espina
Joan Ferrato
Matt Finnerty
Jacqueline Flicker
Helen Fludd
Leigh Summers Frey
Helene Friedman-Hager
Diana Gering
Matthew Giles
Lucy Gill
Steven Gladden
Greg Grambo
Carrie Grodin-Vehling
Stephan Joanides
Kathryn Kadei
Paraskevi Karangunis
Cynthia Kerns
Martine Lalanne
Erin Lalor
Jennifer Lerman
Sara Lugert
Whitney Lukens
Dana Martorella
Christine Mazurek
Janine McGeown
Chevelle McKeever
Kevin Meyer
Jennifer Miller
Nicholas Miller
Diana Neligan
Caitlin Van Ness
Marlyn Orque
Eloisa Gelo Ortiz
Gina Papadopoulos
Tim Perez
Albertha Petrochilos
Christopher Poli
Kristina Rodriguez

Nadiesta Sanchez
Annette Schavez
Hilary Sedgwitch
Elissa Seto
Laura Shectman
Audrey Shmuel
Katherine Silva
Ragini Singhal
C. Nicole Smith
Gitangali Sohit
Justin Stein
Thomas Tapia
Eilish Walsh-Lennon
Lisa Wong
Brian Yanek
Cesar Yarleque
David Zaretsky
Colleen Zarinsky

7th Grade

Mayra Amaro
Emmanuel Anastasiou
Cheryl Barnhill
Bryce Cahn
Ligia Chiorean
Ben Colella
Boris Consuegra
Careen Halton Cooper
Elizabeth Derse
Urmilla Dhanraj
Gina DiCicco
Lydia Doubleday
Lizanne Espina
Matt Finnerty
Steven Gladden
Stephanie Goldberg
Nicholas Graham
Robert Hunter
Charlene Joseph
Ketlynne Joseph
Kimberly Kavazanjian
Christine Kennedy
Bakwah Kotung
Lisa Kraker
Anthony Lett
Herb Lippe
Jennifer Lopez
Jill Mastromarino
Kerry McKie
Christie Morgado
Patrick O'Connor
Agnes Ochiagha
Tim Perez
Nadia Piltser
Chris Poli

Carmelo Ruiz
Kim Sanders
Leslie Schiavone
Ileana Solla
Jacqueline Taylor
Purvi Vora
Ester Wiltz
Carla Yuille
Marcy Sexauer Zacchea
Lidan Zhou

8th Grade

Emmanuel Anastasio
Jennifer Applebaum
Marsha Armstrong
Jenine Barunas
Vito Cipolla
Kathy Critharis
Patricia Davis
Alison Earle
Lizanne Espina
Matt Finnerty
Ursula Fokine
Kirsis Genao
Steven Gladden
Stephanie Goldberg
Peter Gooding
Matthew Herschfeld
Mike Horowitz
Charlene Jenkins
Ruben Jimenez
Ketlynne Joseph
Kimberly Kavazanjian
Lisa Kraker
Dora Kravitz
Anthony Lett
Emilie Lubis
George McCarthy
David Mckinney
Michael McMahon
Paul Melhado
Jen Miller
Christie Morgado
Ms. Oporto
Maria Jenny Pineda
Anastasia Plaunova
Carmelo Ruiz
Riza Sanchez
Kim Sanders
Maureen Stefanides
Dave Thompson
Matthew Ulmann
Maria Verosa
Tony Yaskulski

PLANETARY FORECASTER

Planetary Forecaster was developed by the Geographic Data in Education (GEODE) Initiative and the Center for Learning Technologies in Urban Schools (LeTUS) at Northwestern University. The first version, entitled Create a World, was developed as part of the Supportive Inquiry-Based Learning Environments Project (SIBLE, Brian Reiser, Daniel Edelson, Louis Gomez, PI's). This edition of Planetary Forecaster was developed by the Project-Based Inquiry Science project in conjunction with the Center for Curriculum Materials in Science at Northwestern University (Brian Reiser, Daniel Edelson, Bruce Sherin, PIs). The weather activities in Learning Set 6 were developed by the PBIS and IAT Development Team.

Planetary Forecaster

Project Director

Daniel Edelson

Lead Developers

Jennifer Mundt Leimberer

Darlene Slusher

Developers

Sue Marshall

Gabrielle Matese

Lindsey Own

Virginia Pittsl

Contributors

Matthew Brown

Mary Pat Pardo

Ken Rose

Consultants

LeeAnn M. Sutherland

Rebecca M. Schneider

Research and Evaluation (LeTUS and SIBLE)

Phillip Herman

Sue Marshall

Gabrielle Matese

Pilot teachers (LeTUS and SIBLE)

Bernie Bradley

Barbara Dubielak-Wood

Barb Figlewicz

John Figlewicz

Anne-Marie Fries

Erwin Laskey

Dan Lucas

Jennifer Mundt Leimberer

Mary Pat Pardo

Kavan Yee

Production Assistants

Cara Nelson

Elizabeth Van Buren

Andrew Watson

Valerie Wilson

PBIS Development Team

Michael T. Ryan

Jennifer Mundt Leimberer

The development of *Planetary Forecaster* was supported by the National Science Foundation under grant nos. ESI-0352478, ESI-0227557, ESI-0137807, REC-0087751, REC-9720383, REC-9720377, REC-9720663, and RED-9453715. Any opinions, findings, and conclusions or recommendations expressed in this material are those of the authors and do not necessarily reflect the views of the National Science Foundation.

Planetary Forecaster Teacher's Planning Guide

NOTE: This book contains Student Edition pages from the second printing of the SE. If your students are using the first printing of the SE, the SE pages in this book may look different from those in the book your students are using. The differences are primarily in the design of tables and graphs (e.g., some tables and graphs are now Blackline Masters); the content of the book is largely unchanged.

Table of Contents

Welcome to Project-Based Inquiry Science!

Welcome to Project-Based Inquiry Science (PBIS): A Middle-School Science Curriculum!

This year, your students will be learning the way scientists learn, exploring interesting questions and challenges, reading about what other scientists have discovered, investigating, experimenting, gathering evidence, and forming explanations. They will learn to collaborate with others to find answers and to share their learning in a variety of ways. In the process, they will come to see science in a whole new, exciting way that will motivate them throughout their educational experiences and beyond.

What is PBIS?

In project-based inquiry learning, students investigate scientific content and learn science practices in the context of attempting to address challenges in or answer questions about the world around them. Early activities introducing students to a challenge help them to generate issues that need to be investigated, making inquiry a student-driven endeavor. Students investigate as scientists would, through observations, designing and running experiments, designing, building, and running models, reading written material, and so on, as appropriate. Throughout each project, students might make use of technology and computer tools that support their efforts in observation, experimentation, modeling, analysis, and reflection. Teachers support and guide the student inquiries by framing the guiding challenge or question, presenting crucial lessons, managing the sequencing of activities, and eliciting and steering discussion and collaboration among the students. At the completion of a project, students publicly exhibit what they have learned along with their solutions to the specific challenge. Personal reflection to help students learn from the experience is embedded in student activities, as are opportunities for assessment.

The curriculum will provide three years of piloted project-based inquiry materials for middle-school science. Individual curriculum units have been defined that cover the scope of the national content and process standards for the middle-school grades. Each Unit focuses on helping students acquire qualitative understanding of targeted science principles and move toward quantitative understanding, is infused with technology, and provides a foundation in reasoning skills, science content, and science process that will ready them for more advanced science. The curriculum as a whole introduces students to a wide range of investigative approaches in science (e.g., experimentation, modeling) and is designed to help them develop scientific reasoning skills that span those investigative approaches.

Technology can be used in project-based inquiry to make available to students some of the same kinds of tools and aids used by scientists in the field. These range from pencil-and-paper tools for organized data recording, collection, and management to software tools for analysis, simulation, modeling, and other tasks. Such infusion provides a platform for providing prompts, hints, examples, and other kinds of aids to students as they are engaging in scientific reasoning. The learning technologies and tools that are integrated into the curriculum offer essential scaffolding to students as they are developing their scientific reasoning skills, and are seamlessly infused into the overall completion of project activities and investigations.

Standards-Based Development

Development of each curriculum Unit begins by identifying the specific relevant national standards to be addressed. Each Unit has been designed to cover a specific portion of the national standards. This phase of development also includes an analysis of curriculum requirements across multiple states. Our intent is to deliver a product that will provide coverage of the content deemed essential on the widest practical scope and that will be easily adaptable to the needs of teachers across the country.

Once the appropriate standards have been identified, the development team works to define specific learning goals built from those standards, and takes into account conceptions and misunderstandings common among middle-school students. An orienting design challenge or driving question for investigation is chosen that motivates achieving those learning goals, and the team then sequences activities and the presentation of specific concepts so that students can construct an accurate understanding of the subject matter.

Inquiry-Based Design

The individual curriculum Units present two types of projects: engineering-design challenges and driving-question investigations. Design-challenge Units begin by presenting students with a scenario and problem and challenging them to design a device or plan that will solve the problem. Driving-question investigations begin by presenting students with a complex question with real-world implications. Students are challenged to develop answers to the questions. The scenario and problem in the design Units and the driving question in the investigation Units are carefully selected to lead the students into investigation of specific science concepts, and the solution processes are carefully structured to require use of specific scientific reasoning skills.

Pedagogical Rationale

Research shows that individual project-based learning units promote excitement and deep learning of the targeted concepts. However, achieving deep, flexible, transferable learning of cross-disciplinary content (e.g., the notion of a model, time scale, variable, experiment) and science practice requires a learning environment that consistently, persistently, and pervasively encourages the use of such content and practices over an extended period of time. By developing project-based inquiry materials that cover the spectrum of middle-school science content in a coherent framework, we provide this extended exposure to the type of learning environment most likely to produce competent scientific thinkers who are well grounded in their understanding of both basic science concepts and the standards and practices of science in general.

Evidence of Effectiveness

There is compelling evidence showing that a project-based inquiry approach meets this goal. Working at Georgia Tech, the University of Michigan, and Northwestern University, we have developed, piloted, and/or field-tested many individual project-based units. Our evaluation evidence shows that these materials engage students well and are manageable by teachers, and that students learn both content and process skills. In every summative evaluation, student performance on post-tests improved significantly from pretest performance (Krajcik, et al., 2000; Holbrook, et al., 2001; Gray et. al. 2001). For example, in the second year in a project-based classroom in Detroit, the average student at post-test scored at about the 95th percentile of the pre-test distribution. Further, we have repeatedly documented significant gains in content knowledge relative to other inquiry-based (but not project-based) instructional methods. In one set of results, performance by a project-based class

in Atlanta doubled on the content test while the matched comparison class (with an excellent teacher) experienced only a 20% gain (significance $p < .001$). Other comparisons have shown more modest differences, but project-based students consistently perform better than their comparisons. Most exciting about the Atlanta results is that results from performance assessments show that, within comparable student populations, project-based students score higher on all categories of problem-solving and analysis and are more sophisticated at science practice and managing a collaborative scientific investigation. Indeed, the performance of average-ability project-based students is often statistically indistinguishable from or better than performance of comparison honors students learning in an inquiry-oriented but not project-based classroom. The Chicago group also has documented significant change in process skills in project-based classrooms. Students become more effective in constructing and critiquing scientific arguments (Sandoval, 1998) and in constructing scientific explanations using discipline-specific knowledge, such as evolutionary explanations for animal behavior (Smith & Reiser, 1998).

Researchers at Northwestern have also investigated the changes in classroom practices that are elicited by project-based units. Analyses of the artifacts students produce indicate that students are engaging in ambitious learning practices, requiring weighing and synthesizing many results from complex analyses of data, and constructing scientific arguments that require synthesizing results from multiple complex analyses of data (Edelson et al, 1998; Reiser et al, 2001). Students are engaged in planning, performing, monitoring and revising their investigations, and reporting on their investigation processes as well as their results (Loh et al, 1998). In general, the classrooms engaging in project-based activities reveal substantial moves toward a scientific discourse community in which students focus on arguing from evidence, critiquing ideas, and conjecturing, rather than simply reporting on what they have read or been told (Tabak & Reiser, 1997).

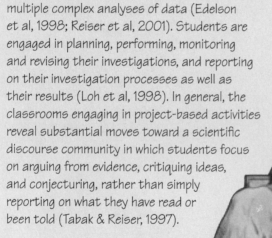

Introducing PBIS

What Do Scientists Do?

1) Scientists...address big challenges and big questions.

Students will find many different kinds of *Big Challenges* and *Questions* in *PBIS* Units. Some ask them to think about why something is a certain way. Some ask them to think about what causes something to change. Some challenge them to design a solution to a problem. Most are about things that can and do happen in the real world.

Understand the Big Challenge or Question

As students get started with each Unit, they will do activities that help them understand the *Big Question* or *Challenge* for that Unit. They will think about what they already know that might help them, and they will identify some of the new things they will need to learn.

Project Board

The *Project Board* helps you and your students keep track of their learning. For each challenge or question, they will use a *Project Board* to keep track of what they know, what they need to learn, and what they are learning. As they learn and gather evidence, they will record that on the *Project Board*. After they have answered each small question or challenge, they will return to the *Project Board* to record how what they have learned helps them answer the *Big Question* or *Challenge*.

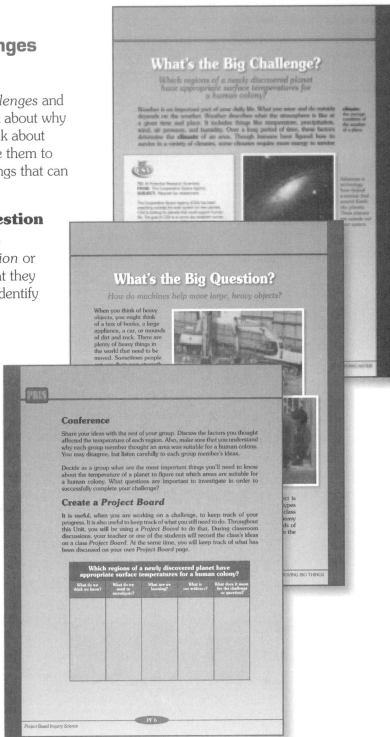

PBIS — *Learning Set 1 • How Do Flowing Water and Land Interact in a Community?*

Learning Set 1

How Do Flowing Water and Land Interact in a Community?

The big question for this unit is *How does water quality affect the ecology of a community?* So far you have considered what you already know about what water quality is. Now you may be wondering where the water you use comes from. If you live in a city or town, the water you use may come from a river. You would want to know the quality of the water you are using. To do so, it is important to know how the water gets into the river. You also need to know what happens to the water as the river flows across the land.

You may have seen rivers or other water bodies near your home, your school, or in your city. Think about the river closest to where you live. Consider from where the water in the river comes. If you have traveled along the river, think about what the land around the river looks like. Try to figure out what human activities occur in the area. Speculate as to whether these activities affect the quality of water in the river.

To answer the big question, you need to break it down into smaller questions. In this *Learning Set,* you will investigate two smaller questions. As you will discover, these questions are very closely related and very hard to separate. The smaller questions are *How does water affect the land as it moves through the community?* and *How does land use affect water*

PBIS

Address the Big Challenge

How Do Scientists Work Together to Solve Problems?

You began this unit with the question, *how do scientists work together to solve problems?* You did several small challenges. As you worked on those challenges you learned about how scientists solve problems. You will now watch a video about real-life designers. You will see what the people in the video are doing that is like what you have been doing. Then you will think about all the different things you have been doing during this unit. Lastly, you will write about what you have learned about doing science and being a scientist.

Watch

IDEO Video

The video you will watch follows a group of designers at IDEO. IDEO is an innovation and design firm. In the video, they face the challenge of designing and building a new kind of shopping cart. These designers are doing many of the same things that you did. They also use other practices that you did not use. As you watch the video, record the interesting things you see.

After watching the video, answer the questions on the next page. You might want to look at them before you watch the video. Answering these questions should help you answer the big question of this unit: *How do scientists work together to solve problems?*

100

Learning Sets

Each Unit is composed of a group of *Learning Sets,* one for each of the smaller questions that needs to be answered to address the *Big Question* or *Challenge*. In each *Learning Set,* students will investigate and read to find answers to the *Learning Set's* question. They will also have a chance to share the results of their investigations with their classmates and work together to make sense of what they are learning. As students come to understand answers to the questions on the *Project Board,* you will record those answers and the evidence they collected. At the end of each *Learning Set,* they will apply their knowledge to the *Big Question* or *Challenge*.

Answer the Big Question/ Address the Big Challenge

At the end of each Unit, students will put everything they have learned together to tackle the *Big Question* or *Challenge*.

Project-Based Inquiry Science

2) Scientists...address smaller questions and challenges.

What Students Do in a Learning Set

Understanding the Question or Challenge

At the start of each *Learning Set*, students will usually do activities that will help them understand the *Learning Set's* question or challenge and recognize what they already know that can help them answer the question or achieve the challenge. Usually, they will visit the *Project Board* after these activities and record on it the even smaller questions that they need to investigate to answer a *Learning Set's* question.

Investigate/Explore

There are many different kinds of investigations students might do to find answers to questions. In the *Learning Sets*, they might

- design and run experiments;
- design and run simulations;
- design and build models;
- examine large sets of data.

Don't worry if your students haven't done these things before. The text will provide them with lots of help in designing their investigations and in analyzing thier data.

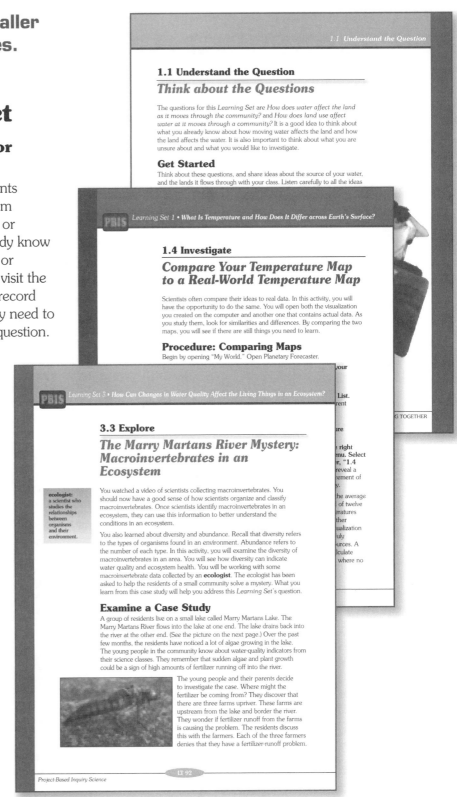

1.1 Understand the Question

1.1 Understand the Question

Think about the Questions

The questions for this *Learning Set* are *How does water affect the land as it moves through the community?* and *How does land use affect water at it moves through a community?* It is a good idea to think about what you already know about how moving water affects the land and how the land affects the water. It is also important to think about what you are unsure about and what you would like to investigate.

Get Started

Think about these questions, and share ideas about the source of your water, and the lands it flows through with your class. Listen carefully to all the ideas

Learning Set 1 • What Is Temperature and How Does It Differ across Earth's Surface?

1.4 Investigate

Compare Your Temperature Map to a Real-World Temperature Map

Scientists often compare their ideas to real data. In this activity, you will have the opportunity to do the same. You will open both the visualization you created on the computer and another one that contains actual data. As you study them, look for similarities and differences. By comparing the two maps, you will see if there are still things you need to learn.

Procedure: Comparing Maps

Begin by opening "My World." Open Planetary Forecaster.

Learning Set 3 • How Can Changes in Water Quality Affect the Living Things in an Ecosystem?

3.3 Explore

The Marry Martans River Mystery: Macroinvertebrates in an Ecosystem

ecologist: a scientist who studies the relationships between organisms and their environment.

You watched a video of scientists collecting macroinvertebrates. You should now have a good sense of how scientists organize and classify macroinvertebrates. Once scientists identify macroinvertebrates in an ecosystem, they can use this information to better understand the conditions in an ecosystem.

You also learned about diversity and abundance. Recall that diversity refers to the types of organisms found in an environment. Abundance refers to the number of each type. In this activity, you will examine the diversity of macroinvertebrates in an area. You will see how diversity can indicate water quality and ecosystem health. You will be working with some macroinvertebrate data collected by an **ecologist**. The ecologist has been asked to help the residents of a small community solve a mystery. What you learn from this case study will help you address this *Learning Set's* question.

Examine a Case Study

A group of residents live on a small lake called Marry Martans Lake. The Marry Martans River flows into the lake at one end. The lake drains back into the river at the other end. (See the picture on the next page.) Over the past few months, the residents have noticed a lot of algae growing in the lake. The young people in the community know about water-quality indicators from their science classes. They remember that sudden algae and plant growth could be a sign of high amounts of fertilizer running off into the river.

The young people and their parents decide to investigate the case. Where might the fertilizer be coming from? They discover that there are three farms upriver. These farms are upstream from the lake and border the river. They wonder if fertilizer runoff from the farms is causing the problem. The residents discuss this with the farmers. Each of the three farmers denies that they have a fertilizer-runoff problem.

Project-Based Inquiry Science

LT 92

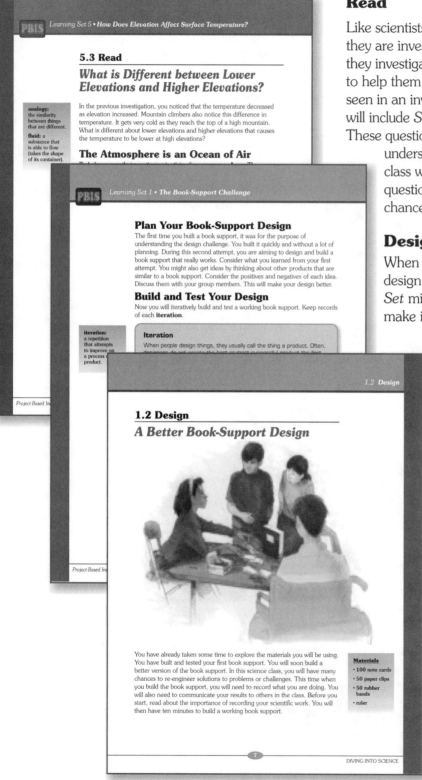

Read

Like scientists, students will also read about the science they are investigating. They will read a little bit before they investigate, but most of the reading they do will be to help them understand what they have experienced or seen in an investigation. Each time they read, the text will include *Stop and Think* questions after the reading. These questions will help students gauge how well they understand what they have read. Usually, the class will discuss the answers to *Stop and Think* questions before going on so that everybody has a chance to make sense of the reading.

Design and Build

When the *Big Challenge* for a Unit asks them to design something, the challenge in a *Learning Set* might also ask them to design something and make it work. Often students will design a part of the thing they will design and build for the *Big Challenge*. When a *Learning Set* challenges students to design and build something, they will do several things:

- identify what questions they need to answer to be successful
- investigate to find answers to those questions
- use those answers to plan a good design solution
- build and test their design

Because designs don't always work the way one wants them to, students will usually do a design challenge more than once. Each time through, they will test their design. If their design doesn't work as well as they would like, they will determine why it is not working and identify other things they need to investigate to make it work better. Then, they will learn those things and try again.

Explain and Recommend

A big part of what scientists do is explain, or try to make sense of why things happen the way they do. An explanation describes why something is the way it is or behaves the way it does. An explanation is a statement one makes built from claims (what you think you know), evidence (from an investigation) that supports the claim, and science knowledge. As they learn, scientists get better at explaining. You will see that students get better, too, as they work through the *Learning Sets*.

A recommendation is a special kind of claim—one where you advise somebody about what to do. Students will make recommendations and support them with evidence, science knowledge, and explanations.

3.5 *Explain*

3.5 Explain
Create an Explanation

After scientists get results from an investigation, they try to make a claim. They base their claim on what their evidence shows. They also use what they already know to make their claim. They explain why their claim is valid. The purpose of a science explanation is to help others understand the following:

- what was learned from a set of investigations
- why the scientists reached this conclusion

Later, other scientists will use these explanations to help them explain other phenomena. The explanations will also help them predict what will happen in other situations.

You will do the same thing now. Your claim will be the trend you found in your experiment. You will use data you collected and science knowledge you have read to create a good explanation. This will help you decide whether your claim is valid. You will be reporting the results of the investigation to your classmates. With a good explanation that matches your claim, you can convince them that your claim is valid.

Because your understanding of the science of forces is not complete, you may not be able to fully explain your results. But you will use what you have read to come up with your best explanation. Scientists finding out about new things do the same thing. When they only partly understand something, it is impossible for them to form a "perfect" explanation. They do the best they can based on what they understand. As they learn more, they make their explanations better. This is what you will do now and what you will be doing throughout PBIS. You will explain your results the best you can based

CIENCE

4.3 *Explain and Recommend*

4.3 Explain and Recommend
Explanations and Recommendations about Parachutes

As you did after your whirligig experiments, you will spend some time now explaining your results. You will also try to come up with recommendations. Remember that explanations include your claims, the evidence for your claims, and the science you know that can help you understand the claim. A recommendation is a statement about what someone should do. The best recommendations also have evidence, science, and an explanation associated with them. In the *Whirligig Challenge*, you created explanations and recommendations separately from each other. This time you will work on both at the same time.

Create and Share Your Recommendation and Explanation

Work with your group. Use the hints on the *Create Your Explanation* pages to make your first attempt at explaining your results. You'll read about parachute science later. After that, you will probably want to revise your explanations. Right now, use the science you learned during the *Whirligig Challenge* for your first attempt.

Write your recommendation. It should be about designing a slow-falling parachute. Remember that it should be written so that it will help someone else. They should be able to apply what you have learned about the effects of your variable. If you are having trouble, review the example in *Learning Set 3*.

Create Your Explanation

Name: _____ Date: _____

Use this page to explain the lesson of your recent investigations.

Write a brief summary of the results from your investigation. You will use this summary to help you write your Explanation.

Claim – a statement of what you understand or a conclusion that you have reached from an investigation or a set of investigations.

Evidence – data collected during investigations and trends in that data.

Science knowledge – knowledge about how things work. You may have learned this through reading, talking to an expert, discussions, or other experiences.

Write your Explanation using the *Claim, Evidence* and *Science knowledge*.

81

DIVING IN TO SCIENCE

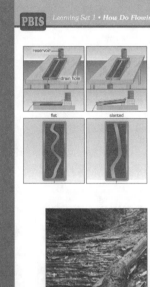

PBIS   *Learning Set 1 • How Do Flowing Water and Land Interact in a Community?*

reservoir
drain hole
flat   slanted

Your teacher will set up the stream table in four different ways, as shown in the diagrams.

Sketch the different models. As you watch the water flow through the model, pay very close attention to the way the land on both sides of the river changes. Pay attention to

- how the soil moves,
- where along the bank the soil moves, and
- where the soil ends up.

Make notes about what you observe for each of these situations. You might want to mark your sketches based on what you observed.

Stop and Think

Look at your sketches and the notes you took about the river models you observed. What did you notice about how the soil was moved by the river? Answer these questions. Be prepared to discuss your answers with your group and the class.

1. When the river was straight and the pan was level, how did the soil move along the river?

2. When your teacher made the pan more slanted by lifting the water end of the pan, how did the water move compared to the level pan? How did that change affect the soil that the river moved?

3. Your teacher also made rivers that were more curved. How did that change the way the soil moved along the river?

Project-Ba

1.3 Read

Reflect

Think about the book support you designed and built so far. Try to think about the science concepts you have read about and discussed as a class. Answer the following questions. Be prepared to discuss your answers with the class.

1. Was your structure strong? If not, did it collapse because of folding, compression, or both?

2. How could you make the structure stronger to resist folding or compression?

3. Was your book support stable? That is, did it provide support so that the book did not tip over? Did it provide this support well? Draw a picture of your book support showing the center of mass of the book and the places in your book support that resist the load of your book.

4. How could you make your book support more stable?

5. How successful were the book supports that used columns in their design?

6. How could you make your book support work more effectively by including columns into the design?

7. Explain how the pull on the book could better be resisted by the use of columns in your design. Be sure to discuss both the strength and the stability of the columns in your design. You might find it easier to draw a sketch and label it to explain how the columns do this.

8. Think about some of the structures that supported the book well. What designs and building decisions were used?

You are going to get another chance to design a book support. You will use the same materials. Think about how your group could design your next book support to better meet the challenge. Consider what you now know about the science that explains how structures support objects.

19

DIVING INTO SCIENCE

---

3) Scientists...reflect in many different ways.

PBIS provides guidance to help students think about what they are doing and to recognize what they are learning. Doing this often as they are working will help students be successful student scientists.

Tools for Making Sense

Stop and Think

Stop and Think sections help students make sense of what they have been doing in the section they are working on. *Stop and Think* sections include a set of questions to help students understand what they have just read or done. Sometimes the questions will remind them of something they need to pay more attention to. Sometimes they will help students connect what they have just read to things they already know. When there is a *Stop and Think* in the text, students will work individually or with a partner to answer the questions, and then the whole class will discuss the answers.

Reflect

Reflect sections help students connect what they have just done with other things they have read or done earlier in the Unit (or in another Unit). When there is a *Reflect* in the text, students will work individually or with a partner or small group to answer the questions. Then, the whole class will discuss the answers. You may want to ask students to answer *Reflect* questions for homework.

Analyze Your Data

Whenever students have to analyze data, the text will provide hints about how to do that and what to look for.

Mess About

"Messing about" is a term that comes from design. It means exploring the materials to be used for designing or building something or examining something that works like what is to be designed. Messing about helps students discover new ideas—and it can be a lot of fun. The text will usually give them ideas about things to notice as they are messing about.

What's the Point?

At the end of each *Learning Set*, students will find a summary, called *What's the Point?*, of the important information from the *Learning Set*. These summaries can help students remember how what they did and learned is connected to the *Big Question* or *Challenge* they are working on.

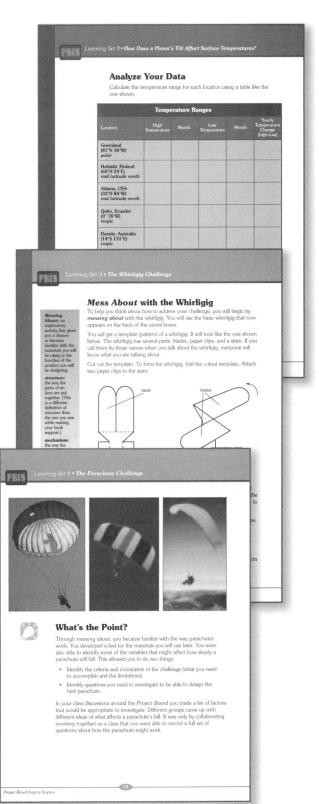

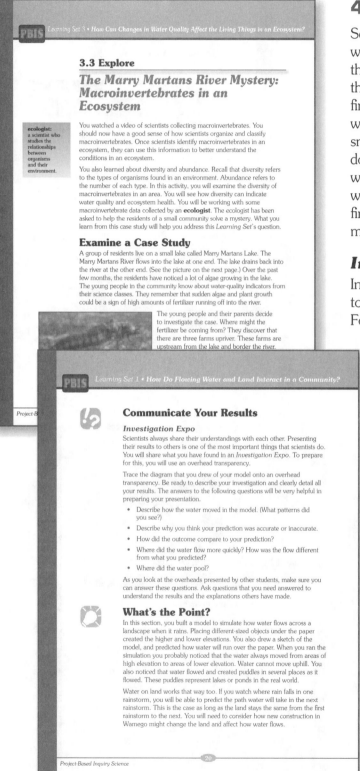

3.3 Explore

The Marry Martans River Mystery: Macroinvertebrates in an Ecosystem

ecologist: a scientist who studies the relationships between organisms and their environment.

You watched a video of scientists collecting macroinvertebrates. You should now have a good sense of how scientists organize and classify macroinvertebrates. Once scientists identify macroinvertebrates in an ecosystem, they can use this information to better understand the conditions in an ecosystem.

You also learned about diversity and abundance. Recall that diversity refers to the types of organisms found in an environment. Abundance refers to the number of each type. In this activity, you will examine the diversity of macroinvertebrates in an area. You will see how diversity can indicate water quality and ecosystem health. You will be working with some macroinvertebrate data collected by an **ecologist**. The ecologist has been asked to help the residents of a small community solve a mystery. What you learn from this case study will help you address this *Learning Set*'s question.

Examine a Case Study

A group of residents live on a small lake called Marry Martans Lake. The Marry Martans River flows into the lake at one end. The lake drains back into the river at the other end. (See the picture on the next page.) Over the past few months, the residents have noticed a lot of algae growing in the lake. The young people in the community know about water-quality indicators from their science classes. They remember that sudden algae and plant growth could be a sign of high amounts of fertilizer running off into the river.

The young people and their parents decide to investigate the case. Where might the fertilizer be coming from? They discover that there are three farms upriver. These farms are upstream from the lake and border the river.

Communicate Your Results

Investigation Expo

Scientists always share their understandings with each other. Presenting their results to others is one of the most important things that scientists do. You will share what you have found in an *Investigation Expo*. To prepare for this, you will use an overhead transparency.

Trace the diagram that you drew of your model onto an overhead transparency. Be ready to describe your investigation and clearly detail all your results. The answers to the following questions will be very helpful in preparing your presentation.

- Describe how the water moved in the model. (What patterns did you see?)
- Describe why you think your prediction was accurate or inaccurate.
- How did the outcome compare to your prediction?
- Where did the water flow more quickly? How was the flow different from what you predicted?
- Where did the water pool?

As you look at the overheads presented by other students, make sure you can answer these questions. Ask questions that you need answered to understand the results and the explanations others have made.

What's the Point?

In this section, you built a model to simulate how water flows across a landscape when it rains. Placing different-sized objects under the paper created the higher and lower elevations. You also drew a sketch of the model, and predicted how water will run over the paper. When you ran the simulation you probably noticed that the water always moved from areas of high elevation to areas of lower elevation. Water cannot move uphill. You also noticed that water flowed and created puddles in several places as it flowed. These puddles represent lakes or ponds in the real world.

Water on land works that way too. If you watch where rain falls in one rainstorm, you will be able to predict the path water will take in the next rainstorm. This is the case as long as the land stays the same from the first rainstorm to the next. You will need to consider how new construction in Wamego might change the land and affect how water flows.

4) Scientists...collaborate.

Scientists never do all their work alone. They work with other scientists (collaborate) and share their knowledge. *PBIS* helps students by giving them lots of opportunities for sharing their findings, ideas, and discoveries with others (the way scientists do). Students will work together in small groups to investigate, design, explain, and do other science activities. Sometimes they will work in pairs to figure out things together. They will also have lots of opportunities to share their findings with the rest of their classmates and make sense together of what they are learning.

Investigation Expo

In an *Investigation Expo*, small groups report to the class about an investigation they've done. For each *Investigation Expo*, students will make a poster detailing what they were trying to learn from their investigation, what they did, their data, and their interpretation of the data. The text gives them hints about what to present and what to look for in other groups' presentations. *Investigation Expos* are always followed by discussions about the investigations and about how to do science well. You may want to ask students to write a lab report following an investigation.

Plan Briefing/Solution Briefing/ Idea Briefing

Briefings are presentations of work in progress. They give students a chance to get advice from their classmates that can help them move forward. During a *Plan Briefing*, students present their plans to the class. They might be plans for an experiment for solving a problem or achieving a challenge. During a *Solution Briefing*, students present their solutions in progress and ask the class to help them make their solutions better. During an *Idea Briefing*, students present their ideas, including their evidence in support of their plans, solutions, or ideas. Often, they will prepare posters to help them make their presentation. Briefings are almost always followed by discussions of their investigations and how they will move forward.

Solution Showcase

Solution Showcases usually happen near the end of a Unit. During a *Solution Showcase*, students show their classmates their finished products—either their answer to a question or solution to a challenge. Students will also tell the class why they think it is a good answer or solution, what evidence and science they used to get to their solution, and what they tried along the way before getting to their answers or solutions. Sometimes a *Solution Showcase* is followed by a competition. It is almost always followed by a discussion comparing and contrasting the different answers and solutions groups have come up with. You may want to ask students to write a report or paper following a *Solution Showcase*.

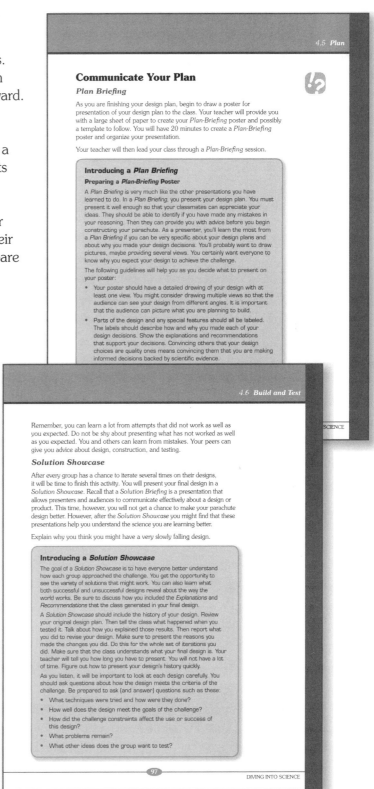

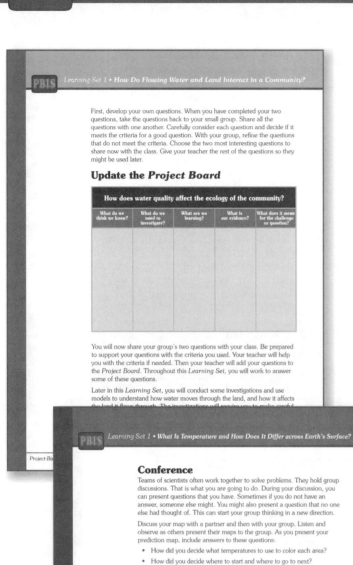

Update the *Project Board*

Remember that the *Project Board* is designed to help the class keep track of what they are learning and their progress toward a Unit's *Big Question* or *Challenge*. At the beginning of each Unit, the class creates a *Project Board*, and together records what students think they know about answering the *Big Question* or addressing the *Big Challenge* and what they think they need to investigate further. Near the beginning of each *Learning Set*, the class revisits the *Project Board* and adds new questions and information they think they know to the *Project Board*. At the end of each *Learning Set*, the class again revisits the *Project Board*. This time, they record what they have learned, the evidence they have collected, and recommendations they can make about answering the *Big Question* or achieving the *Big Challenge*.

Conference

A *Conference* is a short discussion among a small group of students before a more formal whole-class discussion. Students might discuss predictions and observations, they might try to explain together, they might consult on what they think they know, and so on. Usually, a *Conference* is followed by a discussion around the *Project Board*. In these small group discussions, everybody gets a chance to participate.

What's the Point?
Students review what they have learned in each *Learning Set*.

Stop and Think
Student answer questions that help them understand what they have done in a section.

Communicate
Students share their ideas and results with their classmates.

Record
Students record their data as they gather it.

NOTES

NOTES

PBIS

PLANETARY FORECASTER

As a Student Scientist, you will...

Ask
QUESTIONS

APPLY
MEANING

Pursue
ANSWERS

Make
MEANING

Share
ANSWERS

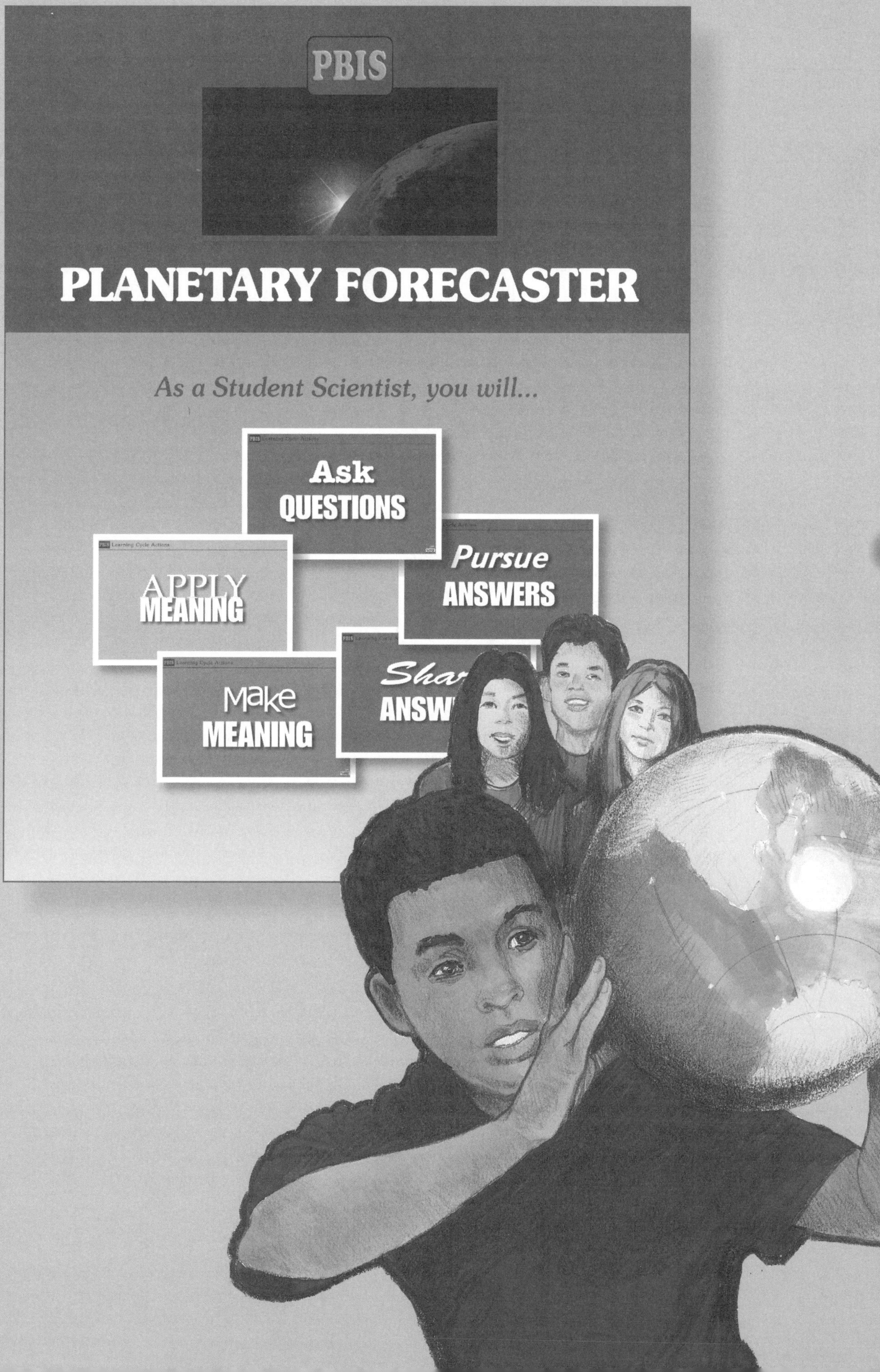

Planetary Forecaster

UNIT OVERVIEW

Content

In this Unit, students explore the major factors affecting temperature on Earth and then use what they learn to make predictions of temperatures and habitable areas on a fictional, newly-discovered planet. Students consider four factors that affect Earth's temperatures:

- shape of the planet
- tilt of the planet's axis
- land/water differences
- surface elevation

Students will apply what they learn to predict the temperatures of *Planet X*. This motivates a series of investigations consisting of both hands-on labs and software-based activities in which students examine the different factors affecting temperatures.

Students begin in *Learning Set 1* by learning about temperature, heat energy, heat conduction, and how to measure temperature. They study Earth's surface temperature using the *My World* software to help them visualize and analyze various data for Earth. The subsequent *Learning Sets* focus on factors that affect Earth's surface temperatures. In *Learning Set 2*, students consider how the planet's shape affects the temperature and how direct and indirect light affect surface temperature. Students are informed that the electromagnetic waves from the Sun transfer light and heat energy to Earth and discuss heat transfer by radiation. They explore the variation of incoming solar energy per area on Earth for different latitudes and read about how the unequal heating from the Sun affects surface temperature and the habitability of an area resulting in Earth's different biomes. *Learning Set 3* focuses on how the tilt of a planet affects surface temperature and causes the seasons. How land and water affect surface temperatures is explored in *Learning Set 4*. Students learn about specific heat capacity and how the absorption and the reflection of light energy affect the temperature of an object. *Learning Set 5* considers how elevation affects surface temperature. Students read about density and explore the relationships between pressure and temperature of air. Applying what they learned about density, pressure, and temperature, students consider how heat energy is transferred through the atmosphere by convection. In the last *Learning Set*, students act as meteorologists and explore the factors that interact to cause Earth's weather patterns. Students read about global warming, explore the water cycle, and the wind patterns on Earth. After each *Learning Set*, students apply what they

$45\frac{1}{2}$ *class periods*

A class period is considered to be one 40 to 50 minute class.

have learned to the fictitious *Planet X* to determine its surface temperatures and make predictions on where it might be habitable.

The Unit concludes with students applying all they have learned to make a recommendation supported by their reasons on where colonists should settle on the fictitious *Planet X*.

Investigations

Each *Learning Set* focuses on a factor that affects the surface temperature of Earth and involves investigations and explorations to provide evidence on how these factors influence the surface temperature. Students begin by using their pre-existing knowledge to predict surface temperatures on Earth in July and then compare an electronic version of their maps to real temperatures in a data visualization program called *My World*. In *Learning Set 2* students investigate the first factor in predicting *Planet X's* surface temperatures: how the shape of the planet affects the incoming solar energy and the temperature of the surface. Students begin by observing how the location of a light beam shines on a ball. They build a model to observe the effects of direct and indirect sunlight striking Earth. The model consists of a flashlight shining on paper placed at various angles. Students measure how the area covered by the light and the intensity of the light are affected by the angle of the paper relative to the light beam. Students relate how the light from the Sun strikes Earth and causes a variation of temperatures due to the difference in the angle it strikes Earth's surface. Students investigate how solar energy varies with latitude on Earth using data in the *My World* software and obtain evidence to support their claims about how the shape of the planet relates to the temperatures on the planet. In *Learning Set 3,* students create a model and measure how the tilt of Earth affects the solar energy striking the planet at different latitudes and at different months of the year. From this they acquire evidence for the cause of the seasons. Students investigate how land and water affect Earth's surface temperature in *Learning Set 4*. Students investigate how light shining on sand and water affect their temperatures, providing a model and evidence for how solar energy affects land and water bodies. Students use *My World* to investigate how the temperatures of land and water compare at similar latitudes. In *Learning Set 5,* students investigate how elevation affects surface temperature. They use data from *My World* to analyze how the elevation of a location on Earth affects its temperature and to investigate how the pressure and temperature decrease as the elevation is increased. This provides students with further reason to investigate how pressure and temperature are related. Through a simple experiment they observe that as the pressure decreases the temperature decreases, which they relate to the atmosphere and apply these ideas as they learn about density and convection. *Learning Set 6* focuses on weather. Students use a model consisting of a jar of hot water with ice cubes sitting on top of the jar. They observe water changing from a liquid to a vapor (steam

Students should work in fixed groups of three or four for the entire Unit. When selecting groups, consider the goals for each student, how the material will challenge them, how they will challenge each other, and how they will share the workload.

Students will use the *My World* software throughout the *Planetary Forecaster* program as a tool to solve the *Big Challenge.* You should be familiar with how to use this software and have it ready and available for the students. Directions on how to use the software are embedded in the student text. It would be best to have one computer available per group of students. If this is not possible, consider how you will efficiently manage computer usage. Students will be constructing maps they will share with the class. Consider having students share their maps using a projection system. Consider how you will save and store students' maps.

Student groups should have a group folder to hold their collective work during the Unit. This folder should stay in the classroom in case of student absences.

from the hot water) and back to a liquid (condensation because of the ice), which provides some evidence for the water cycle. Students conclude the Unit by further investigating the data from *Planet X* and making recommendations supported by evidence from their investigations and science knowledge presented throughout the Unit.

Nature of Science

The *PBIS* curriculum is designed to have students behave as scientists do, engaging in common social practices and processes of science. Students work in groups throughout the Unit as they consider what they know, create questions about what they need to investigate, construct claims supported by evidence from their investigations, and make recommendations supported with evidence on where appropriate locations for a colony exist on a fictitious planet. Students practice the skills of making observations, recording and analyzing data, utilizing available science knowledge, utilizing visual representations, and using models. Students engage in the social practices of scientists as they share ideas within their groups and the results of their investigations with the class. Through sharing ideas, results, and having discussions, students revise and refine their ideas.

Artifacts

Students begin the Unit by creating their class *Project Board* which is a tool designed to keep track of their questions, claims, supporting evidence, explanations, and recommendations. This *Project Board* is updated throughout the Unit as students gather more information to help them address the *Big Challenge*. Students also construct explanations throughout the Unit pertaining to how various factors of a planet affect its surface temperature and apply these explanations when they make their recommendations for habitable locations on *Planet X*. Throughout the Unit, students update prediction maps they create for *Planet X* and prepare presentations for the class. Students construct various other artifacts throughout the Unit. In *Learning Set 1,* students create a prediction map on paper of Earth's surface temperatures and then create a prediction map using the visualization software *My World*. This helps them familiarize themselves with the software and the advantages of using the software. In *Learning Set 2,* students construct a model to help them understand how light from the sun striking Earth is affected by the shape of Earth. The model consists of a flashlight and paper on a clipboard. Students begin constructing prediction maps for the surface temperature and habitability of *Planet X* using the *My World* software. Students make a model of Earth rotating on its axis in *Learning Set 3* to help them understand the motion of the planet around the Sun and to help them consider how tilt affects surface temperatures. Using *My World,* students construct data tables for Earth's surface temperature for various months and latitudes to help them understand how a planet's tilt affects the surface temperature. Students focus on how land and water affect surface temperatures in *Learning Set 4* and construct various data tables to find trends in the data for Earth. In *Learning Set 5*, students construct a model to simulate how the change in air pressure changes the temperature. They use the data from their simulation along with data from *My World* as evidence for how elevation affects surface temperature and apply this to their prediction maps of *Planet X*. *Learning Set 6* focuses on weather, what factors cause weather, and how variables that influence the weather are measured. Students construct rain gauges, a thermometer shelter, a barometer, an anemometer, and a wind vane. Students also construct predictions of the weather patterns on *Planet X*.

Targeted Concepts, Skills, and Nature of Science	Section
Scientists often work together and share their findings. Sharing findings makes new information available and helps scientists to refine their ideas and build on others' ideas. When another person's or group's idea is used, credit needs to be given.	Unit Intro, 1.1, 1.3, 1.BBC, 2.1, 2.2, 2.3, 2.4, 2.5, 2.BBC, 3.1, 3.2, 3.3, 3.4, 3.5, 3.BBC, 4.1, 4.2, 4.3, 4.5, 4.BBC, 5.1, 5.2, 5.7, 5.BBC, 6.1, 6.4, 6.5, 6.6, 6.BBC, ABC II
Scientists must keep clear, accurate, and descriptive records of what they do so they can share their work with others and consider what they did, why they did it, and what they want to do next.	Unit Intro, 1.1, 1.3, 1.4, 1.BBC, 2.1, 2.2, 2.3, 2.4, 2.5, 2.BBC, 3.1, 3.2, 3.3, 3.4, 3.5, 3.BBC, 4.1, 4.2, 4.3, 4.4, 4.5, 4.BBC, 5.1, 5.2, 5.4, 5.5, 5.7, 5.BBC, ABC I, 6.1, 6.3, 6.4, 6.5, 6.6, 6.BBC, ABC II
Graphs, maps, and tables are an effective way to analyze and communicate results of scientific investigation.	1.1, 1.3, 1.4, 1.BBC, 2.2, 2.4, 2.BBC, 3.2, 3.3, 3.BBC, 4.2, 4.4, 4.5, 4.BBC, 5.2, 5.4, 5.5, 5.7, ABC I, 6.1, 6.6, ABC II
Identifying factors that lead to variation is an important part of scientific investigation.	1.1, 1.4, 2.1, 3.1, 4.1, 4.2, 5.1, 6.1
Scientists make claims (conclusions) based on evidence obtained (trends in data) from reliable investigations	1.5, 2.2, 2.4, 3.2, 3.3, 4.2, 4.4, 4.5, 5.2, 5.4, 5.5, 6.3
Explanations are claims supported by evidence, accepted ideas, and facts.	2.3, 2.5, 3.2, 3.5, 3.BBC, 4.3, 4.5, 4.BBC, 5.BBC, ABC I, 6.4, 6.6

Targeted Concepts, Skills, and Nature of Science	Section
Scientists use models to simulate processes that happen too fast, too slow, on a scale that cannot be observed directly (either too small or too large), or that are too dangerous.	2.2, 3.1, 3.2, 6.3,
Heat energy may be transferred through conduction, radiation, or convection.	1.2, 2.1, 4.2, 5.6
Temperature is a measurement of the average kinetic energy of atoms and molecules. Surface temperature is the temperature measured near a planet's surface.	1.2
Temperatures around the Earth's surface vary widely, but can be predicted somewhat by location and season.	1.3, 1.4, 3.3, 3.4, 4.4, 5.2, 5.4, 6.6
Habitable areas of Earth are determined by average temperatures suitable for humans to live in. These areas are often broken up into biomes, which are a group of ecosystems that have the same general climate and similar plants and animals.	1.5, 2.4
The intensity of light on an object depends on its shape and the angle it strikes the object at. As the curvature of the object's surface increases, the angle at which the light strikes increases and the intensity of light on the object decreases.	2.1, 2.2, 2.3, 2.4
The average amount of solar energy that strikes Earth's surface over a year is highest near the Equator and the intensity of the solar energy that strikes the surface decreases as you move farther away from the equator, whether you are moving north or south.	2.4, 2.5, 2.BBC, 3.4
Earth makes one complete rotation every day about its axis that is tilted with respect to the Sun. It takes a year for the planet to revolve around the Sun.	3.1
Earth's tilted axis causes differences in how solar energy strikes its surface as it moves in an orbit around the Sun.	3.2, 3.3
Seasons experienced on Earth are caused by its rotation on a tilted axis. The tilt causes either the Northern or Southern Hemisphere to have more direct sunlight and an increase in the exposure time to the Sun, creating summer conditions. The other hemisphere receives less direct sunlight and less exposure time to the sun and experiences winter.	3.4, 3.BBC

Targeted Concepts, Skills, and Nature of Science	Section
Different substances (such as soil and water) transfer heat energy at different rates and require different amounts of energy to raise their temperatures. The amount of energy needed to raise the temperature of a substance is described by its specific heat capacity.	4.2, 4.3, 4.BBC
The atmosphere is made up of molecules. The density and pressure of air decreases with increasing elevation.	5.3
Surface temperature changes with changes in elevation and air pressure. As elevation increases, the air pressure and temperature decrease. As the pressure increases the temperature increases.	5.4, 5.5, 5.6, 5.BBC
Warm air rises and molecules of air spread out and cool as they reach higher, less-dense elevations. This results in heat being transferred through the atmosphere by the convection process.	5.6
Weather moves in patterns that can be identified and tracked. Weather maps allow scientists to observe weather patterns and make predictions. Some factors that weather depends on are temperature, air pressure, wind direction, wind speed, and humidity.	6.1, 6.2
Trends in weather data show that Earth's climate is changing. Scientists believe these changes are caused by an increase in global warming due to an increase in greenhouse gases in the atmosphere.	6.2
Energy from the Sun drives Earth's water cycle. Water moves between different physical states in a continuous cycle of evaporation, condensation, and precipitation.	6.3, 6.4
Water changes state (solid, liquid, gas) by adding or removing heat energy.	6.4
Wind results from the Sun's energy heating Earth. Solar energy heats air molecules and creates areas of high and low pressure. Wind is created as air molecules move from high to low pressure areas. This is affected greatly by landforms and water on a local scale.	6.5
Changes in weather are caused when air fronts of different temperatures interact with each other. The different pressures of the fronts cause air masses to move and create precipitation and other forms of weather. Special conditions are needed to develop storms, tornados, and hurricanes.	6.6, 6.BBC

Unit Materials List

Quantities for 5 classes of 8 groups.		
Unit Durable Classroom Items	**Section**	**Quantity**
Learning Cycle Action Poster, set of 5	All	1
Project Board, laminated	1.1,1.4, 2.1, 2.3, 2.5, LS 2, 3.1, 3.4, 3.5, 4.1, 4.3, 4.5, LS 4, LS 5, 6.1, 6.4, 6.5, 6.6	5
Project Board transparency	1.1, 1.4, 2.1, 2.3, 2.5, LS 2, 3.1, 3.4, 3.5, 4.1, 4.3.4, 3.5, LS 4, 5.1, LS 5, 6.1, 6.4, 6.5, 6.6	5
My World software	1.3, 1.4, 2.4, LS 2, 3.3, LS 3, 4.4, LS 4, 5.2, 5.4, LS 5	1
US Weather map with weather symbols	6.1, 6.5, 6.6	1
75 Watt Bulb	3.2	1
Tilt mounted globe, 12" diameter	3.2	1
Electronic scale - 0.1 gram readability, 0–1500 grams	4.2, 5.5	1
Push pins, pkg. of 100	6.2	1
Hole puncher	6.2	2
Small stapler	6.2	2
Wide-mouth plastic jar with cap, 16 oz	6.3	1

Quantities for groups of 4-6 students.

Unit Consumable Group Items	Section	Quantity
Battery, D–Cell (for flashlight)	2.2, 2.1	2
Ballpoint pen	2.1, 2.2, 3.1, 3.2	1
Masking tape	2.2, 3.2, 4.2, 6.2	1
Styrofoam ball, 5 cm diameter	3.1	1
250W Reflective heat lamp	4.2	1
White poster board, 4" x 4"	6.2	1

Quantities for 5 classes of 8 groups.

Unit Consumable Classroom Items	Section	Quantity
Graph paper, pkg. of 50	2.2	1
Rubber bands, size #33, 1 lb	2.2, 6.2	1
Restickable easel pad	2.2, 4.2, 5.1, ABC II	2
Wooden skewers, 10" long, pkg. of 50	3.1	1
Construction paper, 12" x 18", pkg. of 50	3.1	1
Fine grain sand, 5 lbs	4.2	1
Duct tape	6.2	1
Paper cup, 5 oz	6.2	200
Ball of string	6.2	1
Transparent drinking straws, pkg. of 100	6.2	1
Modeling clay, 1/2 lb	6.2	1
Food coloring (Red, Blue, Green, Yellow)	6.2	1

Quantities for 5 classes of 8 groups.		
Unit Consumable Classroom Items	**Section**	**Quantity**
Unlined index cards, 3" x 5", pkg. of 100	6.2	1
Pencils, pkg. of 10	6.2	1

Additional Items Needed Not Supplied	**Section**	**Quantity**
Access to outdoor area	1.1	1 per classroom
Cardboard box, 6" x 6" x 6"	2.1	1 per group
Stack of books	2.2	1 per group
Block, cut at various angles	2.2	4 per group
Cardboard	3.2	1 per classroom
Labels (December ,March, June, September)	3.2	1 per classroom
Star to represent the North Star	3.1, 3.2	1 per classroom
Liners for cup lids, black	4.2	2 per group
Water, 200 g	4.2	1 per group
Soda bottle, 2L	5.5	1 per group
Straight-sided jar	6.2	1 per group
Wood stick or post	6.2	1 per group
Milk carton	6.2	1 per group
Small jar	6.2	1 per group
Sticker or decal	6.2	1 per group
Triangle pattern	6.2	1 per group
Ice cubes	6.3	1 per classroom
Hot water	6.3	1 per classroom

What's the Big Challenge?

Which Regions of a Newly Discovered Planet Have Surface Temperatures Appropriate for a Human Colony?

◀ *1 class period*

A class period is considered to be one 40 to 50 minute class.

Overview

Students are introduced to the *Big Challenge* of *Planetary Forecaster: Which regions of a newly discovered planet have surface temperatures appropriate for a human colony?* As part of the *Big Challenge*, students learn that they have the opportunity to work as part of a research team. The research team will make recommendations for a suitable location on *Planet X* for a human colony based on temperature. Students begin by considering what makes a place suitable for a human colony by considering where and how humans live on Earth. They focus on how the temperature and fluctuations of temperature of the region affect human life. Students share their ideas with their group members and decide on what important investigative questions pertaining to the temperature of a planet will need to be answered in order to make good recommendations for the challenge. Groups then share what they think they know and what they think they need to investigate and the class begins constructing its *Project Board*. The *Project Board* is where the class will keep track of all its ideas, questions, claims, evidence, and what it means for the challenge throughout the Unit.

Targeted Concepts, Skills, and Nature of Science	Performance Expectations
Scientists often work together and share their findings. Sharing findings makes new information available and helps scientists to refine their ideas and build on others' ideas. When another person's or group's idea is used, credit needs to be given.	Students should work in groups to identify factors they think affect the temperatures of different regions and construct questions to investigate. The class should begin construction of its *Project Board* by discussing and recording what they think they know about factors that affect temperature and habitability for humans, and what they should investigate.
Scientists must keep clear, accurate, and descriptive records of what they do so they can share their work with others and consider what they did, why they did it, and what they want to do next.	Students should keep a copy of the class *Project Board* — a detailed record to help them organize their ideas, questions, claims, evidence, and explanations.

Materials

1 per class	Class *Project Board*
1 per student	*Project Board* page

NOTES

....

....

....

....

....

....

....

Activity Setup and Preparation

Students should work in fixed groups of three or four for the entire Unit. When selecting groups, consider the goals for each student, how the material will challenge them, how they will challenge each other, and how they will share the workload.

Consider projecting the letter from the *Cooperative Space Agency* describing the *Big Challenge*. This provides a focal point for the class as the challenge is discussed. There is also a copy of the letter in the student text.

Homework Options

Reflection

- **Science Process:** Select two things that need to be investigated that were written on the class *Project Board*. How would you investigate these? What would you measure? *(Students should describe how they would test a relationship between two variables such as temperature and shape. Students should describe how they will measure the values.)*

- **Science Content:** Describe some of the things that make the environment you live in different from other places on Earth. *(Students should be able to identify the temperature or environmental conditions in their location that make it different from other places on Earth.)*

Preparation for 1.1

- **Science Process:** Describe the different ways that you learn about the temperature in your environment every day. *(Answers will vary. Students may describe using weather forecasts on TV, radio, or newspapers. They may also describe looking for clues to the temperature when they look outside.)*

NOTES

UNIT INTRODUCTION IMPLEMENTATION

◀ *1 class period**

What's the Big Challenge?

Which regions of a newly discovered planet have surface temperatures appropriate for a human colony?

Weather is an important part of your daily life. What you wear and do outside depends on the weather. Weather describes what the **atmosphere** is like at a given time and place. It includes things like temperature, precipitation, wind, **air pressure**, and humidity. Over a long period of time, these factors determine the **climate** of an area. Though humans have figured how to survive in a variety of climates, some climates require more energy to survive in than others. How do people who live in the Arctic stay warm in the winter? How do people in Texas stay cool? A group of human colonists traveling to a newly discovered planet would want to find a place to live where the temperatures never get too hot or too cold.

TO: All Potential Research Scientists
FROM: The Cooperative Space Agency
SUBJECT: Request for researchers

The Cooperative Space Agency (CSA) has been searching outside the solar system for new planets. CSA is looking for planets that could support human life. The goal of CSA is to some day establish human colonies on other planets. CSA has found a new planet very similar to Earth that revolves around a star very similar to our Sun. For now, it is called *Planet X*. This planet is the same distance from its star as Earth is from the Sun. There appears to be water on the planet. It also has an atmosphere with enough oxygen to support humans.

However, CSA has not yet found the temperature ranges on *Planet X*. This information is needed to know if the planet is appropriate for a colony. CSA is putting together a team of research scientists to find out this information. You have been selected as a possible member of this team.

Please expect another bulletin with more details at a later date.

atmosphere: the layer of gases (air) that surrounds Earth.

air pressure: the weight of all the air above an area pressing down on that area.

climate: the average condition of the weather of a place.

Advances in technology have helped scientists find several Earth-like planets. These planets are outside our solar system.

*Welcome to Planetary Forecaster.
Enjoy the challenge of being a student scientist.*

PF 3

PLANETARY FORECASTER

What's the Big Challenge

Which regions of a newly discovered planet have surface temperatures appropriate for a human colony?
5 min.

Students are introduced to the Big Challenge *of the Unit.*

○ Engage

Begin by eliciting students' ideas about the weather and making connections to their lives. Record students' ideas.

TEACHER TALK

❝What do you know about weather?

Why is the weather an important part of your life?❞

*A class period is considered to be one 40 to 50 minute class.

Ask students what they think is meant by the climate of a region. Using the student text, describe how the climate is the average condition of the weather of a place. Ask students to describe different climates and how humans survive in these climates. You may want to ask what the climate of the arctic is and what humans wear and how they live in the arctic region.

Describe how scientists have found many planets outside our solar system that they think might be able to support human life. Let students know these planets are far away and have them imagine humans traveling to the planet to form a colony. Ask students what information scientists should look for to determine if the planet could support human life before sending anyone there. Record students' responses.

Have the class read together the letter from the *CSA* in the student text.

NOTES

PBIS

Scientists have recently discovered several planets they think may be a lot like Earth. These planets are outside our solar system, so it is not possible for humans to travel to them, but imagine if they could travel to one... Scientists would want to know where the best place for people to live on that planet would be. Scientists understand a lot about the weather and climate of Earth and the advantages and disadvantages of living in these different climates. They could use what they know about Earth to predict what the climate of this other planet would be like. This is what you will be doing. Read the bulletin on the previous page.

Think About the *Big Challenge*

Your challenge for this Unit is to research one climate factor on *Planet X*. That factor is temperature. The temperature ranges on the planet will determine if it is suitable for a human colony.

habitable: suitable to live on or in.

Before you get started on any challenge, it is a good idea to organize your thinking. You will start this Unit by thinking about what areas here on Earth are **habitable** for humans and what makes them that way.

Get Started

1. What would make a place suitable for a human colony? Make a list of what you think is needed and why you think it is needed to sustain a colony.

2. As you know, people live all over the world. Carefully observe the pictures on the right. They show different regions of the world. As you look at the pictures, think about the following questions:

   • What factors do you think affect the temperatures of the different regions?

   • How much do you think the temperatures change in the different regions at different times of year?

   • Which areas do you think would be best suited for a human colony? Why?

PF 4

Project-Based Inquiry Science

Think About the *Big Challenge*

5 min.

Students are introduced to the concept of the Big Challenge *and become familiar with the work of* Planetary Forecaster.

△ Guide

Using the information in the student text, introduce students to the challenge for the Unit. Emphasize that they will be researching one climate factor—temperature—on the newly discovered *Planet X* and they will be searching for a suitable place for a human colony. Before they begin, let students know they will need to consider what makes a place habitable.

Get Started

10 min.

Students answer questions about temperature and habitability to engage thinking about the Big Challenge.

...r. These planets are ... ... solar system, so ... ...ole for humans to travel to them, but imagine if they could travel to one... Scientists would want to know where the best place for people to live on that planet would be. Scientists understand a lot about the weather and climate of Earth and the advantages and disadvantages of living in these different climates. They could use what they know about Earth to predict what the climate of this other planet would be like. This is what you will be doing. Read the bulletin on the previous page.

Think About the *Big Challenge*

Your challenge for this Unit is to research one climate factor on *Planet X*. That factor is temperature. The temperature ranges on the planet will determine if it is suitable for a human colony.

Before you get started on any challenge, it is a good idea to organize your thinking. You will start this Unit by thinking about what areas here on Earth are **habitable** for humans and what makes them that way.

habitable: suitable to live on or in.

Get Started

1. What would make a place suitable for a human colony? Make a list of what you think is needed and why you think it is needed to sustain a colony.

2. As you know, people live all over the world. Carefully observe the pictures on the right. They show different regions of the world. As you look at the pictures, think about the following questions:

   • What factors do you think affect the temperatures of the different regions?

   • How much do you think the temperatures change in the different regions at different times of year?

   • Which areas do you think would be best suited for a human colony? Why?

△ Guide

Let students know that to suggest a good place for a colony on *Planet X* they will need to consider the following questions: What do we mean when we call a place habitable? What do humans need in order to live? How does the location and environment affect these needs?

Let students know they should look over the pictures of different climate regions of Earth shown in the student text and consider what makes each of these locations different.

Tundra in the Arctic.

Desert in Africa.

Deciduous forest in New York State.

Tropical rainforest in Costa Rica.

Grassland in Wyoming.

PF 5

PLANETARY FORECASTER

⬡ Get Going

Students should write their responses to the questions clearly and in detail so they can later share their responses with their group members. Let students know how much time they have.

☐ Assess

Monitor students' responses to get a sense of where you may want to guide the discussion for the *Project Board*.

1. Students' responses should include a temperature range that allows for plant growth, animal life, and a water source.

2. Students' responses may include:

   • How far north or south the location is, or hours of daylight.

   • A description of a temperature range greatest for areas such as New York State and Wyoming, and less varied for the Tundra in the Arctic, and Desert in Africa.

   • A description of a location with vegetation and water. Students' responses should support their responses to Question 1.

NOTES

PBIS

Conference

Share your ideas with the rest of your group. Discuss the factors you thought affected the temperature of each region. Also, make sure that you understand why each group member thought an area was suitable for a human colony. You may disagree, but listen carefully to each group member's ideas.

Decide as a group what are the most important things you'll need to know about the temperature of a planet to figure out which areas are suitable for a human colony. What questions are important to investigate in order to successfully complete your challenge?

Create a *Project Board*

It is useful, when you are working on a challenge, to keep track of your progress. It is also useful to keep track of what you still need to do. Throughout this Unit, you will be using a *Project Board* to do that. During classroom discussions, your teacher or one of the students will record the class's ideas on a class *Project Board*. At the same time, you will keep track of what has been discussed on your own *Project Board* page.

Which regions of a newly discovered planet have surface temperatures appropriate for a human colony?				
What do we think we know?	What do we need to investigate?	What are we learning?	What is our evidence?	What does it mean for the challenge or question?

Conference

15 min.

Students discuss their responses to the Get Started *questions with their groups and then formulate questions to investigate.*

META NOTES

Many students will give responses indicating that habitability often depends on the presence of food or water. Make sure to follow up these responses with questions asking them to describe the conditions necessary for food or water to be present.

△ Guide

Let the class know that groups should share their responses to the *Get Started* questions making sure they understand each group member's response. When they are done discussing the questions, they should construct new questions to investigate about temperature to successfully complete the challenge.

Create a Project Board

15 min.

Create a Project Board *and start to fill it out.*

Recall that a *Project Board* has space for answering five guiding questions:

- What do we think we know?
- What do we need to investigate?
- What are we learning?
- What is our evidence?
- What does it mean for the challenge or question?

To get started on this *Project Board*, you need to identify and record the important science challenge you need to address: *Which regions of a newly discovered planet have appropriate surface temperatures for a human colony?*

What do we think we know?

In this column of the *Project Board*, you will record what you think you know about surface temperature and temperatures suitable for a colony. Discuss and post the things you and your classmates think you know. Have you studied these concepts before? What did you study? Even if it is a small fact or idea, talk about it. Discuss any factors that you might think affect the temperature of a region.

What do we need to investigate?

In this column, you will record the things you need to investigate. During your group conference, you may have found that you and others in your group disagreed with some of your ideas. You may not know exactly what determines the temperature of a region. This second column is designed to help you keep track of things that are debatable, unknown, and need to be investigated.

Later in this Unit, you will return to the *Project Board.* For now, work with your classmates as you begin filling in the first two columns.

PF 7

PLANETARY FORECASTER

△ Guide

Transition students by reviewing what they have done, what they need to do, and how the *Project Board* will keep track of their ideas and the information they gather.

"You have already begun to address the *Big Challenge* of finding a good place to colonize *Planet X*. You have begun to consider the concepts of temperature, climate, and habitability. We need a good way to keep track of all the information we gather and our ideas about what to investigate. To do this we will use a class *Project Board*."

It may be helpful to review the *Big Challenge* again at this point. If possible, post the letter from the *CSA* as an overhead during the creation of the *Project Board*. This will help stimulate ideas on what must be investigated.

Remind students of the five columns of the *Project Board* using the student text. Let students know that they will be focusing on filling out the first two columns: *What do we think we know?* and *What do we need to investigate?*

Post the *Project Board* in a prominent location in the classroom and tell students that they will be updating it constantly throughout this project as they learn and develop new ideas and questions.

Elicit students' ideas for the first column and record them. Encourage student-led class discussion. Focus on recording all of the thoughts, ideas, and preconceptions expressed by the students.

◇ Evaluate

Students should include a description of temperature range and climate that can support vegetation and animal life. They should also note the need for water.

△ Guide

Ask students what questions they came up with in their groups that they think should be investigated in order to complete the challenge. Record students' questions.

◇ Evaluate

Students' questions should pertain to what affects surface temperature and how temperature relates to the habitability of a region.

META NOTES

The *Big Challenge* will involve learning about the various factors that affect surface temperatures on Earth. The *Planetary Forecaster* program will highlight four main factors: shape, tilt, land/air differences, and elevation. In the beginning, students may be unfamiliar with these concepts. At this point, they only need to be thinking about their concepts of temperature. The four factors will be introduced at the end of *Learning Set 1*.

NOTES

Learning Set 1

What Is Temperature and How Does It Differ Across Earth's Surface?

◀ $5\frac{1}{2}$ *class periods*

A class period is considered to be one 40 to 50 minute class.

Students behave as scientists as they construct prediction temperature maps and surface temperature maps for Earth, and consider what makes a location habitable for humans.

Overview

Students consider the surface temperature of Earth and how it relates to what makes a location habitable. Students are given a bulletin from the *Cooperative Space Agency* describing the discovery of a new planet it wants to colonize. To do so, its scientists need to learn where the habitable places are on the planet and what the planet's temperatures are like. The students are told the planet is much like Earth, but details on the temperature are purposely withheld. Throughout this *Learning Set*, students have to think about what they need to know in order to complete the mission. Students articulate their initial ideas about temperature patterns on Earth and the causes of variations in temperature at different locations. They draw prediction temperature maps of Earth's global temperatures to demonstrate any ideas they might have about temperature variation and its causes. Students share and discuss their predictions with their classmates in groups and as a class. Students familiarize themselves with the *My World* software as they reproduce their paper maps on the computer, compare their predictions with real data, and speculate the causes for any differences. Students explore habitable locations on Earth and patterns in surface temperatures on Earth. From these patterns, students try to determine what factors affect surface temperature.

LOOKING AHEAD

This *Learning Set* will introduce students to *My World* software. Students will use this software throughout the Unit as a tool to solve the *Big Challenge*. You should be familiar with how to use this software and have it ready and available for the students. Directions on how to use the software are in the student text. It would be best to have one computer available per group of students. If this is not possible, consider how you will efficiently set up computer usage. Students will be constructing prediction maps they will share with the class. Consider having students share their maps using a projection system. Consider how you will save and store students' maps.

Targeted Concepts, Skills, and Nature of Science	Section
Scientists often work together and share their findings. Sharing findings makes new information available and helps scientists to refine their ideas and build on others' ideas. When another person's or group's idea is used, credit needs to be given.	1.1, 1.3, 1.BBC

Targeted Concepts, Skills, and Nature of Science	Section
Scientists must keep clear, accurate, and descriptive records of what they do so they can share their work with others and consider what they did, why they did it, and what they want to do next.	1.1, 1.3, 1.4, 1.BBC
Graphs, maps, and tables are an effective way to analyze and communicate results of scientific investigation.	1.1, 1.3, 1.4, 1.BBC
Identifying factors that lead to variation is an important part of scientific investigation.	1.1, 1.4
Scientists make claims (conclusions) based on evidence obtained (trends in data) from reliable investigations	1.5
Heat energy may be transferred through conduction, radiation, or convection.	1.2
Temperature is a measurement of the average kinetic energy of atoms and molecules. Surface temperature is the temperature measured near a planet's surface.	1.2
Temperatures around Earth's surface vary widely, but can be predicted somewhat by location and season.	1.3, 1.4
Habitable areas of Earth are determined by average temperatures suitable for humans to live. These areas are often broken up into biomes, which are a group of ecosystems that have the same general climate and similar plants and animals.	1.5

NOTES

....

....

....

....

....

....

Students' Initial Conceptions and Capabilities

- Students use their prior knowledge to create a prediction map of global surface air temperatures in July and a list of questions they have about differences in temperature at different locations around the world. The maps are designed to elicit students' initial ideas about temperature. Students' ideas should not be assessed for accuracy; rather, their misconceptions should be noted and addressed in subsequent activities.

- The students' abilities to create and use visualizations should be assessed in this *Learning Set.* By the end of the *Learning Set,* students need to be able to interpret and construct temperature maps using a color representation.

- Some students think that some of the less tangible forms of energy such as light, sound, and chemical energy are not capable of making things happen (Carr & Kirkwood, 1988).

- Some students think that energy transformations involve only one form of energy at a time (Brooke & Wells, 1988).

- Students often do not connect heat transfers with an interaction. They tend to believe that objects cool down or release heat spontaneously (Kesidou, 1990; Wiser, 1986).

- Students often do not explain heating and cooling in terms of heat being transferred (Tiberghien, 1983; Tomasini & Balandi, 1987). Some students think that cold is being transferred from a colder to a warmer object (Brook & Driver, 1984). Some students think cold and heat are being transferred simultaneously between two objects of different temperature (Brook & Driver, 1984).

- Students often believe temperature is a measure of heat, and are very resistant to changing this idea (Linn & Songer, 1991). Even after a few courses in physics, students often do not distinguish between heat and temperature when they discuss thermal phenomena (Kesidou & Duit, 1993; Tiberghien, 1983; Wiser 1988).

- Students often bring up the Moon as a possible factor that affects temperature. The Moon has no effect on Earth's temperatures. The gravitational attraction between the Earth, Moon, and Sun causes tides.

Understanding for Teachers

Thermal and Heat Energies

The words thermal energy and heat energy are often interchanged, even though they mean different things. Thermal energy is the internal energy of a substance that is affected when heat is added. Thermal energy depends on the temperature of the substance and its mass.

When heat energy is added to a substance, it may increase the average kinetic energy of the molecules making up the substance. The average kinetic energy of the atoms/molecules making up a substance is its temperature.

If the substance is undergoing a phase change (e.g. solid to liquid, liquid to gas, etc), the temperature does not change because the overall temperature or average kinetic energy of all the atoms/molecules does not change. During a phase change for a substance in its solid state, a transfer of kinetic energy from the more energetic atoms/molecules to the less energetic atoms/molecules occurs until all the atoms/molecules have become energetic enough to break the bonds that held them in place. When this occurs, all the atoms/molecules are in a liquid state. After all the atoms/molecules are in the liquid state, the temperature begins to rise again if more heat is added.

As a liquid substance is heated, the liquid molecules gain kinetic energy. The average kinetic energy rises and so the does temperature. This occurs until the liquid reaches its boiling point. At this point, the atoms/molecules become energetic enough that some of the bonds break and the atoms/molecules fly apart from each other forming a gas. The temperature does not rise because the liquid particles cannot move any faster without escaping the liquid state.

Heat energy is the energy transferred from one object to another during an interaction that increases the average kinetic energy of the substance on the molecular level (the temperature) or changes the phase of the substance. The volume of the substance may also change when heat is transferred to it. Most solids will expand when heated. Their atoms/molecules are more energetic and move back and forth with a greater amplitude even though they are still held in place. Water is an exception to this. At water's freezing point it expands. Ice molecules take up more space than the same number of water molecules in the liquid state.

Fundamentally, thermal energy is the kinetic energy (energy of motion) at the atomic level.

Conduction, Convection, and Radiation Interactions

Heat energy is transferred between two objects of different temperatures by means of conduction, convection, or radiation.

During a conduction interaction, the two interacting objects must be touching each other and one object must be warmer. The two objects could be any state of matter such as a solid cube of ice interacting with the gaseous air around it, or cool liquid interacting with a solid cup. In this case, heat energy is transferred between the two objects through collisions between atoms/molecules. This continues until the two objects have the same average kinetic energy or temperature. When the two objects have the same temperature they are said to be in thermal equilibrium. Collisions still occur between the atoms/molecules. However, no net transfer of energy results from these collisions.

Heat transfer by convection occurs when the atoms/molecules of the substance are not fixed in place (such as in a liquid or gas) and when gravity is acting on the substance. As heat is transferred to the object, its atoms/molecules expand and become less dense. The less dense atoms/molecules rise above the more dense molecules, colliding with less energetic molecules. As they transfer their kinetic energy through collisions they become denser (needing less room to move around) and sink. Heat transferred by convection still requires contact between particles and a temperature difference, but also requires that the particles be able to move through the substance.

Heat transfer by radiation requires no contact between the particles of the warmer object and the cooler object. In this case, electromagnetic radiation emitted by the warmer object is absorbed by the cooler object. The electromagnetic energy absorbed can be transformed into kinetic energy, resulting in the increased motion of the atoms/molecules.

NOTES

....

....

....

....

....

....

....

....

NOTES

LEARNING SET 1 IMPLEMENTATION

◀ 5½ *class periods* *

Learning Set 1

What Is Temperature and How Does It Differ Across Earth's Surface?

Learning Set 1

What Is Temperature and How Does It Differ Across Earth's Surface?

10 min.

Students are introduced to the first step of the Big Challenge, *to understand temperature and to look for surface temperature patterns.*

CSA

TO: All potential research scientists
FROM: The Cooperative Space Agency
SUBJECT: Exploring Earth's temperatures

The Cooperative Space Agency (CSA) suggests that you begin your investigation into the temperatures found on *Planet X* by first understanding temperatures found on Earth. In order to communicate with other scientists on this team, you must be able to use the same language. In your daily life, you may use the words temperature and heat interchangeably. To a scientist, however, they have different meanings. What is temperature and what is heat? How do they relate to one another?

In order to share information and communicate, scientists also use another type of language—the language of measurement. Like all other measurements, temperature is measured with a tool and communicated with a number and unit. How is temperature measured and what units are used to describe it?

From your earlier observation of different regions of Earth, you probably understand that not all regions are heated equally. As you study temperature patterns around the world, you need to begin asking yourself why. Remain confident that everything you discover about temperature on Earth will be of value in your final analysis of *Planet X*.

More details will follow in a future bulletin.

Recall that your *Big Challenge* is to determine if *Planet X* has areas with surface temperatures that can support human life. You have brainstormed ideas about what makes an area habitable. You may have used words, such as "very hot" or "too cold." But what do these words mean? Your next step is to construct some useful knowledge that will help you be more specific.

Read the urgent message on the left. You will find some smaller questions that will help you succeed with the *Big Challenge*.

Project-Based Inquiry Science

META NOTES

Eliciting students' initial ideas will help to identify their misconceptions and address them as needed. Refer to the *Understanding for Teachers* segment in the introduction to this *Learning Set* for common initial ideas that students have.

○ Engage

Ask students what they think the difference is between temperature and heat. Record their responses.

△ Guide

Let students know that heat and temperature are different and people often use these words interchangeably, but scientists do not. Let students know that they will learn more about heat and temperature soon.

*A class period is considered to be one 40 to 50 minute class.

Introduce the bulletin from *CSA*. If possible, project the bulletin in the student text. Let students know that this bulletin discusses how they will begin to answer the *Big Challenge*. Read the bulletin to your class or have your students read it aloud.

If your students are not familiar with astronomy terms, consider briefly discussing that our Sun is the center of our solar system and that the planets are kept in their orbits by gravitational attraction. *Planet X* is in a different solar system, and it is approximately the same distance from its sun as the Earth is from our sun.

◇ **Evaluate**

Ask students to answer the following questions:

1. What is known about *Planet X?*

   Students should describe how Planet X *is similar to Earth. It is the same distance from its star as Earth is from the Sun. There appears to be water on the planet and has an atmosphere with enough oxygen to support humans.*

2. What information does the *CSA* still need to know about *Planet X?*

   Students' responses should clearly state that knowledge of temperature ranges is not known for Planet X.

3. How does the *CSA* want you to get started?

   Students should state that the first step is to investigate and understand temperatures found on Earth.

NOTES

....

....

....

....

....

....

1.1 Understand the Challenge

Think About the Questions

◀ $\frac{1}{2}$ *class period*

A class period is considered to be one 40 to 50 minute class.

Overview

Students begin to consider how temperature is measured, how it varies in different locations, and what factors may affect it. Students do this by measuring the temperature in a given area for different locations and elevations. Using all the data collected, the class considers how the temperatures in the area vary and what factors could have affected the temperatures.

Targeted Concepts, Skills, and Nature of Science	Performance Expectations
Scientists often work together and share their findings. Sharing findings makes new information available and helps scientists to refine their ideas and build on others' ideas. When another person's or group's idea is used, credit needs to be given.	Students should share their data with the class and together consider the factors that could have affected the temperature readings.
Scientists must keep clear, accurate, and descriptive records of what they do so they can share their work with others and consider what they did, why they did it, and what they want to do next.	Students should have clear records of their temperature measurements and they should update the class *Project Board*.
Graphs, maps, and tables are an effective way to analyze and communicate results of scientific investigation.	Students should analyze the class data from a class data chart.
Identifying factors that lead to variation is an important part of scientific investigation.	Students should begin to identify factors that lead to variation in temperatures in a given area.

Materials	
1 per student	Thermometer *Project Board* page
1 per class	Class *Project Board*

Activity Setup and Preparation

Consider if you want students to take more than one measurement reading and get the average temperature of a location. Check the area in which you want students to take temperature readings. An area that contains vegetation, concrete, shade, and sunlight will be good to take temperatures. Students should not wander into unsafe areas while taking readings. Notify students before class so they can prepare and dress appropriately.

Homework Options

Reflection

- **Science Process:** How would you test for the factors that affected the temperature measurements? List the variables and the procedure you would follow. *(Students should describe how they would test the relationship between the factor and the temperature. They should list the variables and the procedure they would follow.)*

Preparation for 1.2

- **Science Process:** What do you think temperature is a measurement of? *(The purpose of this question is to have students think about what temperature is before it is discussed in the next section.)*

SECTION 1.1 IMPLEMENTATION

1.1 Understand the Challenge

Think About the Question

The question for this *Learning Set* is *What is temperature and how does it differ across Earth's surface?* It is a good idea to think about what you already know about temperature. It is also important to think about what you are not sure about and what you would like to investigate.

Get Started

Obtain a thermometer from your teacher. If your thermometer is made of glass or has glass parts, you must be very careful when handling it. With your teacher, go outside and choose a place to measure the temperature. Your teacher will tell you where you can go to measure. Record your temperature readings and the following information:

⚠️ Be careful with glass thermometers. Alert your teacher immediately if a thermometer breaks.

- the location where you measured the temperature

- the approximate height at which you held the thermometer while measuring the temperature

- the scale you used to record the temperature, Fahrenheit (F) or Celsius (C)

PF 9

PLANETARY FORECASTER

1.1 Understand the Challenge

Think About the Question

5 min.

Students share their ideas about temperature.

○ **Engage**

Display the class *Project Board* and review any items the class listed in the first column (*What do we think we know?*) that pertain to temperature.

Ask the class if there is anything they know about temperature that is not listed on their *Project Board*. Record students' ideas.

*A class period is considered to be one 40 to 50 minute class.

Get Started

20 min.

Students obtain and record the temperature of a location outside the classroom.

already know ~~about~~ temperature. It is also important to think about what you are not sure about and what you would like to investigate.

Get Started

Obtain a thermometer from your teacher. If your thermometer is made of glass or has glass parts, you must be very careful when handling it. With your teacher, go outside and choose a place to measure the temperature. Your teacher will tell you where you can go to measure. Record your temperature readings and the following information:

Be careful with glass thermometers. Alert your teacher immediately if a thermometer breaks.

- the location where you measured the temperature
- the approximate height at which you held the thermometer while measuring the temperature
- the scale you used to record the temperature, Fahrenheit (F) or Celsius (C)

△ Guide

Let students know they will be taking measurements of temperature in various locations in a given area outside. Students must stay within the area you specify. Remind students they must record the location of the measured temperature, the approximate height at which the thermometer was held, and the temperature measurement with units. Warn students they will need to be careful with the glass thermometers and discuss glass safety.

Pass out the thermometers and let students examine them. Discuss the temperature scale (Celsius and/or Fahrenheit). All students will need to measure temperature using the same scale so that measurements can be compared.

Emphasize to students that they should not wander out of the area you selected.

◇ Evaluate

Make sure students have recorded all the required information. Students should include a description of the location and the height at which each temperature was recorded.

△ Guide

Record each student's temperature readings and location on a classroom chart. Cover up the information pertaining to location to discuss later.

Have a class discussion on the first two bulleted questions in the student text and record what factors students think affected their temperature readings. Ask students for their reasoning behind the factors they chose.

When you return to your classroom, your teacher will record all your temperature readings on a chart. Discuss the following questions with the class:

- Were everyone's temperature readings the same? If not, how different were they?
- What factors could have affected the temperature readings?

Your teacher will write on the chart the location and the height at which each reading was taken. Look at the chart again and discuss the following questions:

- What factors seemed to affect the temperature readings?
- What factor appeared to cause the biggest difference in the temperature readings?

Update the *Project Board*

Before you begin the investigations and readings in this *Learning Set*, it is a good idea to update the *Project Board*. Look at the last message you received from the CSA. It asked you to think about several questions. You may wish to add these questions to the *Project Board*. You may already have some ideas about the answers to these questions. You can add these to the board as well. The temperature readings you took outside the classroom may also have prompted some interesting questions. Note that questions you put on the *Project Board* should not have a yes/no answer. Also, the questions should help you in addressing the *Big Challenge*.

Which regions of a newly discovered planet have surface temperatures appropriate for a human colony?				
What do we think we know?	**What do we need to investigate?**	**What are we learning?**	**What is our evidence?**	**What does it mean for the challenge or question?**

Display the location data with the temperature data. Ask students to consider the two bulleted questions. Ask students for what they now think the factors are that affect temperature and update their list of factors by removing the ones they no longer think are factors and including new factors. Ask students what factor appeared to cause the biggest difference in temperature ranges and why they think it did. Have the class refer to the chart as they answer the questions using data and information to support their answers.

Update the Project Board

10 min.

• What factor appeared to cause the biggest difference in the temperature readings?

Update the *Project Board*

Before you begin the investigations and readings in this *Learning Set*, it is a good idea to update the *Project Board*. Look at the last message you received from the CSA. It asked you to think about several questions. You may wish to add these questions to the *Project Board*. You may already have some ideas about the answers to these questions. You can add these to the board as well. The temperature readings you took outside the classroom may also have prompted some interesting questions. Note that questions you put on the *Project Board* should not have a yes/no answer. Also, the questions should help you in addressing the *Big Challenge*.

△ Guide

Transition the class to updating the *Project Board*.

❝You have taken various temperature readings and thought about what factors might affect the temperature. Now you should think about how we should investigate these factors. To begin, think about what investigative question you could ask. We will put these on the class *Project Board*.❞

◇ Evaluate

Students should list in Column 2 (*What do we need to investigate?*) questions that relate to the factors they think affect temperature. Some examples are provided below for the possible factor of height above the ground:

- *Does the temperature increase as we move further above the ground?*

- *Does the temperature decrease as we move further above the ground?*

- *How does the temperature vary as we move higher above the ground?*

Assessment Options

Targeted Concepts, Skills, and Nature of Science	How do I know if students got it?
Graphs, maps, and tables are an effective way to analyze and communicate results of scientific investigation.	**ASK:** How did the chart of temperatures and locations help you to analyze the data? **LISTEN:** Students should recogrize that having the available information in a chart makes it easier to view all the data, compare data points, find trends and find possible factors in the data.
Identifying factors that lead to variation is an important part of scientific investigation.	**ASK:** What is a factor and why is it important to identify them? **LISTEN:** Students should define factors as variables that affect temperature. They should also state that it is important to identify the factors that affect temperature in order to understand what makes a climate habitable or not.

Teacher Reflection Questions

- Did students understand the importance of temperature and the factors that affect it for the *Big Challenge?*

- How well were students able to express their thoughts and questions on the *Project Board?*

- How were you able to engage students and keep them focused when they worked with their groups and individually to take temperature readings? What would you do differently?

NOTES

1.2 Read

Measuring Temperature

◀ *1 class period*

A class period is considered to be one 40 to 50 minute class.

Overview

Students read about what temperature is, how a thermometer works, the difference between heat and temperature, and one of the ways heat energy can be transferred. Students begin by considering air on the atomic level and how air particles are constantly moving. They are introduced to the energy associated with movement—kinetic energy. The class discusses temperature as the average kinetic energy of the atoms and molecules in the air around the thermometer. Students read a description about what happens to the liquid in a thermometer as it warms up due to a conduction interaction between the air, the glass bulb of the thermometer, and the liquid in the thermometer. Students will apply this knowledge in the next section when they construct a prediction map of surface temperatures for *Planet X*.

Targeted Concepts, Skills, and Nature of Science	Performance Expectations
Heat energy may be transferred through conduction, radiation, or convection.	Students should describe the difference between temperature (average kinetic energy) and heat (energy transferred), and that heat energy may be transferred through conduction which requires that the objects are in contact with each other and one object is warmer than the other.
	A discussion on radiation is optional. In the discussion, students should describe heat transferred by radiation as an interaction between two objects of different temperatures that do not touch. They interact and transfer heat energy by the warmer object emitting electromagnetic radiation that is absorbed by the cooler object. Students should also be able to provide an example and note that this is how Earth receives energy from the Sun.

Targeted Concepts, Skills, and Nature of Science	Performance Expectations
Temperature is a measurement of the average kinetic energy of atoms and molecules. Surface temperature is the temperature measured near a planet's surface.	Students should describe that the temperature of an area is a measure of average kinetic energy of atoms and molecules in that area and relate this to how a thermometer works.

Homework Options

Reflection

- **Science Process:** Describe the conduction interaction between warm food and a cool dish. What are the requirements for a conduction interaction to occur? *(Students' responses should include that a conduction interaction requires two objects in contact and a temperature difference between them. Heat energy is transferred from the warmer object (warm food) to the cooler object (dish). Students should describe the atoms and molecules of the warm food having more kinetic energy than the molecules in the dish and how the molecules of food transfer kinetic energy to the molecules in the dish during collisions between the two.)*

- **Science Process:** What are the highs and lows of the day for where you live? Where did you get this information? Where do you think these temperatures were taken? How do you think the temperature varies for your street? Where you live? *(Students' responses should include the high and low temperatures of the day and their source. Students should show they understand temperatures vary due to location.)*

Preparation for 1.3

- **Science Content:** What do you think the temperature ranges will be tomorrow for each continent? Describe where the highs and lows might occur for each continent. *(The purpose of this is to get students to think about how temperatures range around the globe and to elicit any ideas they have about how temperature may change with latitude. Consider providing students with a copy of a world map such the one shown in Section 1.3)*

SECTION 1.2 IMPLEMENTATION

1.2 Read

Measuring Temperature

What Is Temperature?

You just used a thermometer to measure the outside **temperature**. Think about what you were actually measuring. You might say that you measured how hot or cold the air was. However, when scientists talk about temperature, they are referring to something more specific.

Air is made up of microscopic particles called **atoms** and **molecules**. Even though you cannot see these particles, you know they are there. You can feel them fill up your lungs when you breathe in, and you can fill up a balloon with them by blowing air into it.

Scientists have discovered that these particles are constantly moving. When these particles absorb energy, they move faster. This faster movement causes the air to feel warm to us. When we measure the temperature of air, we are actually measuring the speed at which the individual molecules and atoms in the air are moving. Scientists call the energy of moving objects "kinetic energy." The temperature measured by a thermometer is the average kinetic energy of the atoms and molecules in the air around the thermometer.

temperature: a measure of the average amount of kinetic energy found in the molecules of a substance.

atom: a tiny particle of matter.

molecule: two or more atoms bound together.

In summer, the high kinetic energy of the air molecules at this South Carolina beach keeps the temperature warm enough to swim.

PF 11

PLANETARY FORECASTER

1.2 Read

Measuring Temperature

5 min.

What Is Temperature?

10 min.

Students have a discussion on what temperature is.

META NOTES

This section will help students understand how surface temperatures are related to energy received from the Sun. It will also give them an understanding of how energy and temperature move along the surface of Earth.

○ **Engage**

Elicit students' ideas on what temperature is and record their ideas.

△ **Guide**

Emphasize that temperature is the average kinetic energy (or energy of motion) of the atoms and molecules near your measuring device. Let students know that all matter (solids, liquids, and gases) is made up of atoms and molecules that are constantly moving.

*A class period is considered to be one 40 to 50 minute class.

Discuss how these particles move faster as they absorb energy and slower when they transfer energy to another particle it interacts with. Again emphasize that the temperature measured by a thermometer is equal to the average kinetic energy of the atoms and molecules surrounding the thermometer.

NOTES

How Do Scientists Measure Temperature?

In this Unit, we will be talking about **surface temperature**. The surface temperature is the temperature of the air a short distance above the ground.

The air closest to Earth's surface is not exactly the same temperature as the actual surface, but it is close. As Earth's surface begins to heat up or cool down, so does the air just above it.

Thermometers are the most familiar tools scientists use to measure temperature. A common type is a bulb thermometer. Bulb thermometers work very simply.

The bulb at the bottom of the thermometer is full of a liquid. When you place the bulb in a location that is hotter or cooler than the bulb, the bulb and its liquid heat up or cool down until they reach the same temperature as their surroundings. As with air, when the liquid heats up, the atoms and molecules in the liquid move faster. When the particles in a liquid move faster, they collide with each other and push each other farther apart. As the particles move faster in the liquid in the thermometer, the liquid expands. Trapped inside the narrow tube, the only place for the expanding liquid to go is into the tube. If you place the bulb in a cooler location, the liquid particles will move more slowly. They will move closer together. The liquid in the tube will now take up less space, and its level will drop down inside the tube.

The marks on the side of the tube are a measure of how much the liquid has expanded. By measuring how much the liquid expands into the tube, you can measure the temperature of the liquid. The distance between the marks on the side of the thermometer is measured in units called degrees (°). Degrees (°) are the units scientists use to measure temperature. Just like meters (or feet) are used to measure distance, degrees are used to measure temperature.

You might wonder what causes the liquid in the bulb to heat up or cool off when it is placed in warm or cool air. Why doesn't it stay the same temperature? The answer is that the kinetic energy in the air gets transferred to the liquid in the bulb through a process called **conduction**. The moving particles in the air collide with the particles in the glass outside the bulb. These collisions cause the particles in the glass to move around.

surface temperature: air temperatures measured around 1.25 m (4 ft. 1 in.) to 2 m (6 ft. 7 in.) above the ground.

conduction: the transfer of heat energy from a substance of higher temperature to one of lower temperature through direct contact.

PF 12

Project-Based Inquiry Science

How Do Scientists Measure Temperature?

10 min.

Students discuss how a thermometer works to measure temperature.

META NOTES

Consider discussing heat transferred by radiation, particularly if it is one of your state standards. Heat transferred by convection is discussed in a later *Learning Set.*

⚠ Guide

Discuss what is meant by surface temperature. Explain that it is the temperature of air from 1.25 m to 2 m above the ground. Let students know they will be trying to predict what the surface temperatures are for *Planet X*.

Discuss how the air closest to Earth's surface is not the same temperature as the surface and it warms up and cools down as Earth's surface warms up or cools down.

Students can read this section before or after you discuss this process.

Consider providing an example such as a cup of hot cocoa. Some heat energy is transferred through the air to nearby hands because of a conduction interaction. Some energy is transferred through electromagnetic radiation to nearby hands because of a radiation interaction. During a conduction interaction, collisions between the molecules of hot cocoa and the molecules in your cup increase the average kinetic energy of the molecules in your cup and they warm up. Collisions between the molecules of your cup and the molecules in air warm the air. Collisions between the energetic molecules of air and the molecules in your hands warm your hands. Your hands are also warmed by electromagnetic radiation emitted from the molecules of the hot cocoa and the cup. These molecules do not interact with the air molecules, but with the molecules in your hand. When this radiation strikes your hand, it increases the kinetic energy of the molecules in your hand and the temperature of your hand.

Ask students what temperature is and what is happening to a molecule that has more kinetic energy, or a higher temperature. Guide them to understand it is moving faster, since the mass has not changed.

Using the information in the student text, discuss the process that takes place between the air and the liquid thermometer.

NOTES

....

....

....

....

....

"When molecules and atoms get warmer, they move around more, causing them to take up more space for movement. This is why an object expands when it is warmed.

The molecules of air around the thermometer bulb are moving and colliding with the glass surrounding the liquid. This gets the molecules of glass moving more. These molecules collide with neighboring molecules of glass until they are all moving with the same average kinetic energy as the surrounding air. These molecules of glass next to the liquid collide with the molecules of liquid and transfer kinetic energy to them. The molecules of liquid start moving around more and have nowhere to go but up the thin glass tube.

The energy transferred during this process is called heat energy. It is the energy that gets transferred from the air to the glass to the liquid. The liquid rises due to its increased average kinetic energy and we read a scale marked next to it to determine the temperature.

This type of interaction is called a conduction interaction. It requires that the objects are in contact with each other, or touching, and that one object has a higher temperature than the other. In this case, the warmer air was in contact with the glass. Then the warmer glass was in contact with the liquid. When they all have the same average kinetic energy, then there is no longer an overall transfer of heat energy and they are said to all have the same temperature."

META NOTES

Students might think heat and cold are different, rather than being opposite ends of a spectrum. Ask them to describe hot and cold in terms of energy. Encourage them to create a drawing or diagram as part of their answer. Emphasize that heat energy is always transferred from the warmer object to the cooler object.

Let students know they will be using the Fahrenheit scale for measuring temperature because it is the scale used in the United States and probably what they are most familiar with.

△ Guide and Assess

Ask students for other examples of heat conduction such as a hot handle on a cooking pot or water that becomes hot as its container is heated.

Stop and Think

15 min.

Students discuss their responses to the reading with the class.

META NOTES

Section 1.2 introduces several physical science concepts to students in order to explain how kinetic energy is responsible for temperature. Students should understand how temperature is related to kinetic energy. It is not necessary for students to have an in-depth knowledge of the content in order for them to understand and progress through the Unit. Make sure that the students understand the basic concepts.

1.2 Read

Conduction

The flame from the candle heats up the metal bar. When you touch the metal bar it feels hot. Heat is being transferred to your hand by conduction.

heat: a form of energy associated with the motion of particles or molecules

As a result, the glass's kinetic energy increases, and its temperature goes up. The particles in the glass then collide with the particles in the liquid, causing them to move faster, as well. In this conduction process, the kinetic energy, or **heat**, gets transferred from the air to the glass and from the glass to the liquid. After a while, the average kinetic energy of the particles in the air, the glass, and the liquid all become equal. They all reach the same temperature.

There are different scales used to measure temperature. The thermometer in the picture on the right shows the Fahrenheit and Celsius scales. When you write a temperature, you should always include the unit and scale, such as 0°C or 32°F. Fahrenheit is commonly used to measure air temperature in the United States. Most other countries use the Celsius scale. Celsius is the scale that most scientists use, as well. In this Unit, you will use the Fahrenheit scale, because that is what is commonly used in the U.S. to describe weather and climate.

Stop and Think

1. What makes some air feel hotter than other air?

2. What is the relationship between temperature and kinetic energy?

3. Why are the marks on a thermometer evenly spaced?

4. Why does the length that the liquid extends into the tube of a thermometer give you a measure of temperature?

5. What areas of Earth do you think have higher average surface temperatures? What areas do you think have lower average surface temperatures? Give your reasoning.

PF 13

PLANETARY FORECASTER

⬡ Get Going

Let students know they should answer all the questions and a class discussion will follow. Inform them of how much time they have.

△ Guide and Assess

Have a class discussion on students' responses. Use the information below to help assess students' responses and guide the discussion.

1. Students' responses should include that the warmer air molecules on average have more kinetic energy than molecules in the cooler air.

2. Students' responses should state that an increase in the average kinetic energy results in an increase of the temperature.

3. The answer to this question is directly related to the answer to Question 4. Consider answering both of these questions together. When designing a thermometer, it is easiest to read in a linear scale because the temperature increases by the same amount for each increment of height. The selection of fluid and the diameter of the tube should be carefully chosen.

4. Students may need more guidance with this question. The thermometer is designed so the liquid rises the same for each equal increase in average kinetic energy. This results in equal spacing for the measuring scale.

5. Students should share their ideas about places they think have higher or lower average surface temperature and give reasons to support their answer. Encourage students to define average surface temperature.

> **META NOTES**
>
> Consider discussing how kinetic energy is related to mass and speed. When comparing the same amount (mass) of the same objects (air and air), the only thing that will make the average kinetic energy different is the speed of the object. Warmer air means air moving with greater speeds.

△ Guide

Remind students that their goal is to determine the temperature ranges of *Planet X* to decide where human life may be supported.

NOTES

....

....

....

....

....

....

What's the Point?

Your goal is to determine if *Planet X* has temperature ranges that can support human life. You will map the temperatures of this planet. Then you will decide where a colony of humans can be established. You know that *Planet X* is the same distance from its star as Earth is from the Sun, and its star is very similar to our Sun. You also know that the two planets are very similar. You will be able to apply what you now know about temperatures on Earth to make recommendations about *Planet X*.

You are a member of the research team investigating this new planet. You will be required to discuss surface temperatures with others. You just read about some basic information about temperature. You should now be able to communicate with others about temperature.

A view of Earth from space, showing its Sun.

Assessment Options

Targeted Concepts, Skills, and Nature of Science	How do I know if students got it?
Heat energy may be transferred through conduction, radiation, or convection.	**ASK:** How is heat transferred between objects? **LISTEN:** Students should describe that heat energy may be transferred from one object to another by conduction. They should also describe the requirements of conduction. Conduction requires the objects to be in contact with each other and that one object is warmer than the other. If you discussed heat transfer by radiation, students should be able to describe how heat transferred to an object from electromagnetic radiation travels from a warmer source to the object. This radiation can travel in vacuum.
Temperature is a measurement of the average kinetic energy of atoms and molecules. Surface temperature is the temperature measured near a planet's surface.	**ASK:** What is temperature? **LISTEN:** Students should describe the temperature of an object as a measure of the average kinetic energy of atoms and molecules of the object.

Teacher Reflection Questions

- What difficulties did students have with the concepts of temperature, heat, and conduction?
- How did the *Stop and Think* questions assist students understanding?
- How did you guide students through the discussions surrounding the *Stop and Think* questions? What would you do differently?

NOTES

1.3 Investigate

Creating a Prediction Map on Paper and in My World

◀ *2 class periods*

A class period is considered to be one 40 to 50 minute class.

Overview

Students examine a temperature map of the United States. They use this map as an example of a visualization that shows temperature data in value and a color code. Students articulate their initial ideas about temperature patterns on Earth and the causes of variations in temperature at different locations. They draw a prediction map of color-coded temperatures for the world to show ideas they have about temperature variation. Students support their ideas with their reasoning. They share and discuss their predictions with their group members, refine them, and map out their final group prediction map using *My World*. This is an introduction to the *My World* software that students will use throughout the Unit.

Targeted Concepts, Skills, and Nature of Science	Performance Expectations
Scientists often work together and share their findings. Sharing findings makes new information available and helps scientists to refine their ideas and build on others' ideas. When another person's or group's idea is used, credit needs to be given.	Students should work individually to construct global temperature prediction maps. In groups they should refine their ideas and come up with a group prediction map.
Scientists must keep clear, accurate, and descriptive records of what they do so they can share their work with others and consider what they did, why they did it, and what they want to do next.	Students should keep clear and descriptive records of the reasoning behind their prediction maps, as well as clear notes of their prediction maps. In the next section, they will compare these maps with real data.

Targeted Concepts, Skills, and Nature of Science	Performance Expectations
Graphs, maps, and tables are an effective way to analyze and communicate results of scientific investigation.	Students should construct global temperature prediction maps to articulate and communicate their ideas. In the next section, students will compare their prediction maps with real data.
Temperatures around Earth's surface vary widely, but can be predicted by location and season.	Students should predict average temperature ranges around Earth for the month of July.

Materials	
6 per student	Colored pencils or crayons (recommended colors: dark blue or purple, blue, turquoise or greenish blue, yellow, orange, and red)
1 per student	Blank world map for coloring
1 per group	Computer with *My World* software
1 per classroom	Computer with *My World* software and projection equipment

Activity Setup and Preparation

Before the class period, try constructing your own global temperature prediction map using the *My World* software and the instructions in the student text.

Decide how you will manage computer time if you do not have enough computers for each group to work simultaneously. Decide on how you want students to save their computer work. Students could save their work by group name and map type (e.g. *smithTempPredJuly.mp3z*) or by a name of a student in the group. You may also want to create folders for students to keep their work in based on class and group.

If computers are limited you might have groups print out their work.

Homework Options

Reflection

- **Science Content:** How did you decide where to put temperatures on your maps? *(Student responses will vary. Students should express the thought processes that went into creating their maps.)*

Preparation for 1.4

- **Science Process:** How could you check your group prediction map? *(The purpose of this is to get students to think about what they should do to test their predictions. Some may suggest experiments collecting data around the world for the month of July. Some may suggest reviewing previous data for temperatures in July around the world. Emphasize the need for multiple data points for reliability.)*

NOTES

NOTES

SECTION 1.3 IMPLEMENTATION

1.3 Investigate

Creating a Prediction Map on Paper and in My World

In this activity, you will use color to show surface temperatures on a map. Then you will be able to see the surface temperatures in different parts of the world. As you do this activity, think about what causes the differences. Consider why you observe different temperatures around the world.

What Is a Visualization?

Scientists who study weather and climate cannot see the weather everywhere around the world. It would take a great deal of time to compare lists of information from different weather stations. Visualizations show a picture of the information. They make it possible to see all the information at once.

The map visualization shows temperatures in the United States on August 14, 2001. By using different colors to represent temperature ranges, you can quickly see which areas are warmer and which are cooler. Carefully observe the map and answer the following questions:

a) Where are the highest temperatures on this map?

b) Where are the lowest temperatures on this map?

c) How are variations in temperature represented on this map?

d) Using the temperatures shown, create a key for this map. The key should allow someone to use the map to identify the temperature of a location, even if the temperature is not shown on the map.

PF 15

PLANETARY FORECASTER

1.3 Investigate

Creating a Prediction Map on Paper and in My World

15 min.

Introduce the class to the idea of visualizing temperature data on a map.

△ **Guide**

Describe for students what a map visualization is.

*A class period is considered to be one 40 to 50 minute class.

"There are many different temperatures. Even across a small area, it would be difficult to analyze the data and find trends if you just looked at all the data values. Temperature data maps often include a color coding in which each color represents a range of temperatures. This is called a map visualization. It helps you view and analyze a lot of data at once.**"**

Discuss the example map in the student text. Have the students imagine how difficult it would be to find patterns in the temperature map if they used numbers to represent actual temperatures at every point instead of colors.

△ Guide and Assess

Ask students what surface temperature is. Students should be able to describe surface temperature as the temperature located near Earth's surface. Let students know the map in the student text shows surface temperatures.

Have students answer the four questions and have a class discussion on each.

a) Students should indicate the highest temperatures are in the southern states: 98°F in southeastern CA, 93°F in the central western part of TX, and 92°F in the southern tip of FL.

b) Students should indicate the lowest temperatures are along the western coast: 55°F and 57°F on the CA coast, 55°F on the WA coastline.

c) Students should describe the representation of temperature by numerical values and color coding where red indicates high values and yellow indicates the low values.

d) From analyzing the map, students should come up with a key such as:

98°F - 80°F = red

79°F – 73°F = orange

72°F – 55°F = yellow

Discuss the importance of how the colors are chosen. Orange is a mixture of red and yellow, so it makes sense to use the color between red and yellow. Discuss the importance of having a map key to provide information on how to translate color to temperature range.

Let students know that they will be making their own prediction map using a color-coded key.

Procedure:
Create a Prediction Map on Paper

1. You often make predictions. In science, predictions are a forecast of what you think will happen or the way things might be. They are based on what you know. In this activity, you will use what you know so far about temperature. You will make a prediction map of surface temperatures around the world.

   Get a world map from your teacher. Begin by making a color key using the information in the table.

   These colors are similar to the colors you observed in the map of temperatures in the United States. They are also similar to the colors used in a real surface-temperature map to which you will later compare your prediction map.

2. Color your map based on what you think Earth's surface temperatures are like in July. Begin by coloring areas you know about. For example, you may want to locate North America and start there. You may also be familiar with areas that you have lived in, visited, read about, or studied. In some cases, you may know nothing about an area. It is fine to make an educated guess. When you do this, think about things such as where the area is located on Earth. Look for patterns in the temperatures of areas with which you are more familiar.

World Map Color Key	
Temperature	**Color**
-30°F to -11°F	dark blue or purple
-10°F to 10°F	blue
11°F to 31°F	turquoise or greenish blue
32°F to 53°F	yellow
54°F to 74°F	orange
75°F to 94°F and over	red

Procedure: Create a Prediction Map on Paper

15 min.

Students create a global temperature prediction map.

△ Guide

Let students know that everyone will be creating a global temperature prediction map for Earth during the month of July.

To make the color scheme more meaningful to the students, try connecting the temperature ranges to students' perceptions and real-life experiences. Ask them, "What temperature ranges would require a heavy coat?", "In what temperature range would you be comfortable swimming?", "What temperature range does our area currently fall into?", etc.

3. There are eight locations indicated on the map below.

   a) Give the reasons why you made the temperature predictions you did for these areas.

   b) In what areas were you confident about your temperature predictions? What information did you use to make these predictions?

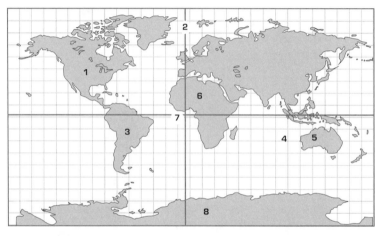

   c) In what areas were you less confident about your temperature predictions? What information did you use to make your predictions in these areas?

   d) Describe any patterns you observed while coloring your map. How do you think these patterns may have helped you complete the map?

   e) Describe any observations or thoughts you may have had while coloring your map that might explain why different regions on Earth's surface are different temperatures at the same time of the year.

PF 17

PLANETARY FORECASTER

⬡ Get Going

Distribute the blank world maps and crayons or colored pencils to each student. Let students know how much time they have.

△ Guide and Assess

Monitor students as they work. Check that they draw a key to their map.

Some students may see this as a coloring exercise and not realize that the colors indicate a temperature value. Students may color the water blue. Let students make these mistakes to use later as a source of discussion.

Check to see if students color the land but not the water. Ask these students if the air above the water has a temperature. They should indicate on their maps what they think it is.

Students should have descriptive answers to Step 3. Let students know that they will be sharing their maps with their group members when they are done.

Check for content misconceptions. For example, students may reveal that they think it is summer in both hemispheres at the same time, or that it is colder at the poles because the energy that reaches Earth from the Sun strikes the Equator and then curves toward the poles, or that the wind moves the heat energy. Some students may believe that the gravitational pull from the moon affects Earth's temperatures. Note these so that they can be brought up and addressed in future discussions as needed.

> **META NOTES**
>
> The more detail-oriented students may take some more time to color these maps. Do not give them more time — remind them that this exercise is just a way to get them to think about what they already know.

NOTES

Conference

10 min.

META NOTES

The idea of this exercise is to allow students to reveal their preconceptions about the temperatures on Earth and to gain an awareness of what they know and what they do not know. It is not important that the maps are accurate. Later, students will be able to compare their maps to actual maps and discuss areas where they were accurate and inaccurate and begin to think about why their own maps are different from actual temperature maps.

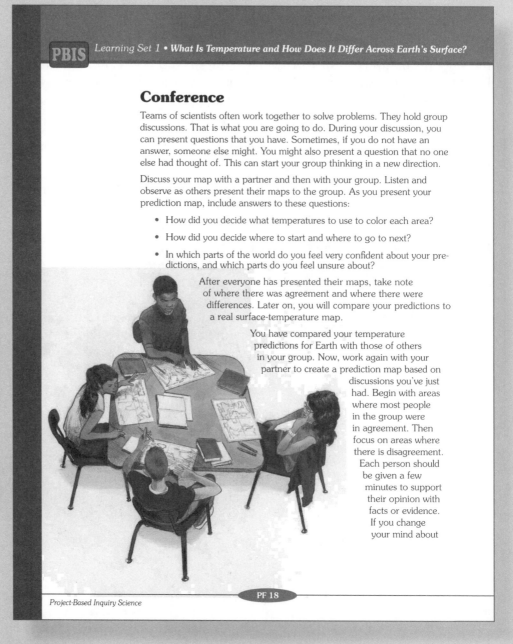

Conference

Teams of scientists often work together to solve problems. They hold group discussions. That is what you are going to do. During your discussion, you can present questions that you have. Sometimes, if you do not have an answer, someone else might. You might also present a question that no one else had thought of. This can start your group thinking in a new direction.

Discuss your map with a partner and then with your group. Listen and observe as others present their maps to the group. As you present your prediction map, include answers to these questions:

- How did you decide what temperatures to use to color each area?
- How did you decide where to start and where to go to next?
- In which parts of the world do you feel very confident about your predictions, and which parts do you feel unsure about?

After everyone has presented their maps, take note of where there was agreement and where there were differences. Later on, you will compare your predictions to a real surface-temperature map.

You have compared your temperature predictions for Earth with those of others in your group. Now, work again with your partner to create a prediction map based on discussions you've just had. Begin with areas where most people in the group were in agreement. Then focus on areas where there is disagreement. Each person should be given a few minutes to support their opinion with facts or evidence. If you change your mind about

Project-Based Inquiry Science

PF 18

△ Guide

Let students know they will be sharing their maps with their group. They will be discussing all the questions in Step 3 of the procedure and answering the three bulleted points.

Describe the procedure students should follow.

"After everyone has presented their prediction maps, they should take note of where there was agreement and where there were differences. The differences should be discussed allowing each group member to give their opinion and their reasoning behind it. Then the group should create a group prediction map. "

⬡ Get Going

Have groups begin their discussions and let them know how much time they have. While groups are sharing and discussing their maps, distribute a blank world maps for the group to fill out.

△ Guide and Assess

Monitor groups' progress, paying attention to how their discussions are going. Check that everyone is participating and taking turns.

Let students know that some will have different questions about their maps due to different experiences. Students from other countries may be able to describe what the temperature was like there or students may know about other places from movies or television. During the discussion, they will have opportunities to ask each other questions and explain the choices they made.

Consider asking students about the different factors that might have affected the temperature.

"Where was the coldest place you ever were? What time of year was it?

Where was the warmest place you ever were? What time of year was it?

Was it in an elevated location?

Was it near water, in a city?"

Be a Scientist: Using *My World*

5 min.

Introduce the My World *software to the class.*

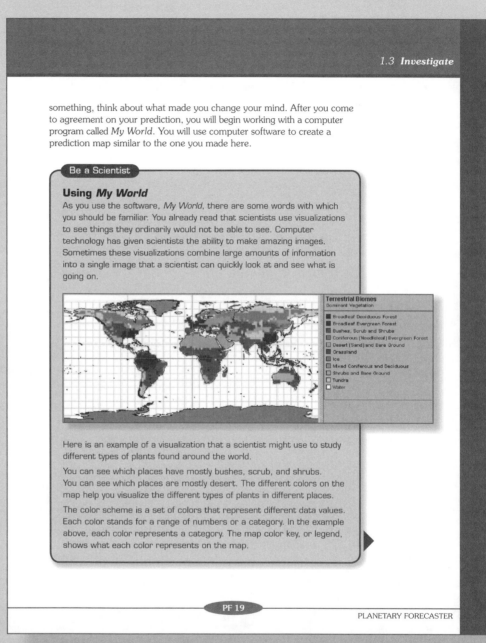

something, think about what made you change your mind. After you come to agreement on your prediction, you will begin working with a computer program called *My World*. You will use computer software to create a prediction map similar to the one you made here.

Be a Scientist

Using *My World*

As you use the software, *My World*, there are some words with which you should be familiar. You already read that scientists use visualizations to see things they ordinarily would not be able to see. Computer technology has given scientists the ability to make amazing images. Sometimes these visualizations combine large amounts of information into a single image that a scientist can quickly look at and see what is going on.

Here is an example of a visualization that a scientist might use to study different types of plants found around the world.

You can see which places have mostly bushes, scrub, and shrubs. You can see which places are mostly desert. The different colors on the map help you visualize the different types of plants in different places.

The color scheme is a set of colors that represent different data values. Each color stands for a range of numbers or a category. In the example above, each color represents a category. The map color key, or legend, shows what each color represents on the map.

△ Guide

Introduce the reason for using *My World* and the software.

Use the example in the student text to describe how this software is used. Conclude this discussion by emphasizing that the main goal of using the software is to become familiar with creating an electronic version of their prediction maps.

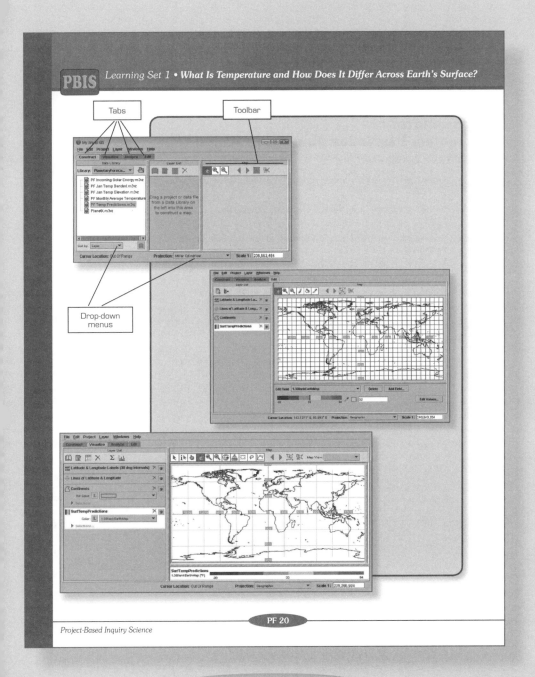

TEACHER TALK

"You have colored your prediction maps and discussed with your group to construct a group prediction map. Now you will reconstruct your prediction map using the *My World* software. This software helps you to visualize your map and easily revise it if needed. "

Procedure: Create a Prediction Map in *My World*

20 min.

Groups construct an electronic version of their prediction maps using My World.

META NOTES

It will probably be helpful to allow some time during the procedure for students to explore the *My World* software, familiarize themselves with it, and become comfortable using it.

META NOTES

Consider having the students save this project using the project name and their names as the title. Also consider creating class and group folders to save their work in.

Students will need to be able to access their electronic maps at various times. This can be managed in a variety of ways. Students could save their work to a server or a portable disk, or they could work on the same computer during all of the *My World* exercises.

1.3 Investigate

Procedure: Create a Prediction Map in *My World*

1. **Prepare a blank map**.

   a) **Open "My World"** by double-clicking on the *My World* icon on your computer screen.

   b) **In the "Construct" tab, select "Planetary Forecaster"** from the Library drop-down menu.

   c) **Double-click on "PF Temp Predictions" to open a blank visualization.** The blank visualization will appear on your screen and the "Visualization" tab will be selected. You cannot "paint" your map in the Visualization screen.

   d) **Select the "Edit" tab. Double-click "SurfTempPredictions" from the Layer List.** Now you'll be able to "paint" the blank temperature map. You will show your temperature predictions using "the paintbrush."

2. **Paint your "Prediction" Map.**

   a) **Click on the paintbrush ✏ in the toolbar.** It is at the top of your *My World* screen, below the Construct, Visualize, Analyze, and Edit tabs. Once it is selected, the paintbrush button should look white instead of gray.

   b) **Notice the Brush Size bar at the bottom of the map.** You can adjust the size of your paintbrush by clicking on the arrow and dragging it left and right on the Brush Size bar. The smallest size you can color is one square, or cell, on the grid at a time. If you drag the arrow to the far right side of the Brush Size bar, you can color a large square, ten cells tall and ten cells wide.

PF 21

PLANETARY FORECASTER

⚠ Guide

Even if your students have used *My World* before, demonstrate the procedures before they start working on the computers. Use a projection system and go through each step in the procedure. This should not take much time.

Let students know how they should save their work and where they should save it. Provide them with an example and ask them to record it so they can refer to it later. Encourage students to save their work regularly.

Let students know if you want them to print out a copy of their map to work from.

◯ Get Going

Remind students to have their group's prediction map with them as they work and let them know how much time they have.

Have students follow the *Procedure t* in their texts. They will access the blank Earth map visualization and color this map. Your students should duplicate their hand-colored group maps into *My World* using the paint tools.

△ Guide and Assess

Monitor students and guide them as needed. Students may ask how to erase cells that they place a color on. Tell them there is no need to erase cells. They can simply paint over the cell with a new value to change it. Make sure students realize that all cells should have some data value. Cells that are not painted do not have a value of zero degrees. These cells are not assigned a value until they are colored and must be colored to indicate they have a value of zero degrees.

As groups finish their computer maps, have students begin working on the *Reflect* questions. Let them know that they should be prepared to discuss their responses with their group and the class.

META NOTES

For a reference guide to the painting tools, please refer to the Help menu in *My World*.

NOTES

....

....

....

....

....

....

....

Reflect

20 min.

Students have a class discussion on their responses.

META NOTES

There are no correct or incorrect answers to the *Reflect* questions. Students should be able to describe their thought processes as they completed the exercise. In the next section, the students will compare their predictions with real data. At this point they should focus on their preconceptions about surface temperatures. Resist the urge to correct students and encourage discussion.

c) **Move the cursor over the color bar.** This is the bar with the range of colors showing the color key. **Position the paintbrush over the color you want to select and click.** In the box to the right of the color bar, you can see what value is selected and the temperature it represents.

d) **Move the paintbrush back over the map and click on a cell to paint it.** To color several cells without changing the brush size, hold down the mouse button and drag it over those cells.

e) **To paint a different part of the map,** change colors by placing the paintbrush over a different color on the color bar and click. If you change your mind about a temperature after you've painted it, just paint over it with a new color.

f) **Fit your map onto your screen.** Make sure you can see your entire map so that you do not miss coloring any areas. Click the "Zoom To All" icon ▦ to fit the map into your screen. To make your screen bigger, click on the bottom right corner of the *My World* screen and drag the corner down and to the right. Click the "Zoom To All" icon again to fit the map into this larger screen.

3. **Save your file** following your teacher's instructions. It is important to save your file because you will need it for later activities. When you are finished saving, **select Quit from the File menu.**

Reflect

Answer the following questions. Be prepared to share your answers with your group and your class.

1. What ideas guided your group as you colored the prediction map? For example, you may have thought, "It is cold at the poles because there is snow and ice there."

2. Were there any areas where your group was unsure about the temperature predictions? What steps did you take to solve these problems?

3. While coloring your group map, were there any situations in which you needed more information? Describe what they were.

4. While painting your prediction map, what patterns did you observe? Were there certain parts of the map that seemed to have a lot of the same color?

○ Get Going

Let students know they should answer the questions on their own and they should be prepared to discuss them with their group and the class. Then let them know how much time they have.

5. Did your thinking change at all since you colored the first map on paper? Describe how and why.

6. How did the use of computer software make the task easier or more difficult? Describe your experience.

7. Make a list of all the information and skills that you gained from this investigation that you can apply to your *Planet X* challenge.

What's the Point?

The Cooperative Space Agency suggested that you discover more about surface temperatures on Earth so you can apply this information to *Planet X*. You are now familiar with the language, tools, and units of measurement used by fellow scientists. This will enable you to communicate with them easily and with accuracy. In completing this activity, you found out how to communicate information in a form that is very easy. You have also used one of scientists' most important tools, the computer. In doing so, you have identified some of the things you and your class already know about surface temperatures on Earth. Perhaps you also identified some of the factors that influence them.

Scientists who study climate and weather often use computers to develop visualizations.

PF 23

△ Guide and Assess

Have a class discussion on students' responses. Consider having each group present at least one answer to the questions and encourage all groups to participate in the discussion. Examples are provided to assist you in guiding and assessing the students. Consider recording students' initial ideas to help guide students as they investigate what factors affect surface temperature.

1. Students should describe their reasoning for selecting the temperatures they did in their prediction map.

2. A good indicator of students' uncertainty about temperature predictions is in group disagreement. Students should describe how they solved locations they were unsure of or where there was disagreement in the group.

3. Areas where students were in disagreement may require more information.

4. Students should describe trends in their prediction maps. They may indicate it is warmer at the equator and cooler at the poles.

5. Students should describe areas in which they refined their maps based on their group discussions.

6. Consider letting students know it will be easier for them to revise their maps.

7. Students should include using the *My World* software and constructing temperature maps.

Assessment Options

Targeted Concepts, Skills, and Nature of Science	How do I know if students got it?
Graphs, maps, and tables are an effective way to analyze and communicate results of scientific investigation.	**ASK:** How does a color-coded temperature map assist in communicating results and analyzing the data? **LISTEN:** Students should describe how it is easier to analyze all the data when you can see it all at once. This makes it easier to find trends and show trends to the class.

Teacher Reflection Questions

- What difficulties did students have using colors to represent their predictions on the map? What ideas do you have for guiding them next time?

- How did the *Conference* session with group members help students with their prediction maps? What were some initial ideas students had?

- How did you manage the computer usage?

SECTION 1.4 INTRODUCTION

1.4 Investigate

Compare Your Temperature Map to a Real-World Temperature Map

◀ *1 class period*

A class period is considered to be one 40 to 50 minute class.

Overview

Students compare the global temperature prediction maps they created in *My World* to *My World* maps of actual temperature data. When comparing their predictions with actual data, students should consider the discrepancies and why they may have occurred. This should lead to new questions to investigate and ideas about how they can use what they have learned to find out more about the surface temperatures on *Planet X*.

Targeted Concepts, Skills, and Nature of Science	Performance Expectations
Scientists often work together and share their findings. Sharing findings makes new information available and helps scientists to refine their ideas and build on others' ideas. When another person's or group's idea is used, credit needs to be given.	Students should work with their group members to compare their global temperature prediction maps with actual data.
Scientists must keep clear, accurate, and descriptive records of what they do so they can share their work with others and consider what they did, why they did it, and what they want to do next.	Students should have clear records of their global prediction maps and reasoning so they can compare their maps and their reasoning with actual data. From this, students should record their thoughts about the comparison to refer back to when predicting surface temperatures for *Planet X*.
Graphs, maps, and tables are an effective way to analyze and communicate results of scientific investigation.	Students should describe how color-coded temperature maps are a useful and efficient way to view and analyze a lot of data simultaneously.

Targeted Concepts, Skills, and Nature of Science	Performance Expectations
Identifying factors that lead to variation is an important part of scientific investigation.	Students may identify possible factors that affect surface temperature from trends in the data.
Temperatures around Earth's surface vary widely, but can be predicted somewhat by location and season.	Students should recognize that Earth's surface temperatures vary widely.

Materials	
1 per group	Computer with *My World* software Optional: copy of world map with countries' names listed
1 per classroom	Computer with *My World* software and projection equipment
1 per class	Class *Project Board*
1 per student	*Project Board* page

Activity Setup and Preparation

Make sure the computers are ready and students' prediction files are available. If you do not have enough computers for each group, consider how to manage computer time. You could have students compare printed copies of their prediction maps to an overhead transparency of the July surface temperatures.

Familiarize yourself with the procedures described in the student text to prepare for how you will demonstrate comparing data.

Homework Options

Reflection

- **Science Process:** What similarities and differences did you see between your temperature prediction map and the temperature data map? *(Students should compare the two maps for similarities and differences.)*

- **Science Process:** What patterns in the data did you notice in the real-world temperature map? From these patterns, what possible factors that affect surface temperature can you identify? *(Students should be able to identify some color/temperature patterns in the data maps they observed such as it gets cooler temperatures closer to the poles.)*

Preparation for 1.5

- **Science Content:** Which locations of Earth have especially high or especially low temperatures? Which areas seem more moderate? What do you imagine these locations look like? Which areas do you think are the best places for human habitat and why? *(Students should begin to identify regions that are most suited for human habitat and be able to visualize the environments of many of these locations. The next section focuses on habitability.)*

NOTES

NOTES

1.4 Investigate

Compare Your Temperature Map to a Real-World Temperature Map

Scientists often compare their ideas to real data. In this activity, you will have the opportunity to do the same. You will open both the visualization you developed on the computer and another one that contains actual data. As you study them, look for similarities and differences. By comparing the two maps, you will see if there are still things you need to know.

Procedure: Comparing Maps

Begin by opening "My World." Open Planetary Forecaster.

1. **Open the temperature map you created earlier, showing your predictions of surface temperatures.**

   a) **Locate the "Visualize" tab and click on it.**

   b) **Click on the "SurfTempPredictions" layer in the Layer List.** There is a drop-down menu within this layer showing different fields. The field containing your temperature predictions is currently selected.

2. **Open a real-world temperature map.**

   a) **Click on the arrow on the right side of the drop-down menu. Select the other field in this layer, "1.4 JulyAvgTempF."** This will reveal a map with the actual measurement of surface temperatures in July.

   The real-world temperature map shows the average temperatures in July over a period of twelve years, from 1982 to 1994. Temperatures are measured at thousands of weather stations around the world. This visualization was made by combining average July measurements from all of these sources. A computer program was used to calculate temperature estimates in locations where no measurements were available.

   PF 24

   Project-Based Inquiry Science

1.4 Investigate

Compare Your Temperature Map to a Real-World Temperature Map

5 to 10 min.

Demonstrate how students will compare their prediction maps with data maps.

META NOTES

This also provides students with a brief review of the procedures that follow.

△ Guide

Let students know that in this section they will be comparing their ideas to real data. They will need to open their electronic prediction data maps and a real data map and look for similarities and differences.

Demonstrate how to do this. Follow the procedures listed in the student text. Open up a prediction map. Show students how to open up a New Child map containing the average July temperatures from 1982 through 1994 and their prediction map.

*A class period is considered to be one 40 to 50 minute class.

Point out that the temperatures in this visualization are an average of the July temperatures over twelve years: 1982-1994. Ask students why it might be better to look at a map of average temperatures over many years rather than choosing any single July map. Students should understand that taking an average over a length of time leads to data that is more representative of the location. This way, unusually cold or warm values would be averaged out.

When students have both maps open and they click the cursor on one of the maps, both maps lock the cursor to that location and provide the temperature value along the color-coded temperature bar below the maps. Point out that this is how they will be able to compare actual temperature values and that they should be able to notice trends from the defined color-coded temperature ranges. Point out that the color coding for the maps are different.

META NOTES

If students select the Synchronize Projection and Zoom box in the New Child Window, the maps will appear the same size.

Procedure: Comparing Maps

20 min.

Students compare their My World prediction maps with maps that display actual temperature data.

you developed on the computer and another one that contains actual data. As you study them, look for similarities and differences. By comparing the two maps, you will see if there are still things you need to know.

Procedure: Comparing Maps

Begin by opening "My World." Open Planetary Forecaster.

1. **Open the temperature map you created earlier, showing your predictions of surface temperatures.**

   a) **Locate the "Visualize" tab and click on it.**

   b) **Click on the "SurfTempPredictions" layer in the Layer List.** There is a drop-down menu within this layer showing different fields. The field containing your temperature predictions is currently selected.

2. **Open a real-world temperature map.**

   a) **Click on the arrow on the right side of the drop-down menu. Select the other field in this layer, "1.4 JulyAvgTempF."** This will reveal a map with the actual measurement of surface temperatures in July.

The real-world temperature map shows the average temperatures in July over a period of twelve years, from 1982 to 1994. Temperatures are measured at thousands of weather stations around the world. This visualization was made by combining average July measurements from all of these sources. A computer program was used to calculate temperature estimates in locations where no measurements were available.

PF 24

Project-Based Inquiry Science

⚠ Guide

Remind students the point of creating their maps was to find out what they know and do not know about the causes of temperature variation. Emphasize that the point of this exercise is to think and form questions as

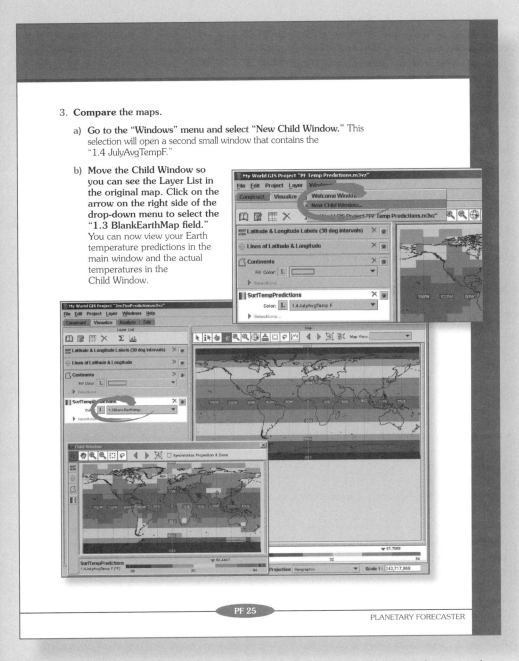

3. **Compare** the maps.

   a) Go to the "Windows" menu and select "New Child Window." This selection will open a second small window that contains the "1.4 JulyAvgTempF."

   b) **Move the Child Window so you can see the Layer List in the original map. Click on the arrow on the right side of the drop-down menu to select the "1.3 BlankEarthMap field."** You can now view your Earth temperature predictions in the main window and the actual temperatures in the Child Window.

part of the investigation and to determine what type of things they need to figure out in order to understand and predict temperature variation.

⬡ Get Going

If students saved their prediction maps on a computer's hard drive, let them know they should use the computers they saved their files on. Then let groups begin.

△ Guide and Assess

Monitor students' progress. It may help students to mark or note where the Equator is on their *My World* map. Students may be used to seeing the Equator bisecting the globe on most maps and this reference may be helpful for interpreting the temperature data.

Show the students how to find the longitude and latitude of the locations by moving the cursor and reading the cursor location window at the bottom of the *My World* window

It may help students to have a world map with the names of the countries for this lesson. You may wish to have students compare and contrast specific areas on the two maps. You can also ask them why a particular color is not a smooth band all the way across the map or why they think there is yellow (an indication of cooler temperatures) on some continents.

As groups complete the procedures, have them begin working on the *Reflect* questions. Let them know they can work on these as a group.

NOTES

c) **Use the "Pointer" tool to compare.** When this button is selected, you can click on any cell on the map. The temperature bar at the bottom of the map will tell you the temperature value for that cell. With a Child Window open, you can click on either the Child Window or the Main Window. The temperature value for the cells in the same position in *both* windows will then be shown. Compare the two maps. Note where your predictions are close to the real temperatures and where they differ. You can track your location by looking at the "cursor location" at the bottom of your map.

Reflect

1. Identify a region on the Real-world Temperature Map where temperatures are in each of the temperature ranges listed below (one region for each temperature range). Use either the name of the region or its cursor location to identify the region.

    -30°F to -11°F

    32°F to 51°F

    73°F to 94°F

2. List at least five places where your predictions are close to the real temperatures. Use either names or cursor locations to identify them.

3. List at least five places where your predictions are very different from the real temperatures. Use either names or cursor locations to identify them.

4. Where were you surprised to see that your map and the actual temperature map were different? Your answer might be an area or a continent. For example: at the North Pole, in the oceans, North America, Australia, Northern Asia.

5. Why might it be better to look at a map of average temperatures over many years rather than a map of the temperatures in any single July?

6. In the Real-world Temperature Map, you notice variation. What do you think is influencing these variations in surface temperature?

Reflect

15 min.

Have a class discussion on students' responses.

⬡ Get Going

Groups should start answering these questions as they complete the procedures. Let them know that they can work on these as a group and how much time they have.

△ Guide and Assess

Have a class discussion on groups' responses to the questions. Consider having the July temperature map projected for students to use when they discuss their results.

1. Check that students have selected areas that fall within the temperature range.

2. Have groups present five locations in which their predictions were similar to the real-world temperatures. Students should describe the location and the temperature range. After each group presents their results, ask the class if any groups had similar results for these locations.

3. Have groups present five locations in which their predictions were different from the actual data. Students should describe the location and the temperature range. After each group presents their results, ask the class if any groups had similar results for these locations.

4. Encourage students to answer this question as completely as they can. Use their responses as a basis for asking further questions that explore why they made their previous predictions.

5. Students should realize there may be one or two years when temperatures are very different from what is normally experienced. By collecting temperatures over several years, a more representative average can be obtained.

6. Encourage students to describe factors they think affect surface temperature and record each groups' ideas. Compare these with what the class has already listed on their *Project Board* and consider updating the class *Project Board*. Let students know they will learn more about these factors in the later lessons.

META NOTES

This will help students articulate what their initial ideas were and evaluate the reasoning behind them.

META NOTES

By comparing the current list of factors with the list students initially constructed on their *Project Board* students can see how their ideas have changed.

NOTES

Update the *Project Board*

You now have an accurate map showing the surface temperatures on Earth in July. You may have observed some patterns on this map. You may have seen where the hottest temperatures are found or where the coldest temperatures are found. At this point, you may have some ideas about what causes these temperature variations. You can add these ideas to your *Project Board*. You should also have a better idea about what you need more information about.

As a class, update the *Project Board*. Some information may need to be moved from *What do we think we know?* to *What do we need to investigate?* New questions will be added, which you will soon investigate.

PF 27

PLANETARY FORECASTER

Update the Project Board

5 min.

⚠ Guide

Have a class discussion updating the first column *(What do we think we know)* and the second column *(What do we need to investigate?).*

If students have found trends in the data where evidence supports one of their claims about a factor or a question previously on the *Project Board*, list these in columns three *(What are we learning?)* and four *(What is our evidence?)*. Students might have the following:

Column 3 (claim): For the month of July, the Northern Hemisphere has warmer temperatures than the Southern Hemisphere.

Column 4 (evidence): By studying a temperature data map showing average temperatures for the month of July from 1982 to 1994, we found that the Southern Hemisphere has cooler temperatures than the Northern Hemisphere as you move equal distances away from the Equator.

NOTES

What's the Point?

In this investigation, you used what you know about temperature to make informed predictions about surface temperatures around the world. You also used many of the same thinking skills and processes that scientists use to solve problems and answer questions. For example, you gathered information. Then you shared your ideas. As a group, you worked together to develop a prediction map.

Scientists often make predictions based on what they know. They then test these ideas. They compare their predictions to data they collect. You were able to compare your predictions to data on a computer. The data were collected by weather stations around the world. In the process, you were able to investigate temperature variations around the world. Investigations done by scientists often raise new questions. These can lead to new areas of research. Your investigation may have raised new questions, as well. For example, you might wonder why there are temperature variations on Earth. You might also question how you could relate what you now know about surface temperatures on Earth to other planets, like *Planet X*.

How you communicate information is also very important. Scientists may have huge amounts of data to work with. Scientists who study weather and climate collect a lot of data. Visualizations enable them to see and study the data much more easily.

Most deserts, like this one in the Southwest U.S., have extremely high surface temperatures during the daytime.

Teacher Reflection Questions

- What trends did students see in the July data maps and what possible factors that affect the surface temperature of Earth did they identify?

- What were the most common misconceptions that students had about temperatures? How were these reflected in their initial predictions?

- How was participation during the class discussions? How do you think the discussions helped students' understanding?

NOTES

1.5 Explore

Which Locations on Earth Are Habitable?

◀ *1 class period*

A class period is considered to be one 40 to 50 minute class.

Overview

Students are notified by the *Cooperative Space Agency* of the guidelines for selecting a temperature range required to meet energy concerns in order to form a habitable colony on *Planet X*. Students consider how they will describe the overall temperatures for a given location. They consider daily and monthly temperature variations, and compare average temperature variations between January and July for Earth's surface. Applying what they have learned, students decide which areas would be considered habitable on Earth within the criteria of the *Cooperative Space Agency*. This prepares students to make predictions about *Planet X* in future *Learning Sets*.

Targeted Concepts, Skills, and Nature of Science	Performance Expectations
Scientists make claims (conclusions) based on evidence obtained (trends in data) from reliable investigations	Students should make claims based on various surface temperature maps of Earth to best describe surface temperatures and what may be factors that affect the surface temperature.
Habitable areas of Earth are determined by average temperatures suitable for humans to live in. These areas are often broken up into biomes, which are a group of ecosystems that have the same general climate and similar plants and animals.	Students should describe what is considered a habitable area on Earth and how these compare to the criteria and constraints for what would be habitable on *Planet X*.

Materials	
1 per classroom (optional)	Projection of the letter from the *Cooperative Space Agency*
1 per group (optional)	Copy of world map with countries' names listed

85

Activity Setup and Preparation

You may want to construct a January habitability map in *My World*. Save a copy of the January average temperatures. Change the temperature scale to be black when it is outside of *CSA's* allowed range of temperatures and white when it is within the allowed range of temperatures.

Homework Options

Reflection

- **Science Content:** How do you find the average daily and average monthly temperatures of a location? *(Students should describe daily averages as the average of the high and low temperatures each day. Monthly average is the average value of all the daily average values for the month.)*

- **Science Content:** Describe one of the patterns of average monthly temperatures found on a global map for January and July. *(Students should be able to describe how temperatures decrease as you move farther away from the Equator.)*

Preparation for Back to the Big Challenge

- **Nature of Content:** List the four factors that you think affect surface temperatures the most and why. *(The purpose of this is to get students to consider the most prominent factors that affect surface temperature. In the next section, they will compare the four factors that the CSA has identified to have the greatest affect on surface temperatures.)*

SECTION 1.5 IMPLEMENTATION

1.5 Explore

Which Locations on Earth Are Habitable?

To determine which locations on Earth are habitable, you have to look at a lot of data. Visualizations are one way people can look at large amounts of data very easily. Think about daily temperatures. Suppose you took a temperature reading every hour for one day. Chances are, the readings would all be different. Now suppose you were asked what the temperature was that day. Think about how you would answer this question. It would take a lot of time to give 24 temperature readings. It might be better to give one or two temperatures that describe the overall day. Learning how to do this will help you communicate the information requested by the CSA. Read the following bulletin to see what the CSA would like to know.

TO: Scientific Research Team
FROM: The Cooperative Space Agency
SUBJECT: Temperature requirements for the new space colony

Other research teams in charge of design and engineering have reported that it is possible for humans to live on *Planet X* as long as temperatures are found to be in a certain range. The engineers have designed a temporary source of energy. It will be able to support about 5000 people if used well. They have asked that you find a region with average surface temperatures between 25°F and 85°F. Humans can survive in temperatures that are lower or higher than this. However, if you can find this temperature range, it will reduce the amount of energy needed for heating and cooling.

CSA is pleased with your progress to date. You may want to refer back to the visualizations you developed to locate any regions in the requested temperature range. In the meantime, please familiarize yourself with daily and monthly average temperatures. This will be important as you move ahead in determining factors that will affect average surface air temperatures on *Planet X*.

The temperature on this Virginia beach changes from hour-to-hour. To report on a day's temperature, you might report a range or an average.

PF 29

1.5 Explore

Which Locations on Earth Are Habitable?

5 min.

Elicit students' ideas about what is habitable and how to describe temperature readings.

◯ Engage

Ask students what they consider a habitable temperature range on Earth and record their responses. Ask them if there are any places on Earth where humans do not live and why.

Project the bulletin from the *Cooperative Space Agency* or instruct students to look at the bulletin in their student text. Read the bulletin as a class. Emphasize to students that because of energy requirements, the only habitable places on *Planet X* will be those with a daily average temperature between 25˚F and 85˚F.

*A class period is considered to be one 40 to 50 minute class.

META NOTES

Making connections with students' everyday experiences may increases students' interest and understanding.

Ask the students to think about what the temperature range 25°F to 85°F feels like. Ask what clothing someone would wear if the temperature was 25°F? What clothing would someone wear if the temperature was 85°F? What is a comfortable room temperature? Ask students if they know of any significant temperature values, and how those values fit into this range. For example, the freezing point of water is 32°F and a healthy human body temperature is 98.6°F. Point out to students that to live in cool regions energy must be used to stay warm and to live in warm regions energy is used to stay cool.

NOTES

Learn About Daily and Monthly Average Temperatures

Recall the last Urgent Message sent by the CSA. Think about what they are asking for in terms of temperature ranges. They are *not* looking for a place that never gets warmer than 85°F or colder than 25°F. They are asking for a location where the **average** temperature for any given month is between 25°F and 85°F. That means some days could be as high as 90°F or even higher. Other days could get as low as 15°F or even lower. These hotter and colder temperatures will affect the average temperature. However, the average can still be inside the given range.

Daily average temperatures are calculated by averaging the highest and lowest temperatures over a 24-hour period. These are usually measured from midnight to midnight. For example, the daily average temperature for a day with a high temperature of 60°F and a low temperature of 40°F would be 50°F.

$$60°F + 40°F = 100°F$$
$$100°F \div 2 = 50°F$$

When solving problems that involve units, whether it is time, temperature, or any measurement, always include the units.

Monthly average temperatures are calculated by adding up all of the daily average temperatures. Then the sum is divided by the total number of days in that month. On Earth, this means that you would divide by a different number of days depending on the month. For example, to find the monthly average temperature for June, you would add up the daily average temperatures for all 30 days in June and divide the total by 30. To find the monthly average temperature for January, you would add up the average temperatures for the 31 days in January and divide the total by 31.

average: the sum of a set of numerical data divided by the number of data items.

daily average temperature: the sum of the highest and lowest temperatures from midnight to midnight, divided by two.

monthly average temperature: the sum of all of the daily average temperatures for a given month divided by the number of days in the month.

Learn about Daily and Monthly Average Temperatures

20 min.

⚠ Guide

Ask students how they would determine the daily temperature if it was recorded every hour for 24 hours. Record students' ideas. Ask how they would determine the average monthly temperature and record students' ideas.

Discuss how the daily and monthly average temperatures are calculated using the information text box entitled *Learn about Daily and Monthly Average Temperatures.* Use the example provided in the student text.

Point out that a low daily temperature of 20°F and a high daily temperature of 30°F results in an average temperature of 25°F, which still fits the criteria of *CSA*.

◇ **Evaluate**

Make sure that the students know how to calculate an average. Have the students who have trouble answering the questions correctly, practice more with averages until they feel comfortable calculating data.

NOTES

1.5 Explore

Stop and Think

Use the temperature data below to answer the following questions.

Temperature Data		
Day	Daily Low (°F)	Daily High (°F)
1	71	89
2	65	93
3	81	84

1. Which day had the highest daily high?

2. Which day had the lowest daily high?

3. Without calculating, estimate which day had the highest average temperature.

4. Calculate the average temperature for each of the three days. Compare your answer to your estimate.

5. Can a day with a high temperature greater than 85°F still have an average temperature that is less than or equal to 85°F? Support your answer.

6. Could a location with any of these average daily temperatures fit the temperature criteria requested by the CSA?

Procedure: Explore the Case on Earth

Patterns in Surface Temperatures

Data, such as daily and monthly average surface temperatures, can be shown on a map. At the top of the next page is a map of average July surface temperatures. Look at that map, and find the places on the map that are habitable according to the CSA guidelines. Remember, you are looking for average temperatures of 25°F to 85°F. Study the map and look for similarities and patterns.

PF 31

Stop and Think

10 min.

Students have a brief discussion on responses.

META NOTES

Students will need to be able to analyze daily and monthly temperatures. The questions here are designed to help identify areas that students do not understand and to apply what they have learned about calculating average temperatures.

META NOTES

Students should work independently answering these questions.

◯ Get Going

Let students know that they will be analyzing the data in the table as they are answering the questions. Then let them know how much time they have and that a brief class discussion will follow.

△ Guide and Assess

Have a class discussion on students' responses. Students should have the information listed below.

1. Students should list Day 2 (93°F) as having the highest daily high temperature.

2. Students should list Day 3 (84°F) as having the lowest daily high temperature. Some students may misread the question and give the lowest daily value.

3. Students should make an educated guess. Encourage students to look at the range and estimate the middle of the range.

4. Students should calculate average temperatures and compare the results with their guess in Question 3. Day 3 has the highest average temperature, with an average of 82.5°F. Day 1 has an average temperature of 80°F and Day 2 has an average of 79°F.

5. Students should answer yes and describe two situations. The first is when a high temperature is greater than 85°F by a given amount and the low temperature is less than 85°F by the same amount, the average of the two numbers will be 85°F. In the second situation, the high temperature is equal to 85°F and the low temperature is also equal to 85°F, then the average temperature is 85°F.

6. Students should answer yes, saying all of these locations fit the criteria requested by the *CSA*. The average daily temperatures are to be between 25°F and 85°F.

△ Guide

Tell the students that the monthly average temperatures for Earth and the daily averages are calculated in a similar way. The only difference is that monthly average temperatures average the daily temperatures for 28-31 days, depending on the length of the month. The calculated averages are represented on the map visualization with color.

META NOTES

Estimating the average as the middle of the range works only because there are only two values. The average of the numbers 2 and 8 is 5, because there are only two values. However, the average of 2, 8, 8, and 8 is 6.5.

air ~~... e that is less tha~~
Support your answer.

6. Could a location with any of these average daily temperatures fit the temperature criteria requested by the CSA?

Procedure: Explore the Case on Earth

Patterns in Surface Temperatures

Data, such as daily and monthly average surface temperatures, can be shown on a map. At the top of the next page is a map of average July surface temperatures. Look at that map, and find the places on the map that are habitable according to the CSA guidelines. Remember, you are looking for average temperatures of 25°F to 85°F. Study the map and look for similarities and patterns.

Procedure: Explore the Case on Earth

20 min.

Groups identify habitable regions that meet CSA's *criteria on Earth and look for patterns in Earth's surface temperatures.*

△ Guide

Ask students to think about the average temperatures at different locations on Earth and how those temperatures change at different times of the year. Tell students they will be identifying the locations on Earth that meet *CSA's* definition of habitable by looking at temperatures at those locations for the months of July and January.

Ask students where they think would be habitable and inhabitable on Earth according to *CSA's* criteria and constraints.

Prompt them to think about the temperatures where they live during the months of January and July, and to consider average monthly temperatures. If the local temperatures rise too high or drop too low on only one or two days in a month, the location is habitable. Tell students the goal for this discussion is to see which locations on Earth would be considered suitable for a colony and which would not be, based on the average monthly temperature.

Ask students if it would be possible for a place to be habitable in one season and not habitable in another season. *(Students should understand that temperature changes in different seasons might mean that many areas would be habitable for some seasons, but not others.)*

○ Get Going

Have groups begin answering the questions and let them know that a class discussion will follow. Let students know how much time they have.

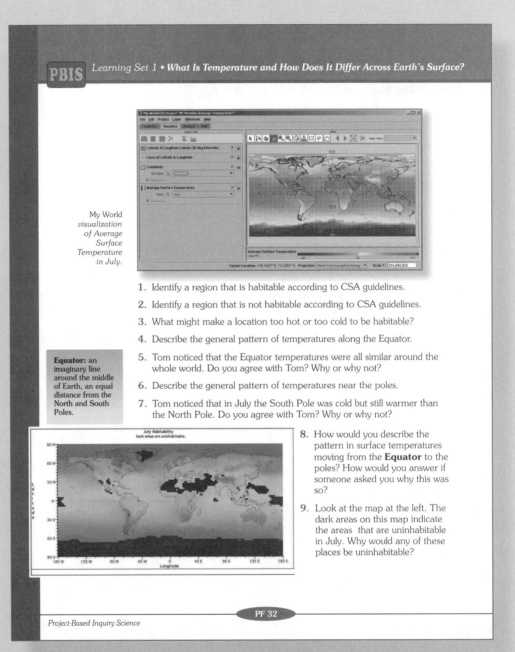

My World
*visualization
of Average
Surface
Temperature
in July.*

1. Identify a region that is habitable according to CSA guidelines.

2. Identify a region that is not habitable according to CSA guidelines.

3. What might make a location too hot or too cold to be habitable?

4. Describe the general pattern of temperatures along the Equator.

Equator: an
imaginary line
around the middle
of Earth, an equal
distance from the
North and South
Poles.

5. Tom noticed that the Equator temperatures were all similar around the whole world. Do you agree with Tom? Why or why not?

6. Describe the general pattern of temperatures near the poles.

7. Tom noticed that in July the South Pole was cold but still warmer than the North Pole. Do you agree with Tom? Why or why not?

8. How would you describe the pattern in surface temperatures moving from the **Equator** to the poles? How would you answer if someone asked you why this was so?

9. Look at the map at the left. The dark areas on this map indicate the areas that are uninhabitable in July. Why would any of these places be uninhabitable?

PF 32

Project-Based Inquiry Science

△ Guide and Assess

Monitor students' progress as they are working and guide them as needed.

When the allotted time is over, have a class discussion on their responses. Consider having projections of the images in the student text as a focal point for the discussion.

1. Students should pick locations that are colored with turquoise, yellow, orange, and orange-red. Purple, dark blue, or red areas should not be selected. Consider projecting the average monthly July temperatures from *My World* by selecting the file *PF Monthly Average Temperature*, selecting the month of July, and selecting the Visualize tab.

2. Students should pick areas shaded in purple, dark blue, or red such as the Antarctic, Northern Africa, Southwestern Asia.

3. Record students' responses. These will be addressed in other *Learning Sets*.

4. Students should recognize that along the Equator the general average temperatures for July are high.

5. Students should provide logical reasoning that supports their responses. Students may observe that most of the temperatures at the Equator are hot as indicated by the predominant dark orange-red colors shown on the map. Students might point out one light orange spot in Africa along the Equator and another along the western coast of South America. Ask students if they can identify these regions. Consider comparing the location with a world map. The mountainous region in Africa is in Kenya and includes Mt. Kilimanjaro. The mountainous region in South America is in Ecuador and is part of the Andes Mountain Range.

> **META NOTES**
>
> This information provides data that suggests elevation affects temperature. This is the topic of *Learning Set 5*. If students infer this, consider exploring other higher elevations like the Himalayan Mountain Range in Asia with the class. This also shows cooler temperatures.

6. Students should describe the general patterns of the poles being cold (32°F or below). Students might note the average temperatures at the North Pole are much warmer (around 32°F) than those of the South Pole (around -45°F).

7. Students should disagree with Tom. The South Pole is cooler than the North Pole during July and can be seen from the color-coded temperature ranges.

8. Students should note that the general trend is for the temperatures to get cooler as you move away from the poles. Consider recording these ideas to discuss later in the Unit.

9. Consider projecting the image for July habitability from the student text. Students should note that the dark areas near the Equator are uninhabitable because the average temperatures are too high (above 85°F) and the dark areas near the poles are uninhabitable because the temperatures are too cold (below 25°F).

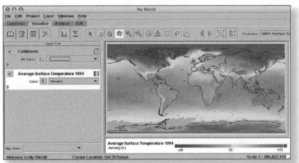

My World
visualization
of Average
Surface
Temperature
in January.

Now look at a map showing average surface temperatures for January.
Compare this map to the one for July.

10. Identify a region that is habitable according to CSA guidelines.

11. Identify a region that is not habitable according to CSA guidelines.

12. Which places are habitable in both January and July?

13. Mike noticed that the latitudes along the Equator were about the same temperature on both Monthly Average Temperature Maps. Do you agree with Mike? How would you answer if someone asked you why this was so?

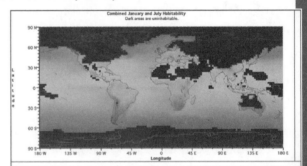

14. Mary noticed that around North America the land and water were different temperatures. She did not notice that on the July map. Do you agree with Mary? How would you answer if someone asked you why this was so?

Consider projecting the *My World* map of the average surface temperatures for January to use as a focal point while answering Questions 10 through 15.

10. Students should select locations in regions that are colored turquoise, yellow, and orange to orange-red colors. Most regions are categorize in this way except for the Arctic and Antarctic regions, and Australia.

11. Students should select locations in regions that are colored purple, dark blue, and red such as the Arctic and Antarctic regions, and Australia.

12. Students may try to determine habitability by combining information from both temperature maps, or by using the combined January and July habitability map shown in the student text. Students should note places that are habitable in both July and January are in the western coastal United States, southeastern United States, parts of Mexico, Central America (not the western islands), most of South America, central and southern Africa, southern Asia, and most of Europe.

13. Students may have trouble determining differences from the images in the text. It would be best if these images were projected. Use *My World* to open up the January map as a Child Map and then open the July map. Adjust the size of the maps so students can view them side by side on the projection screen. Students should notice at 10° North and South of the Equator, temperatures are similar in January and July and there are noticeable differences in the color coding for more northern and southern latitudes.

14. Students' responses should describe a difference in land and sea temperatures for northern United States and Canada in July. The water is cooler than the land. In January, the water is warmer than the land in Canada, the United States, and Mexico. Students may not know why this is so. Record their ideas to refer back to later in the Unit.

> **META NOTES**
>
> Temperature maps provide some evidence that land and sea transfer heat energy at different rates. This is discussed in *Learning Set 4*.

NOTES

....

....

....

....

Niagara Falls in winter.

Niagara Falls in summer.

Mount Rainier in spring.

15. Michelle noticed that in January the Southern Hemisphere was warmer than the Northern Hemisphere. Do you agree with Michelle? How would you answer if someone asked you why this was so?

16. Look at the bottom map of the previous page. The dark areas on this map indicate the areas that are uninhabitable in July and January. Why would any of these places be uninhabitable?

17. Look at the images at the top of this page. They are photos of the same place, one taken in winter and one in summer. Why do you think some places experience such wide temperature variations at different times of the year?

15. Students should provide evidence supporting the claim that the Southern Hemisphere is warmer than the Northern Hemisphere in January. A good comparison is to consider the temperature color-coded information in the Northern Hemisphere between the latitudes of 30°N and 60°N to the information in the Southern Hemisphere between the latitudes of 30°S and 60°S. Much of the

United States is in a range with temperatures below 32°F. In the Southern Hemisphere, Chile, Argentina, and Uruguay are in a region with temperatures above 32°F. Students may not know why this is so. Record their ideas to refer back to later in the Unit.

16. Students' responses should include constraints based on energy needs. The average monthly temperature range for a habitable location on *Planet X* must fall within the range of 25°F and 85°F. If these were the constraints on Earth, all the black areas on the map would be considered uninhabitable because they are outside of this required temperature range. Consider pointing this out by projecting the average monthly temperature maps for January and July side-by-side and asking students which regions are constrained by this temperature range.

17. The purpose of this question is to get students thinking about what causes the seasonal change in temperatures. Consider asking students why temperatures in January and July were used. Students should recognize that most extreme temperatures occur in January and July, and any area that is habitable during both of these months will be habitable during the less-extreme months. Students should be able to describe the seasons, but may not realize what causes the seasons. Record students' responses to refer to later in the Unit and when updating the class *Project Board*.

> **META NOTES**
>
> How elevation affects surface temperature is discussed in *Learning Set 5*.

18. The purpose of this question is to get students thinking about how elevation affects temperature. Students may not realize that elevation changes temperature and they may not know why this is. Record students' responses to refer to later in the Unit and when updating the class *Project Board*.

19. Record students' responses to refer to later in the Unit and when updating the class *Project Board*. Students may note the distance away from the Equator affects the temperature but may not know why. This is discussed in *Learning Set 2*.

Consider concluding with a discussion of how we deal with wide temperature ranges on Earth or in temperature ranges outside of the habitable constraint region and what it means for colonizing *Planet X*.

Ask students, Is special equipment needed to prevent freezing or burning? Do crops and farm animals survive easily? How might the requirement of these extra measures affect the colonization of a new planet?

18. Look at the image to the left.
How do you think there can be snow on a mountaintop at the same time there are spring-like conditions near the base?

19. Look back at the January and July surface-temperature maps. What other factors may cause temperature variations? Observe both surface-temperature maps and record your answer.

What's the Point?

You have worked with different surface-temperature maps. As you did so, it probably became obvious that there are variations across Earth's surface. You have observed temperature differences between the Equator and the poles. You also observed differences between January and July. You can now calculate and understand average daily temperatures and average monthly temperatures. This will be important as you proceed with the *Big Challenge*.

Ice breaking up in the summer in Northern Canada.

Assessment Options

Targeted Concepts, Skills, and Nature of Science	How do I know if students got it?
Scientists make claims (conclusions) based on evidence obtained (trends in data) from reliable investigations	**ASK:** What claims can you make based on the January and July temperature maps you analyzed and how does the data support your claim? **LISTEN:** Students' responses should include a statement about how distance from the Equator affects the average monthly temperature for these two months. They could conclude that there are more regions of higher temperatures in the Southern Hemisphere than in the Northern Hemisphere in January and conversely in July. They may also conclude that lower temperatures occur on high mountains in both January and July.
Habitable areas of Earth are determined by average temperatures suitable for humans to live in. These areas are often broken up into biomes, which are a group of ecosystems that have the same general climate and similar plants and animals.	**ASK:** What temperature ranges on Earth are most suited for human habitation? Humans live all over Earth, what do they have to do to live in less suited climates? **LISTEN:** Students should describe the most suitable temperature ranges for human habitat to be between 25°F to 85°F. They may reduce this range by increasing the low value. Students should describe that to live in climates that fall outside of this temperature region, we must use energy to warm up where we live or cool it down. Food and water sources are also limited in regions outside the most suitable ranges and require importing these items or using innovative methods to sustain food and water sources. These would require energy sources.

Teacher Reflection Questions

- Refer to students' responses to Questions 17, 18, and 19. What difficulties did students have identifying factors that affect surface temperatures?

- How do you think you will use the students' responses for Questions 17, 18, and 19 to guide students in future *Learning Sets?*

- How were you able to engage class discussion during the *Procedure* segment? Were you able to maintain the students' focus on the tasks at hand? What would you try to do next time?

NOTES

Back to the Big Challenge

Which Regions of a Newly Discovered Planet Have Surface Temperatures Appropriate for a Human Colony?

◄ $\frac{1}{2}$ *class period*

A class period is considered to be one 40 to 50 minute class.

Overview

Students are informed that the *CSA* has identified the four most important factors that affect *Planet X*'s surface temperature and will need to investigate each of these factors. Students construct questions to investigate and update their class *Project Board*. In this activity, students act as scientists by breaking up a big question into smaller ones to investigate.

Targeted Concepts, Skills, and Nature of Science	Performance Expectations
Scientists often work together and share their findings. Sharing findings makes new information available and helps scientists to refine their ideas and build on others' ideas. When another person's or group's idea is used, credit needs to be given.	The class should work together to update their class *Project Board*.
Scientists must keep clear, accurate, and descriptive records of what they do so they can share their work with others and consider what they did, why they did it, and what they want to do next.	Students should refer to their previous records to assist them in updating the class *Project Board*.
Graphs, maps, and tables are an effective way to analyze and communicate results of scientific investigation.	Students should recognize that the *Project Board* is an effective table that helps them organize information.

Materials	
1 per class	Class *Project Board*
1 per student	*Project Board* page
1 per classroom	Optional: projection of *CSA* bulletin

Homework Options

Reflection

- **Science Content:** What evidence do you have to support that elevation affects surface temperature of a region? (*Students should use data from the January and July temperature maps to support the claim that elevation affects the surface temperature of a region.*)

Preparation for Learning Set 2

- **Science Process:** You have been asked to determine how the shape of Earth affects its surface temperature. You will need to come up with a way to determine, test, and measure the relationship between a planet's shape and its surface temperature. How will you do this? (*The purpose of this is for students to begin thinking about how they could measure the relationship between a planet's shape and its surface temperature.*)

NOTES

....

....

....

....

....

....

BACK TO THE BIG CHALLENGE IMPLEMENTATION

Learning Set 1

Back to the Big Challenge

Which regions of a newly discovered planet have surface temperatures appropriate for a human colony?

The challenge for *Planetary Forecaster* asks a very big question. The best way to answer this big question is to break it down into smaller questions. You began this *Learning Set* by asking the smaller question: *What is temperature and how does it differ across Earth's surface?*

TO: Scientific Research Team
FROM: The Cooperative Space Agency (CSA)
SUBJECT: Exploration of new planet

The CSA has completed its research to help you determine the habitable regions of *Planet X*. CSA has identified the four factors they think have the greatest effect on *Planet X's* surface temperatures. These factors are

- shape of the planet
- tilt of the planet's axis
- land/water differences
- surface elevation

Your task is to investigate how these factors affect temperatures on Earth. You will then use what you discover to predict the temperature ranges of *Planet X*. Use your predictions and the temperature requirements to identify which parts of *Planet X* are habitable. You will be asked to make a final report to the CSA. It should include your ideas of where a colony might be established. Your report should explain how you came up with your plan. It should also include a possible new name for *Planet X*.

The CSA will continue to gather information about each of the above factors. CSA will send new data to you as it becomes available. Fellow scientists, you are about to join the search for a new frontier! Good luck with your investigation!

You saw that Earth's temperature varies. Temperature can be specific to very small areas. Temperature can change constantly as you move small distances. However, you saw that temperatures on Earth seem to have a pattern. When you looked at average temperatures over longer periods of time, you observed large areas of similar temperature.

Using the CSA criteria, you considered areas that are habitable on Earth. You now know that the CSA feels that habitable areas on *Planet X* must have average monthly temperatures of 25°F to 85°F. Understanding these points is very important for identifying areas on *Planet X* that are suitable for a colony.

Read the bulletin to the left.

You now know the full details of your challenge. You are ready to begin your investigation of the four factors identified by the CSA.

Learning Set 1

Back to the Big Challenge

10 min.

Introduce new information about the Big Challenge.

> **META NOTES**
>
> Students may not know these terms or may have misconceptions relating to the definitions. They may believe that tilt is related to land surface rather than Earth's axis.

△ Guide

Display the bulletin from the *CSA* to the class using an overhead projector. Have the class read the bulletin. Follow this with a class discussion about the four factors the *CSA* has identified to have the greatest affect on the surface temperatures of *Planet X*.

Ask students to think about each of the four factors to elicit what they think each one means. Record all students' ideas.

*A class period is considered to be one 40 to 50 minute class.

Ask students what questions they have about these factors. Record a few questions and point out that this is the process scientists use to answer big questions.

❝We are using the same process as scientists. They often break down big questions into smaller questions. Our *Big Question* is *Which regions of a newly discovered planet have appropriate surface temperatures for a human colony?* In this *Learning Set*, we broke up this question. We explored the questions, *What is surface temperature? What is considered an appropriate range of surface temperatures for a human colony? What factors affect the surface temperature?* Now we need to ask, *How do the factors affect the surface temperature?*❞

NOTES

....

....

....

....

....

....

....

....

....

....

Update the *Project Board*

Discuss the bulletin with your class. As a class, update the *Project Board*, listing any ideas or investigation questions that resulted from the activities you completed. By now you should have some very good ideas about the factors that cause temperature variations. You should also have some evidence to support your ideas. The next steps will be to start asking questions about some of the factors that influence Earth's temperatures. You can then see if these factors will apply to *Planet X* as well.

PF 37

PLANETARY FORECASTER

Update the Project Board

15 min.

The class updates their Project Board *with new ideas they have about temperature and Earth's surface.*

△ Guide

Begin by revisiting the factors students determined during their brainstorming when presented with the *Big Challenge*. Ask them to relate their brainstorming to the factors that the *CSA* has identified. Students may connect "it is cold on mountains" to the factor of surface elevation. They might connect "it is hot on islands near the Equator" to the factor of shape of the planet or land/water differences.

Let students know their ideas are not wrong or unrelated to surface temperatures if they do not match the four factors addressed in the bulletin from the *CSA*. There are many factors that affect that planet, these are the most influential according to the *CSA*. Ask students which of the factors they listed involve human influence and would not apply to *Planet X*. Students may have inferred that areas near big factories are warmer or areas where the rainforest was cut down are warmer in their brainstorming session. Students should be able to recognize that these factors would not affect *Planet X* because there are no humans there.

Ask students what they would like to put in the first column *(What do we think we know?)* about the four factors identified by *CSA*. Then ask students what they think they need to investigate. Ask students to put these in the form of a question in the second column of the class *Project Board*.

Students should have formed more questions in response to the new bulletin and the knowledge they gained in *Learning Set 1*. Make sure they take the time to add these questions and ideas to the *Project Board*. It may be helpful to draw out these questions by asking general questions.

META NOTES

Students should now have a fuller understanding of the challenge in this Unit. In order to make accurate temperature predictions for *Planet X*, they will be research four factors: shape, tilt, land/water differences, and elevation. By eliminating areas with any average monthly temperatures below 25 ° F or above 85 ° F, students will use temperature predictions to determine the best areas to settle.

TEACHER TALK

❝What do you think causes the planet's surface to warm up and cool down?

What questions could we ask to determine the relationship between the shape of the planet and surface temperature? What type of measurements could you make to determine this relationship?

What questions do you have based on what you have done in this *Learning Set?* ❞

Teacher Reflection Questions

- What misconceptions did students have about the four factors indicated by the *CSA*?

- How did students use their previous records? Did they see the benefit of keeping good records?

- How did you encourage each students' participation in updating the *Project Board?*

LEARNING SET 2 INTRODUCTION

Learning Set 2

How Does a Planet's Shape Affect Surface Temperatures?

◀ *7 class periods*

A class period is considered to be one 40 to 50 minute class.

Students use models to explore how the shape of Earth affects how energy from the Sun is spread over its surface. Students analyze data of solar energy over Earth's surface using My World *software.*

Overview

Students investigate how the shape of a planet affects the amount of solar energy it receives. The *Learning Set* begins with a bulletin from the *Cooperative Space Agency* confirming that the shape and size of *Planet X* are similar to Earth. Students explore how direct and indirect light affect how a box and ball are illuminated. By gathering information about the illuminated area and the brightness, students begin to understand this relationship and the effect of the Sun's light on Earth. Using a model, students investigate the relationship between the incident light beam and the angle it strikes an object. From the data they collect, they consider its application to solar radiation striking Earth and how it affects Earth's surface temperature. Using *My World* students analyze data of incoming solar energy striking Earth's surface and obtain evidence to assist them in understanding the relationship between planet shape and surface temperature. Students read about how the Sun's energy affects habitability and are introduced to biomes. Throughout the *Learning Set* students revise explanations they have constructed about how shape affects surface temperature, adding with each revision more evidence and science knowledge to support their claim. Students use the information they have to make an initial prediction of the surface temperatures on *Planet X*. Their final task is to make an initial habitability prediction for *Planet X* based on their predicted surface temperatures.

Targeted Concepts, Skills, and Nature of Science	Section
Scientists often work together and share their findings. Sharing findings makes new information available and helps scientists to refine their ideas and build on others' ideas. When another person's or group's idea is used, credit needs to be given.	2.1, 2.2, 2.3, 2.4, 2.5, 2.BBC
Scientists must keep clear, accurate, and descriptive records of what they do so they can share their work with others and consider what they did, why they did it, and what they want to do next.	2.1, 2.2, 2.3, 2.4, 2.5, 2.BBC
Graphs, maps, and tables are an effective way to analyze and communicate results of scientific investigation.	2.2, 2.4, 2.BBC
Identifying factors that lead to variation is an important part of scientific investigation.	2.1
Scientists make claims (conclusions) based on evidence obtained (trends in data) from reliable investigations	2.2, 2.4
Explanations are claims supported by evidence, accepted ideas and facts.	2.3, 2.5
Scientists use models to simulate processes that happen too fast, too slow, on a scale that cannot be observed directly (either too small or too large), or that are too dangerous.	2.2
Heat energy may be transferred through conduction, radiation, or convection.	2.1
Habitable areas of Earth are determined by average temperatures suitable for humans to live in. These areas are often broken up into biomes, which are a group of ecosystems that have the same general climate and similar plants and animals.	2.4
The intensity of light on an object depends on its shape and the angle it strikes the object at. As the curvature of the object's surface increases the angle at which the light strikes increases, and the intensity of light on the object decreases.	2.1, 2.2, 2.3, 2.4
The average amount of solar energy that strikes Earth's surface over a year is highest near the equator and the intensity of the solar energy that strikes the surface decreases as you move farther away from the Equator, whether you are moving north or south.	2.4, 2.5, 2.BBC

Students' Initial Conceptions and Capabilities

- Most students will know that Earth is colder at the Poles and warmer at the Equator. Some students may have some ideas why this is so, but many students will not understand the effect that shape has on surface temperature and many students will have misconceptions about how energy from the Sun reaches Earth, affects Earth, and the role that Earth's shape has (Sherin, B., Edelson, D., & Brown, M., 2005).

- In studies of students learning about Earth Science topics, students have several recurring misconceptions about how the shape of a planet affects the incoming solar energy and temperatures of the planet. Most students believe the Equator is the warmest place on Earth, but explanations for why vary widely. Students may mistakenly believe that the Equator is warmer than other areas because solar energy only strikes at the Equator and is then distributed over the rest of the planet from there (Sherin, B., Edelson, D., & Brown, M., 2005).

- Students may believe that the Equator sticks out from the surface of Earth, receiving more sunlight. A related misconception is that the Equator is warmer because it is closer to the Sun. This will be proven incorrect in *Learning Set 3* (Sherin, B., Edelson, D., & Brown, M., 2005).

- Another common misconception is that different parts of Earth receive energy from different parts of the Sun, believing warmer areas on Earth get energy from warmer parts of the Sun. If students do not know of the straight-ray model of solar radiation, they may also believe that some areas are cooler because the energy must curve to reach those areas (Sherin, B., Edelson, D., & Brown, M., 2005).

NOTES

....

....

....

....

....

....

Understanding for Teachers

Learning About Shape

Students begin their investigation of surface temperature looking at the shape factor because it is the simplest to investigate. The spherical shape of Earth and *Planet X* causes differential heating of the planet. Parallel rays of solar radiation strike the curved surface of a planet at different angles, depending on latitude. Rays that strike at exactly 90 degrees are considered direct rays. The smaller the angle at which the rays strike (the farther from 90 degrees), the more indirect they are. When the rays strike directly, the energy is more intense than when the rays strike indirectly. When striking at a 90 degree angle, the same amount of solar energy heats a smaller area than when striking indirectly. Locations farther from Earth's Equator such as Canada, Northern Europe, and Siberia are known to be very cold. Locations on the Equator such as the Sahara Desert and the South American Rainforest are known to be very warm. When students understand how the curvature of Earth affects the temperatures in these different locations, they will be able to predict the effects of curvature on *Planet X* and make their initial recommendations for habitable locations based on realistic temperature predictions.

Earth's Shape

For the purpose of the investigations in this *Learning Set*, Earth is assumed to be a sphere. However, Earth is actually an imperfect sphere. Earth is slightly flatter at the poles and bulges at the Equator because of its spinning motion. Earth is also very slightly pear-shaped. Any latitude in the Southern Hemisphere has a slightly larger circumference than the corresponding latitude in the Northern Hemisphere

How Earth's Atmosphere Affects Incoming Solar Radiation

Earth's atmosphere further contributes to changes in incoming solar radiation as it strikes Earth at different angles. The more acute the angle at which solar radiation enters Earth's atmosphere, the more of the atmosphere it must pass through to reach the surface. At any given location, incoming solar radiation must pass through the most atmosphere before reaching ground at sunrise and sunset. At these times, solar energy is passing through significantly more air and is being scattered and absorbed by more molecules. As solar radiation passes through more air, more energy at blue and violet wavelengths is scattered, leaving red and orange light. This is why sunsets and sunrises are typically red and orange. Clouds, humidity, and pollution in the air all scatter different wavelengths of light, and contribute to varied hues in Earth's sunrises and sunsets.

112

2.0

LEARNING SET 2 IMPLEMENTATION

◄ *7 class periods**

Learning Set 2

How Does a Planet's Shape Affect Surface Temperatures?

You saw that average daily and monthly temperatures vary as you move from the Earth's Equator to the poles. The temperatures near the Equator are very warm all year-round. The poles are much colder year-round. Your task is to investigate the factors that are responsible for these temperature differences on Earth. In this *Learning Set*, you are going to explore the answer to the question, *How does a planet's shape affect surface temperatures.* Begin by reading the following urgent message.

Earth's surface temperatures vary widely depending on where you are on the planet.

CSA

TO: Scientific Research Team
FROM: The Cooperative Space Agency
SUBJECT: Shape of *Planet X*

Data has confirmed the size and shape of *Planet X.* The new planet is in the form of a sphere. It is very close in size to Earth.

Your next task is to investigate the ways in which shape affects temperature and why. You will use this information to make temperature predictions for *Planet X.* Then you can determine the most habitable area for the new colony.

PF 38

Project-Based Inquiry Science

Learning Set 2

How Does a Planet's Shape Affect Surface Temperatures?

5 min.

Introduce the Learning Set.

◯ **Engage**

Let students know they will be investigating the relationship between a planet's shape and surface temperatures.

*A class period is considered to be one 40 to 50 minute class.

"To begin your investigation of *Planet X* and make your recommendations for habitability to the *CSA*, you must begin investigating the four factors *CSA* has determined to effect surface temperatures the most. They are shape of the planet, tilt of the planet's axis, land and water differences, and surface elevation. The focus of this *Learning Set* is to answer the question *How does a planet's shape affect surface temperatures?*"

Project the bulletin from *CSA* or have students read it from the student text to make students aware that the size and shape of *Planet X* are similar to Earth's size and shape. Elicit students' ideas about how the shape of a planet affects the surface temperature and why it affects the surface temperature. Record students' ideas.

Let students know that they will investigate this factor over the next several days and will make their first predictions about *Planet X*'s surface temperatures based on what they have learned. Let students know they will make their first drafts of their recommendations to the *CSA* identifying the locations on *Planet X* that will be habitable.

NOTES

2.1 Understand the Challenge

What are the Effects of a Planet's Shape on its Temperatures?

◀ *1 class period*

A class period is considered to be one 40 to 50 minute class.

Overview

Students explore how shape affects the way an object is illuminated and consider what this implies for surface temperature. Students explore how the location of a light source affects how a box's surface is illuminated, using flashlights to simulate this process. They explore how the same locations of the light source effect the illumination of a sphere's surface. By comparing the results of a ball and a box, they conclude that different shapes are illuminated differently by the same light source. Students read about how Earth gets its energy from the radiation emitted by the Sun, direct and indirect light sources, and they consider how their observations model the illumination of Earth by the Sun. Students consider four statements about how the shape of a planet could affect surface temperature and then construct their own predictions about how shape affects surface temperature. The class concludes the section by updating their *Project Board*.

Targeted Concepts, Skills, and Nature of Science	Performance Expectations
Scientists often work together and share their findings. Sharing findings makes new information available and helps scientists to refine their ideas and build on others' ideas. When another person's or group's idea is used, credit needs to be given.	Students should work in groups to obtain evidence of how a light beam shines differently on a box and a sphere. Groups should discuss their observations with the class and the class updates their *Project Board*.
Scientists must keep clear, accurate, and descriptive records of what they do so they can share their work with others and consider what they did, why they did it, and what they want to do next.	Students should keep accurate records of their results to refer back to when answering questions during discussions and when updating the Project Board.

Targeted Concepts, Skills, and Nature of Science	Performance Expectations
Identifying factors that lead to variation is an important part of scientific investigation.	Based on their observations of light striking a box and a sphere, students should be able to describe the shape of an object as a factor that affects how it is illuminated.
Heat energy may be transferred through conduction, radiation, or convection.	Students should describe how energy from the Sun warms Earth through radiation.
The intensity of light on an object depends on its shape and the angle it strikes the object at. As the curvature of the object's surface increases the angle at which the light strikes increases, and the intensity of light on the object decreases.	Students should describe how the intensity and area of illumination of an illuminated object is affected by the object's shape, and where the light beam strikes the object.

Materials	
1 per group	Flashlight Ball Box Marker Metric tape measure or flexible ruler
1 per class	Class *Project Board* Optional: projection of the bulletin from *CSA*
1 per student	*Project Board* page *Getting Started Observations* page

NOTES

....

....

....

....

Activity Setup and Preparation

Try out the experiment before class. You will need to determine how dark your room needs to be and how far from the center line on the spheres and cubes the flashlight should be. Consider marking the locations of the point where the hand holding the flashlight should be and where the front edge of the box and ball should be. Students should drop a straight edge, such as a meter stick, from the ball to position its front edge to the marked location. They can also use a straight edge to position their hand. Consider marking the balls and boxes with parallel lines indicating where students should shine the light beam. These should be marked at equal increments above and below the center line as shown in the image in the student text. Masking tape is an option for marking these distances and locations.

Homework Options

Reflection

- **Science Content:** Based on your observations, what claim can you make about how the shape of an object affects how it is illuminated? Support your claim with evidence. *(Students should state that the shape of an object affects how it is illuminated and they should support their answers with their observations.)*

- **Science Process:** During your investigation, what were the manipulated (independent) and responding (dependent) variables? Which variables were kept constant? *(Students should describe their two experiments. One tested the sphere and another tested the cube. Results were compared across the two objects. The independent variable for each experiment was the location of the light source (the height the flashlight was held), and the dependent variable was the illumination on the object (brightness and area). The controlled variables were the distance the flashlight was held away from the object, the intensity of the flashlight, and the object. The observations for the illumination of the two objects were compared to determine how shape affects illumination.)*

Preparation for 2.2

- **Science Content & Process:** How do you think illumination and temperature are related? How could you test this? *(Students' responses should include a way to measure how temperature changes as the amount of illumination changes.)*

NOTES

SECTION 2.1 IMPLEMENTATION

2.1 Understand the Challenge

What Are the Effects of a Planet's Shape on its Temperatures?

To predict the temperatures on *Planet X*, you will need to investigate how the shape of the planet affects surface temperatures. Before you begin your investigations, you will develop a prediction about the effect of a planet's shape on its surface temperatures. Then you will investigate to find out more and test your prediction. To get started with making a prediction, you are going to explore how light behaves when it strikes objects with different shapes.

Materials
• flashlight
• ball
• box
• marker
• metric tape measure or flexible ruler

Get Started

Get the materials from your teacher. If lines are not already drawn on the ball and the box, draw lines around them as shown in the pictures. Make sure your lines are parallel to each other.

Place the ball on a desktop so the lines you drew are parallel to the top of the desk. You may need to have someone hold the ball or place something behind it so it will not roll away.

Hold the flashlight parallel to the top of the desk about 8 cm (approx. 3 in.) from the farthest edge of the ball. It should be level with the middle line you drew around the ball. Shine the light on the ball. Observe the brightness of the light. Measure the distance between the top and bottom of the beam where it strikes the ball.

Next, shine the light just below the centerline, and measure the distance between the top and bottom of the beam. Then, shine the light near the bottom of the ball and measure again. Do this for the two positions above the centerline, also. Make sure to keep the flashlight parallel to the top of the desk each time.

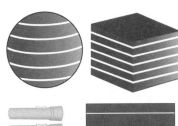

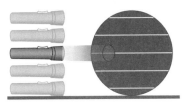

measure this distance

PLANETARY FORECASTER

2.1 Understand the Challenge

What Are the Effects of a Planet's Shape on its Temperatures?

5 min.

Introduce what students will be exploring.

META NOTES

Review the misconceptions listed in the segment *Students' Initial Conceptions and Capabilities*. Monitor the emergence of these misconceptions in student predictions and try to address them directly when possible throughout this *Learning Set*. Because students can often have two contradictory beliefs about a given phenomenon and students' prior conceptions often directly interfere with new content, it is most effective to teach the scientifically accepted explanation of a phenomenon and discredit content misconceptions.

○ Engage

Let students know that in order to develop a prediction about the surface temperatures on *Planet X*, they will need to investigate how the shape affects the surface temperature. Elicit students' ideas about how shape affects surface temperature. Record their ideas.

Let students know they will be investigating how light behaves when it strikes an object. Ask students why they think they will be investigating this and record their responses.

*A class period is considered to be one 40 to 50 minute class.

⚠ Guide

Let students know that Earth gets its energy from the Sun. Electromagnetic energy from the Sun strikes Earth and warms it. We can see some of the energy such as visible light and some we cannot such as x-ray, ultraviolet, and infrared.

Get Started

20 min.

Students explore how an object is illuminated.

META NOTES

Consider comparing students' predictions to their results when discussing the results.

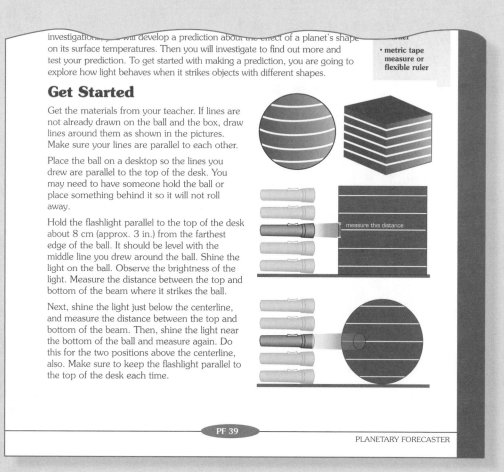

investigation... will develop a prediction about the effect of a planet's shape on its surface temperatures. Then you will investigate to find out more and test your prediction. To get started with making a prediction, you are going to explore how light behaves when it strikes objects with different shapes.

• metric tape measure or flexible ruler

Get Started

Get the materials from your teacher. If lines are not already drawn on the ball and the box, draw lines around them as shown in the pictures. Make sure your lines are parallel to each other.

Place the ball on a desktop so the lines you drew are parallel to the top of the desk. You may need to have someone hold the ball or place something behind it so it will not roll away.

Hold the flashlight parallel to the top of the desk about 8 cm (approx. 3 in.) from the farthest edge of the ball. It should be level with the middle line you drew around the ball. Shine the light on the ball. Observe the brightness of the light. Measure the distance between the top and bottom of the beam where it strikes the ball.

Next, shine the light just below the centerline, and measure the distance between the top and bottom of the beam. Then, shine the light near the bottom of the ball and measure again. Do this for the two positions above the centerline, also. Make sure to keep the flashlight parallel to the top of the desk each time.

measure this distance

PF 39

PLANETARY FORECASTER

⚠ Guide

Let students know what they will be exploring. Use the student text to describe the experiment.

TEACHER TALK

"You will explore how the light illuminates a surface by shining a light beam from a flashlight onto a sphere and a cube. You will position the flashlight at different heights, but keep it at a fixed distance, like the picture in your text books. Then you will compare your observations of the sphere and cube to determine how shape affects how an object is illuminated."

Ask students to predict what will happen and record their predictions.

If you have not marked the parallel lines on the boxes and spheres, demonstrate how to measure and mark parallel lines. Make sure the students measure the lines so they are at equal distances from each other.

Demonstrate how to shine the flashlight onto the objects at different heights above the table surface. Make sure the students understand the flashlight needs to move up and down in its location, not toward or away from the object. The object must stay in its location. The distance between the center line and the flashlight's middle position should be the same for the sphere and the cube. Emphasize that the flashlight needs to be held parallel to the table.

◯ Get Going

Distribute the objects, flashlights, tape measures, and markers to the students and let groups begin their activities. Let students know how much time they have and that after collecting their data they should begin the *Stop and Think* segment.

☐ Assess

Monitor students as they gather their measurements. Make sure students have the ball, the box, and the flashlight in the correct locations. Check to see that students are properly holding the flashlight and measuring the distances.

Students should observe that the brightness of the beam does not change as the flashlight moves up and down the surface of the box. They should notice a difference in the brightness of the beam as it moves up and down the surface of the sphere. As the surface of the sphere curves away, the light beam on the surface will appear less bright and spread out over a larger surface area. Some students may be confused by the term brightness because the brightness of the flashlight does not actually change. It is the illuminated surface's brightness that changes. Students should observe that the illumination (or amount of brightness) per surface area changes. Let students know this is related to the intensity of light. Define intensity as the rate at which energy reaches a surface. Let students know that the brighter the light per surface area, the more intense it is and the dimmer the light per surface area, the less intense it is.

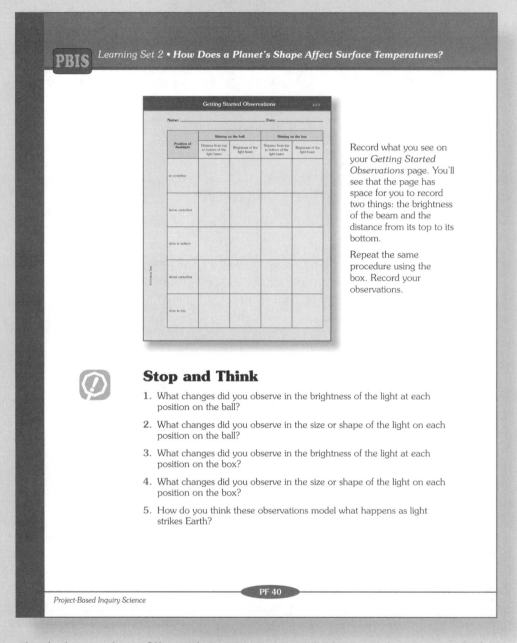

Record what you see on your *Getting Started Observations* page. You'll see that the page has space for you to record two things: the brightness of the beam and the distance from its top to its bottom.

Repeat the same procedure using the box. Record your observations.

Stop and Think

1. What changes did you observe in the brightness of the light at each position on the ball?

2. What changes did you observe in the size or shape of the light on each position on the ball?

3. What changes did you observe in the brightness of the light at each position on the box?

4. What changes did you observe in the size or shape of the light on each position on the box?

5. How do you think these observations model what happens as light strikes Earth?

PF 40

Project-Based Inquiry Science

Check that students fill out the *Getting Started Observations* page with their observations. Encourage them to use whatever descriptions or terms they feel best describes their observations in the table.

When students have completed gathering data have them begin answering the *Stop and Think* questions as a group.

△ Guide and Assess

If any groups observed something differently, consider asking them to describe it in more detail or show it by demonstration.

1. Students should have observed that as they moved the light farther away from the center, the brightness decreased as it shined on a more curved surface area.

2. Students should have observed that the shape of the light beam changed as the flashlight moved farther away from the center. The flashlight beam appears to stretch out as they move the flashlight away from the horizontal center line (equator) of the ball.

3. Students should have observed that the beam does not change brightness as it moves along the flat surface of the box.

4. Students should have observed that the size and shape of the beam do not change as the beam moves along the flat surface of the box.

5. After the class is in agreement about what they observed, have each group present their response to this question. Students' responses should include comparisons between the Sun shining on Earth and the flashlight shining on the ball.

Stop and Think

15 min.

Students have a class discussion on their responses.

NOTES

....

....

....

....

....

....

Direct and Indirect Light

5 min.

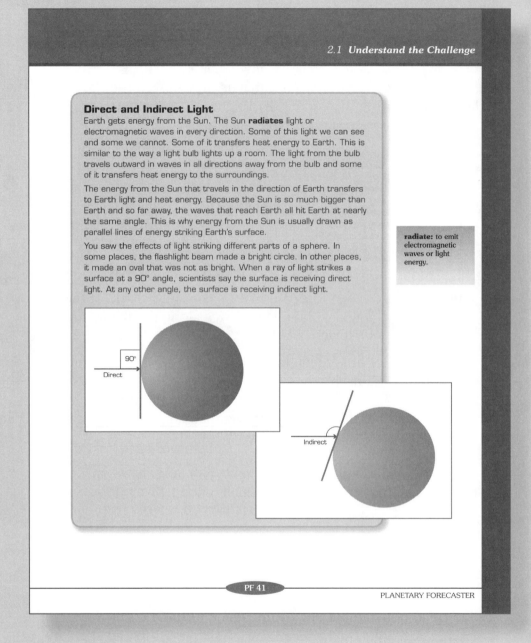

Direct and Indirect Light

Earth gets energy from the Sun. The Sun **radiates** light or electromagnetic waves in every direction. Some of this light we can see and some we cannot. Some of it transfers heat energy to Earth. This is similar to the way a light bulb lights up a room. The light from the bulb travels outward in waves in all directions away from the bulb and some of it transfers heat energy to the surroundings.

The energy from the Sun that travels in the direction of Earth transfers to Earth light and heat energy. Because the Sun is so much bigger than Earth and so far away, the waves that reach Earth all hit Earth at nearly the same angle. This is why energy from the Sun is usually drawn as parallel lines of energy striking Earth's surface.

You saw the effects of light striking different parts of a sphere. In some places, the flashlight beam made a bright circle. In other places, it made an oval that was not as bright. When a ray of light strikes a surface at a 90° angle, scientists say the surface is receiving direct light. At any other angle, the surface is receiving indirect light.

radiate: to emit electromagnetic waves or light energy.

90°

Direct

Indirect

PF 41

PLANETARY FORECASTER

△ Guide

Define and discuss direct and indirect light using the information in the student text.

Begin with a discussion about the Sun's radiation and how it transfers energy to Earth. Discuss how heat energy is transferred through radiation.

> ## TEACHER TALK

> "The Sun radiates light in electromagnetic waves. We can see some of that light with our eyes. This is called visible light. We cannot see the rest of the light that is ultraviolet light, x-rays, and infrared light. One of the ways that Earth's surface temperature heats up is through the interaction between infrared radiation and Earth, which causes Earth to warm up.
>
> When heat energy is transferred by radiation, one object must be warmer than the other and the interacting objects do not need to be touching each other. Radiation emitted from the warmer object (such as the Sun) can travel through a vacuum (nothing, such as space) to the cooler object (such as Earth). This is not the same as a conduction interaction that requires heat energy transferred through collisions between particles of matter. During a conduction interaction, the particles of matter have to touch each other. When heat energy is transferred between two objects due to an interaction involving electromagnetic radiation, the radiating object does not have to touch the other object. Heat energy is transferred by radiation (electromagnetic waves) interacting with the object being warmed. The radiation causes the atoms and molecules in the object to move around more."

Ask students to provide an example of how heat energy can be transferred through radiation. Provide them with an example that exhibits both conduction and infrared radiation interactions. In *Section 1.2*, you may have already discussed the process of conduction using the example of a cup of hot cocoa. You may want to remind students of this example and assess their understanding.

Define direct light as light that strikes an object perpendicularly (at 90°). Give students the examples of the light from the flashlight shining on the sphere's center line and light shining anywhere on the cube.

Define indirect light as light that shines on an object at any angle other than 90°. Use the example of light shining on the sphere at locations other than the center line shown in the student text to guide this explanation.

Describe how light traveling from the Sun to Earth usually strikes at the same angle and the light shining on Earth from the Sun is usually drawn as parallel lines.

◇ Evaluate

Make sure that the students understand the terms direct light and indirect light as they are used in this activity.

Predict

10 min.

Students consider how Earth's shape affects its temperature.

META NOTES

The goal is for students to connect their observations with ideas they have about how Earth's spherical shape affects its surface temperatures.

Predict

Below are some students' ideas about how planetary shape might affect surface temperature. Read and think about each student's ideas.

Jimmy: "I don't think shape makes a difference. The Sun hits all surfaces the same. The differences in temperature are caused by something else."

Ella: "I think the shape of Earth does matter. Earth is round. There are places on a round object where the light is brighter than in other places."

Tariq: "I think it definitely makes a difference. Since Earth is round it bulges out. That part is closer to the Sun, so it is hotter there. If Earth were flat or like a cube, it would not have a part that bulges out, and the temperature would be the same across the surface."

Jin: "I don't really know...but, when I pointed the flashlight at the center of the ball, it made a brighter, smaller circle than when I pointed it above and below the center. I guess if that is happening between Earth and the Sun, then shape could matter."

Now it is your turn. Based on your observations, record your prediction about the relationship between shape and surface temperatures. Discuss your prediction with your group. You may wish to modify your prediction after your discussion. Also, record questions you think you need to investigate to test your prediction. Be prepared to share your predictions and questions with the class.

Project-Based Inquiry Science

PF 42

△ Guide

Have the class read through the four ideas listed in the student text. These ideas deal with some of the misconceptions of how shape affects surface temperature. Encourage discussion on these ideas by asking students to make follow-up comments.

Ask students to create predictions for how Earth's shape affects its surface temperatures based on their observations. Then have groups meet to discuss their predictions. Students may revise their predictions at this time.

Have a class discussion on students' predictions. Students should note any disagreements in the discussion because these could provide questions they should investigate.

☐ Assess

Have a class discussion on students' predictions. Check that students use the observations they made in the exercise to make predictions. Some students will create very solid predictions using their observations; others may focus on trivial observations. The goal is to get students to think about the concepts and to use them to move forward in the challenge.

NOTES

Update the Project Board

5 min.

The class updates the Project Board *with new knowledge and questions about surface temperature.*

Update the *Project Board*

From your group discussion, you may have new questions or new ideas about how shape might influence the temperature of *Planet X*. Record these ideas, predictions, and explanations under *What do we think we know?* Consider what you need to investigate to answer the question, *How does a planet's shape affect surface temperatures?* Record your questions under *What do we need to investigate?*

Which regions of a newly discovered planet have surface temperatures appropriate for a human colony?				
What do we think we know?	What do we need to investigate?	What are we learning?	What is our evidence?	What does it mean for the challenge or question?

What's the Point?

In *Learning Set 1*, your class started a *Project Board* to help you keep track of your understandings and questions about surface temperatures. After the observations you made in this section, you probably had more ideas about how shape might affect the temperature of *Planet X*. Your initial prediction helped you to become aware of your understanding of this relationship. Now that everybody's ideas are out in the open, your class can pursue investigations that focus on these predictions.

PF 43

PLANETARY FORECASTER

△ Guide

Have a class discussion about new ideas or questions students have about how shape influences the temperature of *Planet X*. Remind students that the first column of the *Project Board* lists *What do we think we know?* Record students' ideas in this column. Remind students that the second column lists *What do we need to investigate?* Emphasize to students that they should consider questions to investigate. Record students' questions on the class *Project Board*.

◇ Evaluate

Students should have questions listed about how Earth's spherical shape affects how radiation from the Sun affects Earth's temperature.

Assessment Options

Targeted Concepts, Skills, and Nature of Science	How do I know if students got it?
Heat energy may be transferred through conduction, radiation, or convection.	**ASK:** How does the Sun interact with Earth to transfer energy? Describe the energy involved. How does this affect how heat energy is transferred through radiation? How does this differ from transferring heat by conduction? **LISTEN:** Students should describe how energy from the Sun warms Earth through radiation and that energy is in the form of electromagnetic waves. Students should describe that the infrared radiation from the Sun travels through space (vacuum) to Earth and transfers heat to Earth. Heat transferred by radiation does not require two interacting objects (Sun and Earth) to touch each other. Heat transferred by conduction requires that the objects are touching each other.

META NOTES

Students will be describing how heat energy is transferred by conduction, radiation, or convection as they learn more about the factors that affect surface temperatures. As they start filling in Columns 3 and 4 of their *Project Board*, they should use their science knowledge about heat transfers as part of their evidence. You could have them explicitly describe each type of interaction (conduction, radiation, and convection), or you could have an entry in Columns 3 and 4 specifically for each type of interaction that transfers heat. If you choose to do this, you should already have an entry for conduction and radiation.

Teacher Reflection Questions

- Were students able to discern the differences in brightness and connect this to intensity of solar energy? How can this connection be better explained?

- What misconceptions did students have? What ideas do you have about addressing these ideas?

- What difficulties did students have updating to the *Project Board?* How could these be addressed?

NOTES

2.2 Investigate

How Do Direct and Indirect Light Affect Surface Temperatures?

◀ *2 class periods*

A class period is considered to be one 40 to 50 minute class.

Overview

Students use a model of the Sun/Earth system to determine how the angle between the incident light and the object affects the illumination of the object. The model consists of a flashlight for the light source (the Sun), and a clipboard with paper for the object being illuminated (Earth). The clipboard is placed at various angles with respect to the incident light rays. Students observe how the brightness decreases and the area of illumination increases as the angle increases. Students share their results with the class and determine from the data that the intensity of light decreases with increasing angle and the solar energy striking Earth at an angle to its surface decreases as the angle increases.

Targeted Concepts, Skills, and Nature of Science	Performance Expectations
Scientists often work together and share their findings. Sharing findings makes new information available and helps scientists to refine their ideas and build on others' ideas. When another person's or group's idea is used, credit needs to be given.	Students should work in groups investigating how the brightness and area of an illuminated surface are affected by the angle that the light shines on the object. Groups should share their results with the class during an *Investigation Expo* and the class compares and analyzes the results.
Scientists must keep clear, accurate, and descriptive records of what they do so they can share their work with others and consider what they did, why they did it, and what they want to do next.	Students should have clear, descriptive, and accurate records to share with the class and to refer to as needed during the Unit.
Graphs, maps, and tables are an effective way to analyze and communicate results of scientific investigation.	Students should use their data tables when sharing their results and discussing their analysis.

Targeted Concepts, Skills, and Nature of Science	Performance Expectations
Scientists make claims (conclusions) based on evidence obtained (trends in data) from reliable investigations	Students should make claims about how the brightness and area of illumination are affected by the angle that the light source makes with the object. Students should also make claims about how the intensity of light changes as you move away from the Equator and how the surface temperature changes as the light becomes less direct.
Scientists use models to simulate processes that happen too fast, too slow, on a scale that cannot be observed directly (either too small or too large), or that are too dangerous.	Students should describe that they are using a model because the Earth/Sun system is on a scale that is very large and sometimes difficult to observe. Students should also describe what the parts of the model represent. The flashlight represents the Sun and the clipboard represents a location on a planet. The angle the clipboard is at represents how the planet's curve.
The intensity of light on an object depends on its shape and the angle it strikes the object at. As the curvature of the object's surface increases the angle at which the light strikes increases, and the intensity of light on the object decreases.	Students should begin to make claims based on their observations that the intensity of light on an object depends on the objects' shape and the angle the light strikes the object. They should also recognize that the shape of the object and the location of the source determine the angle the light strikes the object and at larger angles the intensity of illumination on the object decreases.

Materials	
1 per group	Clipboard
	Stack of books
	Wide rubber band
	Masking tape
	Flashlight
	Pencil or marker
	Ruler
	Recording Your Data page

Materials	
4 per group	Blocks, cut at various angles Sheet of graph paper
1 per classroom	Optional: globe

Activity Setup and Preparation

Go through the procedures and run the model to get an idea of where students may have difficulty. Check that your flashlights are working and have extra batteries as backup.

To avoid the illumination area exceeding a standard piece of graph paper you will need to consider the distance between the light source and the clipboard for the greatest angle of the clipboard. Mark the locations for the stack of books and clipboard with masking tape prior to students running the model.

Some types of flashlights may project several concentric circles of light onto the graph paper. If students are using a flashlight like this, make sure they choose one of those circles of light and consistently monitor the changes to that circle of light throughout the lab.

Homework Options

Reflection

- **Science Content:** How is sunlight connected to surface temperatures on Earth? *(Students' responses should include that light energy from the Sun reaches Earth and provides light energy and transfers heat energy to Earth's surface by radiation.)*

Prepare for 2.3

- **Science Content:** Explain how shape affects surface temperature. *(Students are asked to construct an explanation in the next section. This provides them with their first attempt at constructing an explanation for how shape affects surface temperature and will prepare students for discussion.)*

NOTES

SECTION 2.2 IMPLEMENTATION

◀ *2 class periods**

2.2 Investigate

How Do Direct and Indirect Light Affect Surface Temperatures?

simulate: to imitate how something happens in the real world by acting it out using a model.

Materials
- flashlight
- graph paper
- clipboard
- four blocks cut at various angles
- stack of books
- wide rubber band
- masking tape
- pencil or marker

In the previous activity, you saw that shape could affect how light strikes a surface. You noticed that the brightness of a beam was different when it struck curved and flat surfaces. Your measurements of the light beams were also different for the curved surface and the flat surface. At the centerline, both the surfaces were receiving direct light. The brightness and size of the beam were approximately the same for the flat and curved surfaces. However, as you moved away from the centerline, the beam spread out more and was less bright on the curved surface than on the flat surface. The curved surface was receiving indirect light.

Scientists often use models to re-create the real world in a lab. In this investigation, you will use a model to **simulate** how the Sun's light rays strike the surfaces of spherical planets. You will use a flashlight to represent the Sun's rays. You will change the angle at which light strikes a flat surface. This will model how the Sun's light rays strike the surfaces of spherical planets at different places.

Procedure: Build Your Model

1. Place 2 pieces of tape 3-4 inches apart on a flat surface. Make sure the pieces of tape are parallel to each other.

2. Place the flashlight on top of a stack of books so the flashlight is 1-2″ above the surface. Secure the flashlight in place with a rubber band around the top book. Make sure the stack of books is aligned with the tape and the flashlight is aligned with the stack of books.

3. Label 4 sheets of graph paper 90°, 110°, 130°, and 150°. Place the 90° sheet on the clipboard.

4. Line the 90° block up with the second piece of tape. Using the block as a guide, place the clipboard up against the block.

5. Turn on the flashlight. Make sure the flashlight will not move.

2.2 Investigate

How Do Direct and Indirect Light Affect Surface Temperatures?
30 min.

Students are introduced to the simulation model.

⚠ Guide

Remind students how in the previous activity the changing shape of the surface affected how the light shined on the surface. Consider reviewing the images from the previous section to show the direct and indirect rays of light.

Ask students why models are used. Refer to the information in the student text and discuss when models are used and the model they will use.

*A class period is considered to be one 40 to 50 minute class.

Using the flashlight in this lab demonstrates the rays of the Sun extending perfectly parallel towards Earth. Because the flashlight is always held horizontally, the radiation from the flashlight is always traveling in the same direction. However, the Sun does not radiate in only one direction and the rays of the Sun are actually not parallel. The Sun radiates energy outwards in all directions. The Sun is millions of times larger than Earth, as well as millions of miles away. When the radiation actually reaches Earth, the angle of the rays is so small that, for the purposes of understanding solar radiation's effect on Earth, we can assume the rays are parallel.

TEACHER TALK

"Scientists use models to simulate processes that happen too fast, too slow, on a scale that cannot be observed directly (either too small or too large), or that are too dangerous to observe. In this investigation, you will use a model to simulate how the Sun's light rays strike the surfaces of spherical planets. You will use a flashlight to represent the Sun's light and a clipboard with paper on it to represent a location on Earth that the light strikes. You will be able to change the angle at which the light strikes the clipboard. This will model how the Sun's light rays strike the surface of Earth at different locations. Later you will apply all that you learned to predicting a good location for a colony on *Planet X*."

Some students might wonder how a flat board models a spherical surface. Remind them that this is a model and has limitations. The clipboard represents a location on a spherical surface. The angle represents latitude above the Equator. You may want to refer back to the *Direct and Indirect Light* textbox in *Section 2.1* to refresh students with the tangent angle of Earth and light rays. Note that this experiment only estimates how the light strikes a curved surface with a large radius and we are only looking for trends and not accuracy.

Describe how the flashlight represents the rays from the Sun and discuss the similarities (parallel rays, visible light, and infrared light) and differences (Sun emits radiation in the x-ray region, ultraviolet region, and other parts of the electromagnetic spectrum that the flashlight does not) between the flashlight and the Sun.

NOTES

....

....

....

....

....

**Procedure:
Build Your
Model**

5 min.

*Students are provided
with materials and
build their models.*

2.2 Investigate

How Do Direct and Indirect Light Affect Surface Temperatures?

simulate: to imitate how something happens in the real world by acting it out using a model.

In the previous activity, you saw that shape could affect how light strikes a surface. You noticed that the brightness of a beam was different when it struck curved and flat surfaces. Your measurements of the light beams were also different for the curved surface and the flat surface. At the centerline, both the surfaces were receiving direct light. The brightness and size of the beam were approximately the same for the flat and curved surfaces. However, as you moved away from the centerline, the beam spread out more and was less bright on the curved surface than on the flat surface. The curved surface was receiving indirect light.

Materials
• flashlight
• graph paper
• clipboard
• four blocks cut at various angles
• stack of books
• wide rubber band
• masking tape
• pencil or marker

Scientists often use models to re-create the real world in a lab. In this investigation, you will use a model to **simulate** how the Sun's light rays strike the surfaces of spherical planets. You will use a flashlight to represent the Sun's rays. You will change the angle at which light strikes a flat surface. This will model how the Sun's light rays strike the surfaces of spherical planets at different places.

Procedure: Build Your Model

1. Place 2 pieces of tape 3-4 inches apart on a flat surface. Make sure the pieces of tape are parallel to each other.

2. Place the flashlight on top of a stack of books so the flashlight is 1-2″ above the surface. Secure the flashlight in place with a rubber band around the top book. Make sure the stack of books is aligned with the tape and the flashlight is aligned with the stack of books.

3. Label 4 sheets of graph paper 90°, 110°, 130°, and 150°. Place the 90° sheet on the clipboard.

4. Line the 90° block up with the second piece of tape. Using the block as a guide, place the clipboard up against the block.

5. Turn on the flashlight. Make sure the flashlight will not move.

PF 44

Project-Based Inquiry Science

△ Guide

Have a set of materials ready to show students how they should have their materials set up. Show how masking tape marks the location for the flashlight edge and the base of the clipboard. Then show students how they will change the angle of the clipboard.

Get Going

Provide each group with the materials to complete the investigation. Have the students construct the model according to the directions in their student texts. Let students know they should read the procedure before beginning the simulation and that you will check their models before running them.

Assess

Check that students' setup is correct. Let students tell you how they will run the model. Make sure they understand the procedure, how they will change the angles, and what they will mark on the graph paper. Students should have some idea of how to count the squares to determine area, but you may have to guide them further when they are measuring it. Make sure students are aware that they need to fill out the information in the table.

NOTES

Procedure: Run Your Model

2.2 *Investigate*

When everyone is set up, your teacher will darken the room.

1. Make sure the flashlight is shining directly on the graph paper. Also, make sure the flashlight and clipboard are lined up with the tape.

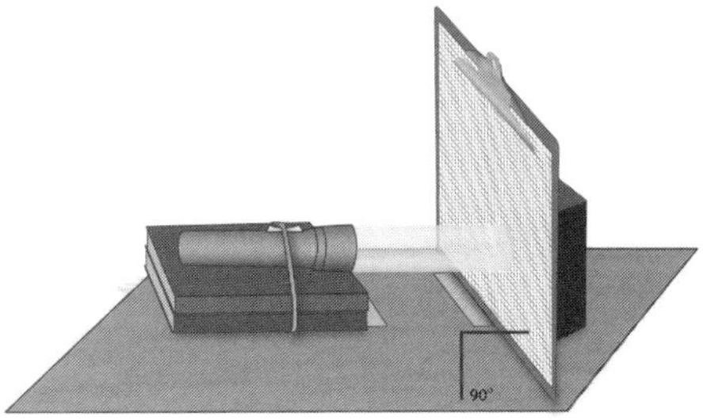

2. Trace with a marker the area covered by the light. Describe the brightness of the light.

3. Remove the square block and replace it with the block marked "110°." Put the paper marked "110°" on the clipboard. Make sure the flashlight and the clipboard are lined up with the tape.

4. Have a team member hold the clipboard against the angled side of the block. Again, trace the area covered by the light. Record the brightness of the light compared to the way you described it on the 90° paper. Note if the area of light is brighter or less bright than the 90° circle of light.

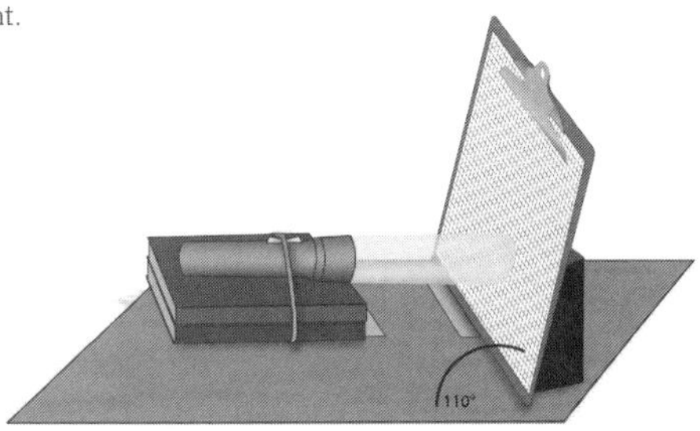

Procedure: Run Your Model

10 min.

Students run their models.

△ Guide and Assess

Students should begin the procedures after you check their setup.

Once students are familiar with the procedure, let them begin their simulations. Monitor their progress during the investigation. Check that students are not moving the flashlight. It should be kept the same distance away from the clipboard and the same height above the table. Check to see that they draw the beam of light properly on the graph paper and note the angle of the clipboard on the graph paper. Check that they are recording their results.

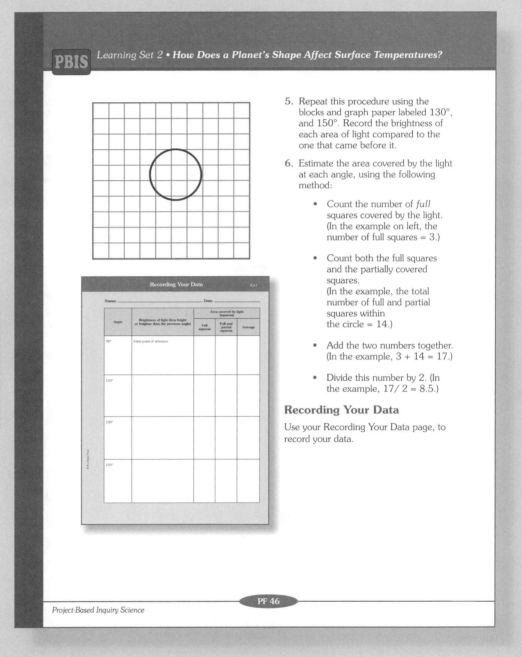

5. Repeat this procedure using the blocks and graph paper labeled 130°, and 150°. Record the brightness of each area of light compared to the one that came before it.

6. Estimate the area covered by the light at each angle, using the following method:

   • Count the number of *full* squares covered by the light. (In the example on left, the number of full squares = 3.)

   • Count both the full squares and the partially covered squares. (In the example, the total number of full and partial squares within the circle = 14.)

   • Add the two numbers together. (In the example, 3 + 14 = 17.)

   • Divide this number by 2. (In the example, 17/ 2 = 8.5.)

Recording Your Data

Use your Recording Your Data page, to record your data.

META NOTES

If the flashlight distance is changed or measured from some other part of the graph paper, it will skew the results.

Ask questions to make sure that students understand how the model relates to the Sun/Earth system. Students should understand when the clipboard is more upright, the graph paper represents land that is nearer to the Equator and pointed more directly toward the Sun. When the clipboard is at a greater angle, it represents land that is closer to the poles.

Check that students understand how to count the squares on the graph paper. Show them how to do it if they are having difficulties. Make sure they are filling out the *Recording Your Data* pages correctly.

◯ Get Going

As students finish collecting their data, have them complete the *Analyze Your Data* questions and let them know that an *Investigation Expo* will follow.

NOTES

Analyze Your Data

15 min.

Students complete the questions using observations from the experiment.

Analyze Your Data

1. How does the brightness of the light you observed change as the angle of the surface it strikes changes?

2. How does the area (number of squares inside the circle) change when the light strikes at a different angle?

3. What is the relationship between the angle at which the light strikes and the area covered by the light? For example, "As the angle increases, the area (*increases, stays the same, or decreases*)."

4. What does it mean to say that light is "direct" or "indirect"? How does that relate to the investigation?

5. Based on your results of this investigation, what do you think happens to the intensity of light as you move away from the Equator? Is the light more direct or less direct?

6. As light becomes less direct, what do you think happens to the temperature in those areas?

7. Why does the angle at which incoming solar energy (sunlight) strikes Earth change?

8. Draw a picture showing how different parts of Earth receive different intensities of incoming solar energy (sunlight).

Communicate Your Results

Investigation Expo

Your group will share the results and analysis of your investigation with other groups in an *Investigation Expo*. For your presentation, you will create a poster that includes the following information:

- the question you were trying to answer in your investigation

- your prediction

- your results and confidence level about them

- your interpretation of the results

Your teacher will collect all the groups' posters and display them together. As a class, you will compare the different results and discuss the analyses.

PF 47

PLANETARY FORECASTER

△ Guide and Assess

As groups are analyzing their data, check their responses and consider if they need further guidance or if there are any responses you want to emphasize during the *Investigation Expo*.

1. Students should indicate that as the angle increases, the brightness of light on the surface decreases.

2. Students should indicate that as the angle increases, the area that the light strikes increases.

3. Students should explain the relationship using the sample explanation given in the question. They should fill in that as the angle increases, the area the light strikes increases.

4. Students should define direct light as light that strikes the surface at a 90° angle (perpendicular, or head on) and indirect light as light that strikes the surface at an angle different from 90°. Using a direct light source models light striking Earth's surface at or near the Equator.

5. Students should note that the angle of the clipboard is like latitude from the Equator and the light gets less direct as the angle of the clipboard increases, just as the light is less direct further away from the Equator. They should connect this with their observations of how when the angle increases, the brightness decreases and the areas that are illuminated increase. Students need to recognize that the intensity of the light is related to the rate energy strikes a surface. The intensity of light leaving the flashlight is assumed to be constant. They should make the connection that as the light shines less directly the area it covers is greater and the intensity is less.

> **META NOTES**
>
> Sun's light strikes Earth directly at different locations above, below, and on Earth's equator due to Earth's axis being tilted. This is discussed in the next *Learning Set*.

6. Students should recognize that radiation from the Sun striking Earth transfers heat energy to Earth. The more direct the light, the more intensely it shines on Earth. They may infer that the more direct the light, more heat is transferred and there is a greater increase in temperature. This fits with the observations that the surface temperature of Earth is warmest at/near the Equator. The less direct the light, the less intensity and less heat transferred and lower temperatures result.

7. Students should describe how Earth's spherical shape causes incoming radiation to strike Earth's surface at different angles because the surface falls away from the direct beam, much like the clipboard leaning back at a greater angle does.

8. Students' drawings should indicate more solar energy reaching the Equator than the poles.

◯ Get Going

Let the class know that each group will need to create a poster that includes the four bulleted items listed in the student text. Point out that their results should be clearly presented with their claims or interpretations of their results. Tell students the *Analyze Your Data* questions will be discussed during the *Investigation Expo*, particularly Questions 5 through 8. Then let students know how much time they have.

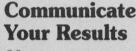

Communicate Your Results

20 min.

Groups share and discuss their results during an Investigation Expo.

---

8. Draw a picture showing how different parts of Earth receive different intensities of incoming solar energy (sunlight).

Communicate Your Results

Investigation Expo

Your group will share the results and analysis of your investigation with other groups in an *Investigation Expo*. For your presentation, you will create a poster that includes the following information:

- the question you were trying to answer in your investigation

- your prediction

- your results and confidence level about them

- your interpretation of the results

Your teacher will collect all the groups' posters and display them together. As a class, you will compare the different results and discuss the analyses.

△ Guide and Assess

Monitor students as they make their posters. Encourage the students to use data tables and graphs to help communicate their observations. Posters should include information that led to the question being answered in the investigation as well as the prediction made before running the investigation. Students should include their interpretations on their poster and the supporting evidence.

◯ Get Going

Display the posters around the room and let students visit each poster for about a minute before discussing them.

△ Guide and Assess

Have a class discussion on each poster. Consider having teams present and discuss their results with the class. Ask each group to share their responses to Questions 5 through 8 from the *Analyze Your Data* section.

What's the Point?

The data from your investigation may have provided you with the evidence needed to support your prediction about the effects of shape on Earth's temperature. During the *Investigation Expo*, you should have seen a consistent pattern in the data. You probably saw the area covered by the light ray getting larger and the light intensity decreasing as the angle increased. As the amount of solar energy (sunlight) is spread out, the result is less heat and lower temperatures.

You may now have a better idea of how shape relates to temperature on a planet. In the next section, you will create an explanation of how a planet's shape affects its temperature. Be sure to consider the investigation you just completed and the data you collected.

PF 48

Project-Based Inquiry Science

Encourage students to discuss any differences they found, especially in their conclusions and interpretations.

Make sure to take time to compare the angled graph paper/clipboard results to different locations on a globe so that students can recognize connections between what they observed in the simulation and the way light reaches Earth's surface. You may wish to have the students look at a globe and imagine the Sun or a flashlight shining directly on the Equator. Then have the students identify places on the globe where the different angles they observed would be located.

☐ Assess

Students should recognize the connection between the amount of surface area covered by a particular amount of incoming solar energy and the intensity. In their simulations, students observed the flashlight emit the same radiation each time. When the light struck a surface more indirectly (at greater angles), the area it illuminated was greater. When the light is more indirect, the amount of energy striking the surface is the same, but the area over which it strikes is greater and the energy per area is smaller. The intensity is the rate at which energy strikes a surface. It can be inferred that the intensity decreases as the light strikes more indirectly. Point out to students that less light (electromagnetic) energy striking an area will correspond to lower overall energy and lower temperatures.

Assessment Options

Targeted Concepts, Skills, and Nature of Science	How do I know if students got it?
Scientists often work together and share their findings. Sharing findings makes new information available and helps scientists to refine their ideas and build on others' ideas. When another person's or group's idea is used, credit needs to be given.	**ASK:** How was the *Investigation Expo* helpful? **LISTEN:** Students should describe how sharing results helped them refine their own.
Graphs, maps, and tables are an effective way to analyze and communicate results of scientific investigation.	**ASK:** How did graphs, tables, and/or maps help you communicate your results or understand the results of others? **LISTEN:** Students should describe how tables are useful for showing trends in data. If students chose to construct a graph or map, they should discuss these as well.

Targeted Concepts, Skills, and Nature of Science	How do I know if students got it?
Scientists use models to simulate processes that happen too fast, too slow, on a scale that cannot be observed directly (either too small or too large), or that are too dangerous.	**ASK:** What did the light/clipboard model represent and why did we use it? **LISTEN:** Students should describe why they are using a model. The Earth/Sun system is on a scale that is very large and sometimes difficult to observe. Students should also describe what the parts of the model represent. The flashlight represents the Sun and the clipboard represents a location on a planet. The angle the clipboard is at represents how the planet's surface is curving away.
The intensity of light on an object depends on its shape and the angle it strikes the object at. As the curvature of the object's surface increases the angle at which the light strikes increases, and the intensity of light on the object decreases.	**ASK:** What is intensity and how does the shape of Earth affect the intensity of light striking it? **LISTEN:** Students should describe intensity as the amount of light or brightness of light per area. Students should make claims based on their observations. They should explain how the intensity of light on an object depends on the objects' shape and the angle the light strikes. The shape of the object and the location of the source determine the angle the incoming light strikes. At larger angles, the intensity of illumination on the object decreases.

Teacher Reflection Questions

- What difficulties did students have with the concept of intensity and how shape affects it?

- What evidence shows that students understand the need for a clear procedure that can be replicated and the need for repeatable results?

- How did students express their attitudes towards success and making mistakes during investigations? Were students discouraged or challenged by making mistakes during a procedure? What methods worked best to encourage them to see mistakes as a challenge they can learn from?

NOTES

SECTION 2.3 INTRODUCTION

2.3 Explain

How Shape Affects a Planet's Temperature

◀ *1 class period*

A class period is considered to be one 40 to 50 minute class.

Overview

Students construct an explanation for how the shape of a planet affects its surface temperature based on their observations of illumination. Students use an iterative process like scientists do to come up with an explanation the class agrees on. They begin by sharing their explanations with their group members, the group discusses and decides on one explanation to present, and then share their explanations with the class and the class constructs an explanation.

Targeted Concepts, Skills, and Nature of Science	Performance Expectations
Scientists often work together and share their findings. Sharing findings makes new information available and helps scientists to refine their ideas and build on others' ideas. When another person's or group's idea is used, credit needs to be given.	Students should work on their explanations, discuss, and revise their explanations with their group. Together they should construct a group explanation and share their explanations with the class and the class should construct an explanation together.
Scientists must keep clear, accurate, and descriptive records of what they do so they can share their work with others and consider what they did, why they did it, and what they want to do next.	Students should refer back to their observations and claims from previous sections to construct their explanations and share these with the class.
Explanations are claims supported by evidence, accepted ideas and facts.	Students should write an explanation for how the shape of a planet affects its temperatures based on the observations they made and science knowledge.

Targeted Concepts, Skills, and Nature of Science	Performance Expectations
The intensity of light on an object depends on its shape and the angle it strikes the object at. As the curvature of the object's surface increases the angle at which the light strikes increases, and the intensity of light on the object decreases.	Students should use their observations of how an object's shape affects how light strikes it, and how this affects the intensity of light for the Sun/Earth system. Students should further discuss how this affects the surface temperature.

Materials	
3 per student	*Create Your Explanation* page
1 per student	*Project Board* page
1 per class	Class *Project Board*

Homework Options

Reflection

- **Science Process:** Why is it important to keep clear, accurate, and descriptive records? *(Students' responses should describe how they rely on their records to help remember what they have done and to communicate to others what they have done.)*

Preparation for 2.4

- **Science Content:** What is latitude and longitude and how are they used? *(Students should recognize that latitude is a measure of distance north or south from the Equator and longitude is a measure of distance east or west from the Prime Meridian. These are used to describe locations on Earth.)*

SECTION 2.3 IMPLEMENTATION

2.3 Explain

How Shape Affects a Planet's Temperature

Your challenge was to determine how the shape of a planet might affect its temperatures. Through a variety of activities and investigations, you have discovered some things about how shape affects the way sunlight strikes a planet's surface and the resulting heat energy. Now you will create an explanation for how shape affects planetary temperatures.

Explain

A good explanation has this structure:

- your claim
- your evidence
- your science knowledge
- a statement connecting your claim to your evidence and the science you know

If you have created explanations before, you know that after scientists get results from an investigation, they make a claim based on what their evidence shows. A claim is a statement of what you understand or a conclusion that you have reached based on data from an investigation. You will now make a claim based on the results of your investigation into shape and temperature. Using the *Create Your Explanation* page, develop a statement declaring your claim.

Next, you will state your evidence. Describe the data, including any **trends** in the data that support your claim. You may want to include visuals, such as tables, charts, or graphs to help communicate this information.

Science knowledge is knowledge about how things work. This knowledge comes through reading, discussion, talking to an expert, or other experiences. You may include information that you read in this *Learning Set* or knowledge you have gained from other resources. Put this all together to write an

trend: pattern.

PF 49

PLANETARY FORECASTER

2.3 Explain

How Shape Affects a Planet's Temperature
5 min.

Students create explanations of what they have been doing in the Learning Set.

△ Guide

Remind students of the goal of this *Learning Set* is to determine how shape affects surface temperature. Ask students what they have done so far. Discuss how they have already observed how light illuminates shapes differently in the box and ball activity and how the angle of the surface affects how the surface is illuminated. From this work, they should now understand how the greater the angle of the surface, the less bright the light shining on the surface will be and the more area will be covered.

*A class period is considered to be one 40 to 50 minute class.

Let students know they will construct their explanation of how the shape of a planet affects its surface temperature.

Explain

10 min.

Students construct an explanation of how a planet's shape affects its surface temperature.

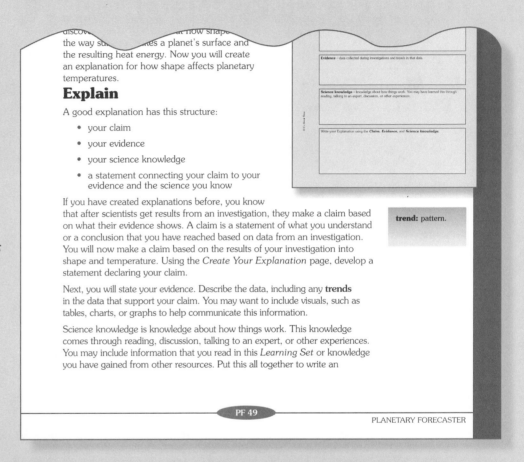

discov... ...at how shape the way su... ...es a planet's surface and the resulting heat energy. Now you will create an explanation for how shape affects planetary temperatures.

Explain

A good explanation has this structure:

- your claim
- your evidence
- your science knowledge
- a statement connecting your claim to your evidence and the science you know

If you have created explanations before, you know that after scientists get results from an investigation, they make a claim based on what their evidence shows. A claim is a statement of what you understand or a conclusion that you have reached based on data from an investigation. You will now make a claim based on the results of your investigation into shape and temperature. Using the *Create Your Explanation* page, develop a statement declaring your claim.

Next, you will state your evidence. Describe the data, including any **trends** in the data that support your claim. You may want to include visuals, such as tables, charts, or graphs to help communicate this information.

Science knowledge is knowledge about how things work. This knowledge comes through reading, discussion, talking to an expert, or other experiences. You may include information that you read in this *Learning Set* or knowledge you have gained from other resources. Put this all together to write an

trend: pattern.

Evidence – data collected during investigations and trends in that data.

Science knowledge – knowledge about how things work. You may have learned this through reading, talking to an expert, discussion, or other experiences.

Write your Explanation using the *Claim*, *Evidence*, and *Science knowledge*.

PF 49

PLANETARY FORECASTER

△ Guide

Let students know they will be working on their own to construct an explanation. Later, they will share these with their group and construct an explanation they all agree on. Then they will share their group explanations with the class and the class will work together to construct a class explanation.

Remind students what a good explanation is and what they will need to do to construct it.

"A good explanation has a claim you make that is supported by evidence and science knowledge in a logical way. This information is in your student text. You should refer back to it as needed when constructing your explanations.

You will need to refer back to the data you collected and claims you made in previous sections. These will help you in constructing your explanation. Your evidence will be based on your data and trends you find in your data. You might even want to include tables, charts, or graphs to help communicate this information.

Don't worry if your explanation is not perfect. The idea is to construct an explanation based on what you know now."

Get Going

Distribute one *Create Your Explanation* page to each student, let them know how much time they have to complete their explanations and let them begin.

Guide and Assess

Monitor students as they are working. Check students' explanations to see if they contain all the parts of a scientific explanation. Consider asking them to point out the specific parts. Guide students as needed, but do not correct them.

Help students as needed if they decide to create a chart or graph that shows the relationship between the surface angle and the area of the circle created by the beam of light.

META NOTES

Many students will already have ideas about what an explanation is. In science and *PBIS*, an explanation needs to be a claim backed up by evidence and science knowledge in a logical way.

META NOTES

Students will be revising and refining their explanations with their group and then with the class. During this process, students should correct each other.

NOTES

Conference

10 min.

Students meet in groups to discuss their explanations and construct a group explanation.

explanation on your own. Do not worry if you cannot create a perfect explanation. Just work with the information you have for now. There will be opportunities for you to revisit and refine your explanation as you learn more.

Conference

With your group, take turns sharing explanations. Then work together to create a group explanation.

Communicate
Share Your Explanation

Your class will meet to discuss each group's explanation. Together, you will select or create the explanation that best explains the relationship between shape and temperature.

Update the *Project Board*

At the beginning of this *Learning Set*, you began a *Project Board* that most likely included more questions and need-to-know items than answers and evidence. After all you have accomplished, you can now update the *Project Board* by adding your explanations and evidence to the next two columns, *What are we learning?* and *What is our evidence?* You might even add some information to the last column, *What does it mean for the challenge or question?*

Make sure you record the same information in your own *Project Board*. You can use these notes during class discussions. The *Project Board* is a great place to start discussions. You may find that you disagree with other classmates about what you have learned or the evidence presented. This is a part of what scientists do. Such discussions help participants identify what they still do not know or understand and what else they still need to learn or investigate. These things should be added to the *Project Board*, as well.

What's the Point?

You and your class created an explanation for how shape affects planetary temperatures. Scientists gain understanding by investigating and explaining. They make claims and support their claims with evidence from their investigations and their science knowledge. Your explanation may not be perfect at this time. You may need to learn more science or do further investigations. You will get a chance to refine your explanation later in this *Learning Set*.

PF 50

△ Guide

Let groups know they will be meeting to share their explanations and to create a group explanation. They should begin by having each group member present their explanation to the group. After everyone has presented, they should discuss the similarities and differences between their explanations. They should look at the data supporting the parts of the explanations where there are differences to help determine what their best explanation will be.

⬡ Get Going

Distribute a *Create Your Explanation* page to each student. Ask them to write Group Explanation on this page and let students know how much time they have.

△ Guide and Assess

Monitor groups and assist them as needed. Model appropriate language as needed.

> **TEACHER TALK**
>
> **"**I don't understand how the science knowledge backs up your explanation. Could you walk me through it?
>
> I don't see how ... is supported by your data. Could you show me?
>
> This statement doesn't make sense to me. Could you state it another way?
>
> I'm not sure if I understand this. Do you mean: ... *(Students should state their understanding using their own words.)***"**

△ Guide

Let students know that each group will be presenting their explanation. After each presentation, students should ask questions to the presenting group to make sure they understand the explanation and how the evidence and science knowledge supports the claim. When needed, model appropriate language.

If the presenting group is not getting many questions from the class, consider having the class pick out the claim, the evidence, and the science knowledge. Encourage the presenting group to answer the person asking the question.

After all groups have presented, guide the class to discussing the similarities and differences between all the explanations. Record the points the class agrees on. Discuss why the differences arise and what the class thinks would be best to include in the explanation.

Have the class construct an explanation. Once the class explanation is completed, distribute another *Create Your Explanation* page and have the class record their explanation indicating at the top of the page that it is the Class Explanation.

Communicate: Share Your Explanation

15 min.

Students participate in a class discussion about groups' explanations and then create a class explanation.

Update the Project Board
10 min.

The class updates their Project Board *with new knowledge and questions.*

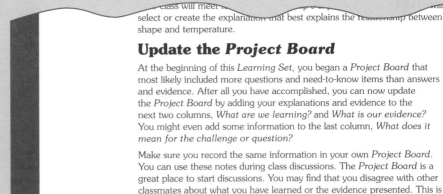

...class will meet ... will select or create the explanation that best explains the relationship between shape and temperature.

Update the *Project Board*

At the beginning of this *Learning Set,* you began a *Project Board* that most likely included more questions and need-to-know items than answers and evidence. After all you have accomplished, you can now update the *Project Board* by adding your explanations and evidence to the next two columns, *What are we learning?* and *What is our evidence?* You might even add some information to the last column, *What does it mean for the challenge or question?*

Make sure you record the same information in your own *Project Board.* You can use these notes during class discussions. The *Project Board* is a great place to start discussions. You may find that you disagree with other classmates about what you have learned or the evidence presented. This is a part of what scientists do. Such discussions help participants identify what they still do not know or understand and what else they still need to learn or investigate. These things should be added to the *Project Board,* as well.

What's the Point?

META NOTES

Distribute *Project Board* pages as needed.

△ Guide

The explanations that students have made contain a lot of new knowledge that students have learned in this *Learning Set.* Help students consider this when the update their *Project Boards.*

Remind the class that the third column (*What are we learning?*) is a place to put claims and the fourth column (*What is our evidence?*) is a place to put the evidence that supports these claims. Emphasize that these two columns always go together.

Ask students what claim they would like to put in Column 3 and what evidence supports that claim. Remind students to record the class's final entries on their *Project Board* pages.

Record students' responses.

◇ Evaluate

Students should have the following information on their *Project Boards.*

> **Column 3 (claim):** Shape affects the illumination of an object.
>
> **Column 4 (evidence):** The angle that light strikes an object affects how brightly the object is lit and the area that is lit. As the angle increases, the surface brightness decreases, and the area of illumination increases. An objects' shape affects the angle that incoming light strikes its surface. If the surface is curved, the light will strike the surface at different angles depending on how it is curved.

Column 3 (claim): The shape of a planet affects its surface temperature.

Column 4 (evidence): Shape affects how a planet is illuminated. As a planet's surface curves away from incoming rays of light, the light energy strikes its surface indirectly. This light energy is spread out over a greater area so less light energy strikes a given location. Light can interact with the planet and transfer heat, warming the planet's surface. If less light (radiation) strikes the planet, less heat energy is transferred to warm the planet's surface. This results in lower temperatures for locations further away from where the sunlight (solar energy) strikes directly.

> **META NOTES**
>
> Students may combine these two claims.

Teacher Reflection Questions

- How successful were students in creating explanations and communicating their reasons? Did students provide support in the form of scientific observations or did they rely on opinion?

- What is your sense of how students felt about constructing an explanation on their own, with their group, and with the class?

- How did you guide and assess group and class discussions? What would you do differently next time?

NOTES

NOTES

2.4 Investigate

What is the Incoming Solar Energy at Different Distances From the Equator?

◀ *1 class period*

A class period is considered to be one 40 to 50 minute class.

Overview

Students analyze data in *My World* to determine how solar energy striking Earth varies with location. Students begin by reviewing latitude and longitude to ensure they understand how locations on Earth are described. Students use a data file from *My World* to compare how the incoming solar energy changes for different latitudes. Students infer how the shape of the planet affects the amount of solar energy it receives and how that affects its surface temperature. To further connect surface temperatures with habitable locations, students read about biomes. They review data for biomes and observe that biomes tend to fall into different latitudes on Earth.

Targeted Concepts, Skills, and Nature of Science	Performance Expectations
Scientists often work together and share their findings. Sharing findings makes new information available and helps scientists to refine their ideas and build on others' ideas. When another person's or group's idea is used, credit needs to be given.	Students should share their results with the class and the class should discuss any questions students still have about how a planet's shape affects its surface temperature.
Scientists must keep clear, accurate, and descriptive records of what they do so they can share their work with others and consider what they did, why they did it, and what they want to do next.	Students should keep clear, descriptive records to refer back to when sharing their results in future sections.
Graphs, maps, and tables are an effective way to analyze and communicate results of scientific investigation.	Students should construct tables and read maps of data to help further understand their observations from *My World*.

Targeted Concepts, Skills, and Nature of Science	Performance Expectations
Scientists make claims (conclusions) based on evidence obtained (trends in data) from reliable investigations	Students should make claims about the amount of solar energy striking Earth's surface at different latitudes based on data from *My World*.
Habitable areas of Earth are determined by average temperatures suitable for humans to live in. These areas are often broken up into biomes, which are a group of ecosystems that have the same general climate and similar plants and animals.	Students should describe biomes as classifications of areas on Earth with similar climates, plants, and animals. Biomes tend to vary according to latitude on Earth.
The intensity of light on an object depends on its shape and the angle it strikes the object at. As the curvature of the object's surface increases the angle at which the light strikes increases, and the intensity of light on the object decreases.	Students should describe how Earth's shape causes solar energy to strike it less directly, resulting in a decreased intensity of illumination.
The average amount of solar energy that strikes Earth's surface over a year is highest near the equator and the intensity of the solar energy that strikes the surface decreases as you move farther away from the Equator, whether you are moving North or South.	Students should be able to describe how light intensity changes in relation to latitude.

Materials

1 per classroom	Computer with *My World* software and projection system Globe or spherical object
1 per group	Computer with *My World* software
1 per student	*Solar Energy Data* page

Activity Setup and Preparation

Go through the procedure before the class period to familiarize yourself with the *My World* software. Determine what you want to emphasize to students and where you think students may have difficulties.

If you do not have enough computers for the class, you could collect the data as a class using a projection system. If you need to do this, consider having students take turns obtaining data points.

Homework Options

Reflection

- **Science Process:** How do visuals such as graphs and maps help communicate scientific data? *(Students should describe how graphs and maps showing data help communicate relationships between large amounts of data by showing trends or patterns.)*

- **Science Content:** How does data on the amount of solar energy connect to the concept of direct and indirect sunlight? *(Students' response should include how indirect light reduces the intensity of sunlight or the rate of solar energy per area that strikes Earth's surface. Students may indicate that the Sun's light shines directly on Earth near the Equator.)*

Preparation for 2.5

- **Science Content:** Explain how Earth's shape affects its temperature. *(This question is meant to have students recognize and apply any new knowledge they learned in this section and to prepare students for the revisions they will make to their explanations in the next section.)*

NOTES

SECTION 2.4 IMPLEMENTATION

2.4 Investigate

What Is the Incoming Solar Energy at Different Distances From the Equator?

You have determined that incoming solar energy (sunlight) is different at different distances from the Equator. Because Earth is curved, incoming solar energy strikes the surface at different angles. This means that solar energy is less direct farther from the Equator. You have also started to make a connection between temperature and incoming solar energy. Since shape affects incoming solar energy, it also affects temperature.

In this activity, you will determine the amount of solar energy at different latitudes. You will use this information to predict how the temperature on *Planet X* is affected by its curved shape.

The map shows the average intensity of incoming solar energy received by different locations on Earth.

The intensity of solar energy can be measured as solar energy per square meter. Using what you discovered in the previous investigation, think about where you would expect to find more solar energy per square meter. In this investigation, you will examine the amount of solar energy per square meter at different latitudes on Earth. The goal is to see if there is a relationship between the latitude and the amount of solar energy per square meter.

PF 51

PLANETARY FORECASTER

2.4 Investigate

What is the Incoming Solar Energy at Different Distances From the Equator?
5 min.

Students are introduced to the section while reviewing latitude and longitude.

△ Guide

Let students know they will analyze average incoming solar energy values for different latitudes and longitudes to determine the relationship between Earth's shape and the average amount of solar energy that Earth's surface receives.

*A class period is considered to be one 40 to 50 minute class.

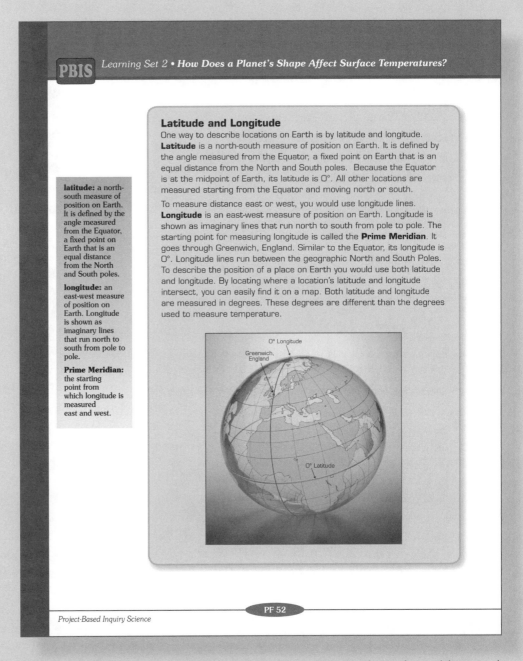

Latitude and Longitude

One way to describe locations on Earth is by latitude and longitude. **Latitude** is a north-south measure of position on Earth. It is defined by the angle measured from the Equator, a fixed point on Earth that is an equal distance from the North and South poles. Because the Equator is at the midpoint of Earth, its latitude is 0°. All other locations are measured starting from the Equator and moving north or south.

To measure distance east or west, you would use longitude lines. **Longitude** is an east-west measure of position on Earth. Longitude is shown as imaginary lines that run north to south from pole to pole. The starting point for measuring longitude is called the **Prime Meridian**. It goes through Greenwich, England. Similar to the Equator, its longitude is 0°. Longitude lines run between the geographic North and South Poles. To describe the position of a place on Earth you would use both latitude and longitude. By locating where a location's latitude and longitude intersect, you can easily find it on a map. Both latitude and longitude are measured in degrees. These degrees are different than the degrees used to measure temperature.

latitude: a north-south measure of position on Earth. It is defined by the angle measured from the Equator, a fixed point on Earth that is an equal distance from the North and South poles.

longitude: an east-west measure of position on Earth. Longitude is shown as imaginary lines that run north to south from pole to pole.

Prime Meridian: the starting point from which longitude is measured east and west.

0° Longitude

Greenwich, England

0° Latitude

Use the information box in the student text to review latitude and longitude. Emphasize that scientists use two main midpoints to describe locations on Earth. The Equator is midway between the two poles and the Prime Meridian runs from the North Pole to the South Pole. Have students look at the image of Earth in the student text and use a globe or spherical object to describe these two important lines.

Latitude is a measure of how far north or south a location is from the Equator and longitude is a measure of how far east or west a location is from the Prime Meridian. Let students know that these are measured in degrees. This unit defines an angle from the center of the planet rather than a temperature. Point out that 0° latitude is at the Equator and 0° longitude is at the Prime Meridian.

◇ Evaluate

Make sure that students understand the difference between using degrees for temperature and degrees for latitude and longitude.

NOTES

Procedure: Compare Incoming Solar Energy at Different Latitudes

10 min.

Procedure: Compare Incoming Solar Energy at Different Latitudes

1. **Open the Incoming Solar Energy Visualization.**

   a) **Open My World and select "Planetary Forecaster"** from the Data Library drop-down menu.

   b) **Open the "IncomingSolarEnergy" project file,** PF Incoming Solar Energy. m3vz.

   c) **Fit your map into the window** using the "Zoom to All" tool 🔲. Select the "IncomingSolarEnergy" data layer.

2. **Collect Incoming Solar Energy Data for Different Latitudes.**

   a) **Select the "Get Information" tool.** This tool can give you information about the data layer selected.

   b) **Move the cursor to the desired longitude.** As you move the cursor over the visualization, the latitude and longitude are being tracked in the lower left corner.

   c) **Select a cell to get information.** A small window will open when you click on a cell on the map. This window has a chart including the amount of incoming solar energy, the latitude, and the longitude for that cell. Try to get as close as possible—it is difficult to be exact.

Recording Your Data

Use the *Solar Energy Data* page to record your data.

△ Guide

Students will be using *My World* for this investigation. Demonstrate how to open the project file, *IncomingSolarEnergy* and explain what the map shows.

"The map shows the average intensity of solar energy received by Earth over a year. The red color indicates 0 or very little solar energy received. Yellow indicates a lot of solar energy received, about 500 watts per meter squared. Orange is in the middle at about 250 watts per meter squared. Remember that the units for intensity are watts per meter squared. This is the rate at which solar energy strikes a square meter."

Remind students that their goal is to determine the relationship between latitude and solar energy.

△ Guide

Briefly go through the steps described in the student text, demonstrating for students how they can collect data using the information tool and clicking on a location in the map. Let students know that they will be selecting a longitude and will take data for every 20° of latitude north and south of the Equator. Students will need to fill out the table on the *Solar Energy Data* page.

Make sure students know they may not be able to record information on exact latitude locations using *My World*. They may not be able to get to zero degrees exactly. Tell them to get as close as possible without spending too much time.

⬡ Get Going

Let students know after they have collected their data they should begin answering the *Analyze Your Data* questions and how much time they have to collect data. Distribute the *Solar Energy Data* pages to students or have them near the computer stations.

△ Guide and Assess

Monitor students' progress and assist them as needed if they are having difficulties using *My World*. Check to see that they are collecting data and filling out their *Solar Energy Data* page properly. As groups finish collecting data, have them start the *Analyze Your Data* segment.

Sample data is shown below. Students should get values close to those shown.

Solar Energy Data

2.4.1

Name: _____ Date: _____

Incoming Solar Energy

Latitude	Amount of incoming solar energy (units/m²)
80°N	179
60°N	231
40°N	334
20°N	391
0° (Equator)	417
20°S	391
40°S	324
60°S	231
80°S	178

Change in Incoming Solar Energy

More direct solar energy (units/m²)	minus	Less direct solar energy (units/m²)	equals	Difference in the amount of solar energy (units/m²)
60°N: _231_	-	80°N: ``179	=	52
40°N: _334_	-	60°N: _231_	=	103
20°N: _391_	-	40°N: _334_	=	57
0°: _417_	-	20°N: _391_	=	26
0°: _417_	-	20°S: _391_	=	26
20°S: _391_	-	40°S: _324_	=	67
40°S: _324_	-	60°S: _231_	=	93
60°S: _231_	-	80°S: _178_	=	53

© It's About Time

NOTES

....

....

....

PBIS | *Learning Set 2 • How Does a Planet's Shape Affect Surface Temperatures?*

Analyze Your Data

Calculate how much the amount of incoming solar energy changes over every 20° of latitude. You can do this by subtracting the amount of incoming solar energy (units/m²) for the more direct solar energy from the amount of incoming solar energy (units/m²) for the less direct solar energy. You can see that it does not change the same amount for every 20° interval. Use the *Solar Energy Data* page and fill it in using these calculations.

PF 54

Project-Based Inquiry Science

Analyze Your Data

5 min.

Students analyze their data and summarize their results.

⬡ Get Going

Students should work with their group to answer these questions. Let students know how much time they have and that a class discussion on their responses will follow.

△ Guide and Assess

Monitor students' progress and guide students as needed using the information below. Note any responses that you want to address during the class discussion.

1. Students' should note that the most incoming solar energy is at the Equator and at latitudes near it. The incoming solar energy decreases as you move to latitudes away from the Equator.

2. Students' responses should connect the planet's shape, direct and indirect light, and the effect this has on incoming energy. Because Earth's surface is curved, some locations receive sunlight more directly than other locations. The Sun shines most directly at or near Earth's Equator, and more indirectly at locations away from the Equator. The more indirectly the light strikes the planet, the larger the area it covers and the light energy is spread out over a greater area. When the sunlight is spread over a greater area, there is less incoming energy per location.

3. Students should connect the amount of incoming solar energy per area or intensity with the amount of energy that can be transferred to warm up the area. The locations around the Equator should have the highest temperatures because these areas receive the most incoming solar energy per area, or the highest intensity of sunlight. Sunlight is electromagnetic radiation and heat energy can be transferred by some of this radiation. The more solar energy there is, the more heat energy can be transferred, resulting in higher temperatures.

4. Students should note that the areas between 40° and 60° North or South of the Equator, have the greatest difference in the amount of incoming solar energy received.

5. Students' responses should state that the locations between 0° and 20° North or South of the Equator experience the smallest changes in incoming solar energy.

6. Students should infer that the latitudes with the greatest difference in incoming solar energy should have the greatest difference in temperature. They should note that between 40° and 60° on either the north or south side of the Equator should experience the greatest change in temperature. They should further connect this difference in incoming solar energy with how the angle the sunlight strikes Earth changes due to Earth's shape.

7. Students should infer that locations within 20° of the Equator all have very similar experiences in the directness of solar energy they receive. Within these areas there is little change in amount of solar energy received and the temperature should not vary much.

What is the Incoming Solar Energy at Different Distances from the Equator?

2.4

Answer these questions to help you summarize the data from your investigation. Remember, your goal was to determine how the shape of a planet affects the amount of solar energy at different latitudes. Be prepared to share your answers with your group and your class.

1. Which latitudes had the most incoming solar energy? Which latitudes had the least incoming solar energy?

2. Why do some latitudes receive different amounts of incoming solar energy than others? Use your understanding of *direct* and *indirect* solar energy to support your answer.

3. Which latitudes will have the highest temperatures? Justify your answer using your understanding of *intensity* of incoming solar energy.

4. Looking at your chart, which range(s) in latitude showed the largest difference in the amount of solar energy? That is, which 20° intervals had the greatest change in the amount of incoming solar energy?

5. Which range(s) had the smallest change in the amount of incoming solar energy?

6. Which 20° intervals of latitude will have the greatest change in temperature within that interval? Use evidence from the investigations you have been doing to support your answer.

7. Which 20° intervals of latitude will have the smallest change in temperature within that range? Use evidence from the investigations you have been doing to support your answer.

Communicate

Now that you have analyzed your data and summarized your data from this investigation, take some time to discuss this with your class. Did you notice a trend? Discuss this along with any questions you may still have.

What's the Point?

Your investigation should have provided each group with a trend in the data collected. This trend in the data provides you with some evidence to understand the relationship between planet shape and temperature. The discussions you had within your group, as well as with other groups, should have focused on this trend. You may have a better idea of how shape relates to temperature on a planet.

Communicate

15 min.

Have a class discussion on students' results.

△ Guide

Let the class know that each group will present their results and the goal.

META NOTES

Earth's atmosphere further contributes to changes in incoming solar energy as it strikes Earth at different angles. The more acute the angle at which solar energy enters Earth's atmosphere, the more of the atmosphere it must pass through before reaching the surface. At any given location, incoming solar energy must pass through the most atmosphere before reaching ground at sunrise and sunset. At these times, solar energy is passing through significantly more air and is being scattered and absorbed by more molecules. As solar energy passes through more air, more energy at blue and violet wavelengths is scattered, leaving red and orange light. This is why sunsets and sunrises are typically red and orange. Clouds, humidity, and pollution in the air all scatter different wavelengths of light and also contribute to different hues in Earth's sunrises and sunsets.

TEACHER TALK

"Each group will be presenting their results and analysis, along with how they think the information relates to surface temperature. You should be checking if all groups observed the same trends and why a difference might have occurred. As a class, we will try to discuss everyone's ideas about how what we have done so far relates to surface temperature, and any questions you still may have."

Have groups present their responses to the questions.

As groups present their results consider having them use a globe or a spherical object to show the class how the angle between the Sun's rays and the surface changes with latitude.

◇ **Evaluate**

Students should realize the difference between 40° to 60° latitude shows the largest drop in the amount of solar energy received. Make sure that students think and discuss how the changes in latitude are related to the angles on which solar energy strikes Earth. Students should also understand that Earth gets most of its energy from the Sun and that incoming radiation from the Sun can transfer heat energy to Earth and warm its surface.

NOTES

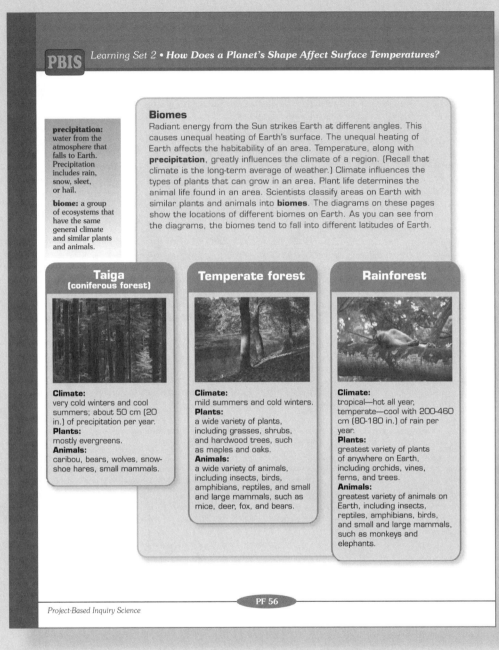

precipitation: water from the atmosphere that falls to Earth. Precipitation includes rain, snow, sleet, or hail.

biome: a group of ecosystems that have the same general climate and similar plants and animals.

Biomes

Radiant energy from the Sun strikes Earth at different angles. This causes unequal heating of Earth's surface. The unequal heating of Earth affects the habitability of an area. Temperature, along with **precipitation**, greatly influences the climate of a region. (Recall that climate is the long-term average of weather.) Climate influences the types of plants that can grow in an area. Plant life determines the animal life found in an area. Scientists classify areas on Earth with similar plants and animals into **biomes**. The diagrams on these pages show the locations of different biomes on Earth. As you can see from the diagrams, the biomes tend to fall into different latitudes of Earth.

Taiga (coniferous forest)

Climate: very cold winters and cool summers; about 50 cm (20 in.) of precipitation per year.
Plants: mostly evergreens.
Animals: caribou, bears, wolves, snowshoe hares, small mammals.

Temperate forest

Climate: mild summers and cold winters.
Plants: a wide variety of plants, including grasses, shrubs, and hardwood trees, such as maples and oaks.
Animals: a wide variety of animals, including insects, birds, amphibians, reptiles, and small and large mammals, such as mice, deer, fox, and bears.

Rainforest

Climate: tropical—hot all year, temperate—cool with 200-460 cm (80-180 in.) of rain per year.
Plants: greatest variety of plants of anywhere on Earth, including orchids, vines, ferns, and trees.
Animals: greatest variety of animals on Earth, including insects, reptiles, amphibians, birds, and small and large mammals, such as monkeys and elephants.

PF 56

Project-Based Inquiry Science

Biomes

10 min.

Students have a class discussion on biomes.

△ Guide

Have a class discussion on the *Biomes* information box. Emphasize that because the Sun's radiation strikes Earth at different angles, there is unequal heating of Earth's surface. Ask students how this connects with the observations they just made between incoming solar energy and latitude.

Let students know that the greatest influences of the climate of a region are temperature and precipitation, and that the climate influences the types of plants and animals that live in a region. Let students know that scientists classify areas on Earth with similar plants and animals as biomes.

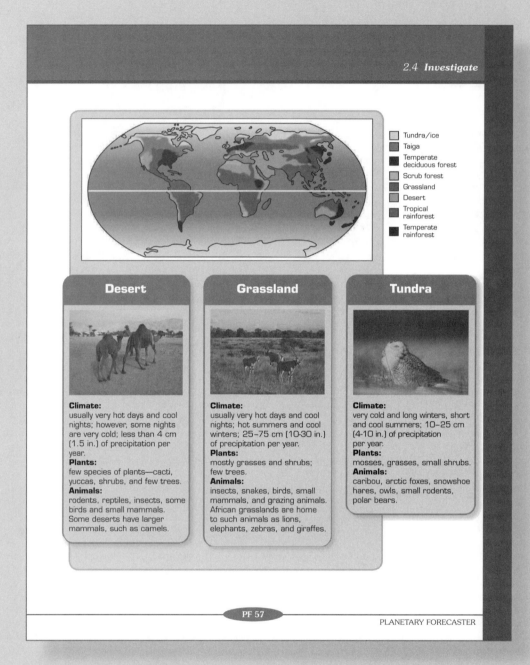

2.4 Investigate

Tundra/ice
Taiga
Temperate deciduous forest
Scrub forest
Grassland
Desert
Tropical rainforest
Temperate rainforest

Desert

Climate:
usually very hot days and cool nights; however, some nights are very cold; less than 4 cm (1.5 in.) of precipitation per year.
Plants:
few species of plants—cacti, yuccas, shrubs, and few trees.
Animals:
rodents, reptiles, insects, some birds and small mammals. Some deserts have larger mammals, such as camels.

Grassland

Climate:
usually very hot days and cool nights; hot summers and cool winters; 25–75 cm (10-30 in.) of precipitation per year.
Plants:
mostly grasses and shrubs; few trees.
Animals:
insects, snakes, birds, small mammals, and grazing animals. African grasslands are home to such animals as lions, elephants, zebras, and giraffes.

Tundra

Climate:
very cold and long winters, short and cool summers; 10–25 cm (4-10 in.) of precipitation per year.
Plants:
mosses, grasses, small shrubs.
Animals:
caribou, arctic foxes, snowshoe hares, owls, small rodents, polar bears.

PF 57

PLANETARY FORECASTER

Discuss the various biomes described in the student text. Then ask students to find trends in the data map shown. Students should recognize a trend between biome type and latitude.

Assessment Options

Targeted Concepts, Skills, and Nature of Science	How do I know if students got it?
Habitable areas of Earth are determined by average temperatures suitable for humans to live in. These areas are often broken up into biomes, which are a group of ecosystems that have the same general climate and similar plants and animals.	**ASK:** What is a biome and how does climate play a role in where biomes are located? **LISTEN:** Students should define a biome as a group of ecosystems that have the same general climate and similar plants and animals. Students should describe biomes as a result of the climate of the region most dependent on temperature and precipitation. Because the surface temperature is dependent on the incoming solar radiation, there is a trend that different biomes fall in different latitudes.
The intensity of light on an object depends on its shape and the angle it strikes the object at. As the curvature of the object's surface increases the angle at which the light strikes increases, and the intensity of light on the object decreases.	**ASK:** How does the shape of a planet affect the amount of incoming solar energy per area? **LISTEN:** Students should describe how the shape of the planet affects the angle that sunlight strikes and the amount of incoming energy per area. The less direct the light strikes, the less incoming energy per area there is. This is because for indirect light the same incoming energy strikes a larger area.
The average amount of solar energy that strikes Earth's surface over a year is highest near the Equator and the intensity of the solar energy that strikes the surface decreases as you move farther away from the equator, whether you are moving North or South.	**ASK:** Where is the average yearly solar energy the most? **LISTEN:** Students should describe how on Earth, the Equator is where the Sun shines most directly on its surface.

Teacher Reflection Questions

- What difficulties did students have making connections between shape, incoming solar energy per area, and surface temperature?

- What misconceptions did students have and how were they addressed?

- What issues arose from using the *My World* software? How was use of the software helpful?

NOTES

SECTION 2.5 INTRODUCTION

2.5 Revise Your Explanation

Shape and Temperature

◀ *1 class period*

A class period is
considered to be one
40 to 50 minute class.

Overview

Students revise their class explanation for how the shape of a planet affects
its surface temperature to include information about how the shape of the
planet affects the intensity of solar radiation and how this affects the surface
temperature. Students use an iterative process like scientists to come up with
an explanation the class agrees on. They share their revised explanations
with their group members to construct an explanation the group agrees on.
Groups then share their explanations with the class and the class constructs
an explanation. The class updates their *Project Board* to include what they
are learning and the evidence that supports it.

Targeted Concepts, Skills, and Nature of Science	Performance Expectations
Scientists often work together and share their findings. Sharing findings makes new information available and helps scientists to refine their ideas and build on others' ideas. When another person's or group's idea is used, credit needs to be given.	Students should revise their previous class explanation, meet with their group members and refine their explanations to come up with a group explanation. Then the groups should share their explanations with the class and the class should decide on an explanation.
Scientists must keep clear, accurate, and descriptive records of what they do so they can share their work with others and consider what they did, why they did it, and what they want to do next.	Students should refer to their previous records to construct their revised explanations.
Explanations are claims supported by evidence, accepted ideas and facts.	Students should revise their previous class explanation for how shape affects surface temperature to include the data they analyzed on incoming solar energy.

Targeted Concepts, Skills, and Nature of Science	Performance Expectations
The average amount of solar energy that strikes Earth's surface over a year is highest near the equator and the intensity of the solar energy that strikes the surface decreases as you move farther away from the Equator, whether you are moving North or South.	Students should include in their explanations how the incoming solar energy per area decreases as you move away from the Equator.

Materials	
3 per student	*Create Your Explanation* page
1 per student	*Project Board* page
1 per class	Class *Project Board*

Homework Options

Reflection

- **Science Content:** Draw a diagram showing how a planet's shape affects its surface temperature. *(Students should demonstrate in their drawings direct and indirect sunlight shining on Earth and how the more indirect the light shines, the less intense the light is.)*

Preparation for Back to the Big Challenge

- **Science Process:** Based on what you now know, how do you think the surface temperatures on *Planet X* will vary? *(Students should apply and indicate their understanding of surface temperatures decreasing with increasing latitude.)*

SECTION 2.5 IMPLEMENTATION

2.5 Revise Your Explanation

Shape and Temperature

You have studied shape and its effects on temperature. Recall what you read about direct and indirect light. Think about what you learned about how much incoming solar energy changes at higher latitudes compared to the Equator.

Look at your original prediction on shape and its effects on temperature. Think about what you have discovered so far. You are ready to revise your explanation.

Review and Revise Your Explanation

You have studied how the shape of Earth affects the incoming solar energy that strikes an area. Think about the connections you have begun to make between incoming solar energy and temperature. You are ready to revise your explanation about shape as a factor in predicting surface temperature.

Earlier, your class wrote an explanation of how shape affects the surface temperature. Review this explanation keeping in mind your results from this last investigation.

Answer the questions below before you revise your explanation. These questions will help you analyze the last class explanation. If the explanation is not as good as it could be, the questions will help you create a better explanation. Answer these questions on your own.

- Review the prediction you made in *Section 2.1*. What evidence do you have that supports or goes against you first prediction of how a planet's shape affects its surface temperature?

- Describe how the relationship between incoming solar energy and latitude supports or goes against the class's explanation from *Section 2.3*.

- How has your understanding of why shape influences temperature changed since you started the *Learning Set*?

PF 58

2.5 Revise Your Explanation

Shape and Temperature

5 min.

Introduce the section to the class.

△ **Guide**

Let students know they will each revise the class explanation they constructed previously to include the new information they have about incoming solar energy.

Review and Revise Your Explanation

5 min.

Students revise the class explanation.

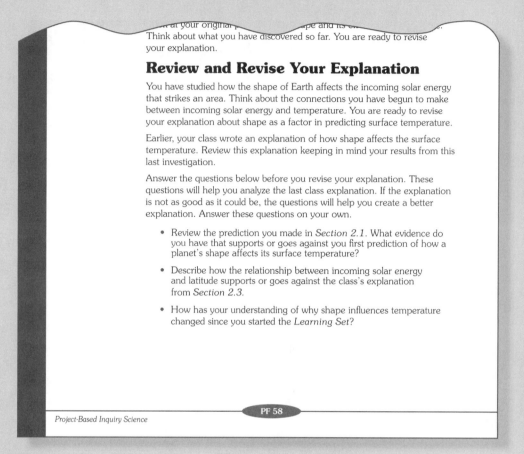

...at your original ...pe and its ...

Think about what you have discovered so far. You are ready to revise your explanation.

Review and Revise Your Explanation

You have studied how the shape of Earth affects the incoming solar energy that strikes an area. Think about the connections you have begun to make between incoming solar energy and temperature. You are ready to revise your explanation about shape as a factor in predicting surface temperature.

Earlier, your class wrote an explanation of how shape affects the surface temperature. Review this explanation keeping in mind your results from this last investigation.

Answer the questions below before you revise your explanation. These questions will help you analyze the last class explanation. If the explanation is not as good as it could be, the questions will help you create a better explanation. Answer these questions on your own.

- Review the prediction you made in *Section 2.1*. What evidence do you have that supports or goes against you first prediction of how a planet's shape affects its surface temperature?

- Describe how the relationship between incoming solar energy and latitude supports or goes against the class's explanation from *Section 2.3*.

- How has your understanding of why shape influences temperature changed since you started the *Learning Set*?

PF 58

Project-Based Inquiry Science

⬡ Get Going

Let students know the bulleted questions should help them revise their explanations and they should answer these first. They will be sharing their explanations with their group and their class in the same way as before.

Distribute the *Create Your Explanation* pages and let students know how much time they have.

△ Guide and Assess

Monitor students to make sure they are answering the questions. They should be referring to their initial prediction from *Section 2.1*, their data and claims from *Section 2.4*, and the class explanation from *Section 2.3*.

Make sure students understand these temperatures are taken outside from the air a meter or two above the ground. These temperatures are gathered from the places where humans are living. Have students recall the investigation in *Learning Set 1*, where they took temperature data from their environment.

2.5 Revise Your Explanation

Once you have considered these, you should be ready to revise your explanation. Using a new *Create Your Explanation* page revise your previous explanation to include all that you know now. Make sure you explanation answers how, why, and how much shape affects surface temperature. Remember that your explanation should have one or more claims that are supported with evidence and science knowledge in a logical way.

Conference

Share your answers to the questions and your explanation with your group. After you consider everyone's explanations, your group will create a group explanation.

Communicate

Your class will meet to discuss the answers to the questions and the group explanations. Then the class will select or create a new class explanation that best explains the relationship between shape and temperature.

Update the *Project Board*

Now that you have done this investigation, you know more about how a planet's shape affects surface temperature. You are now ready to fill in the *Project Board* more completely.

Once again you are going to focus on the *What are we learning?* and *What is our evidence?* columns. You will still have questions in the *What do we need to investigate?* column. As you record what your new knowledge in the *What are we learning?* column, you will be answering some of those questions. Describe what you have determined from your investigations. Provide evidence for your new knowledge.

You will fill in the *Project Board* as a class. Make sure to record the same information on your own *Project Board* page.

Conference
10 min.

Groups meet to discuss their explanations and construct a group explanation.

▲ Guide

Let groups know they will be meeting to share their explanations and to create a group explanation. They should begin by having each group member present their responses to the questions and their explanation to the group. After everyone has presented, they should discuss the similarities and differences between their explanations. They should look at the data supporting the parts of the explanations where they have differences to help them determine what their best explanation will be.

⬡ Get Going

Distribute a *Create Your Explanation* page to each student and ask them to indicate that is the Group Explanation. Let students know how much time they have.

△ Guide and Assess

Monitor groups and assist them as needed. Model appropriate language as needed.

TEACHER TALK

"I don't understand how the science knowledge backs up your explanation. Could you walk me through it?

I don't see how ... is supported by your data. Could you show me?

This statement doesn't make sense to me. Could you state it another way?

I'm not sure if I understand this. Do you mean: ..."

Communicate

15 min.

Students have a class discussion on groups' explanations and then create a class explanation.

Share your answers to the questions and your explanation with your group. After you consider everyone's explanations, your group will create a group explanation.

Communicate

Your class will meet to discuss the answers to the questions and the group explanations. Then the class will select or create a new class explanation that best explains the relationship between shape and temperature.

Update the *Project Board*

Now that you have done this investigation, you know more about how a planet's shape affects surface temperature. You are now ready to fill in the *Project Board* more completely.

△ Guide

Let students know that each group will be presenting their explanation. Emphasize that after each presentation students should ask questions to the presenting group to make sure they understand the explanation and how the evidence and science knowledge supports the claim. When needed, model for students appropriate language.

If students are having trouble questioning the presenting group, consider having the class pick out the claim, the evidence, and the science knowledge. Encourage the presenting group to answer the person asking the question.

After all groups have presented, discuss with the class the similarities and differences between all the explanations. Record the points that the class agrees on. Discuss why the differences arise and what the class thinks would be best to include in the explanation.

Have the class construct an explanation. Once the class explanation is completed, distribute another *Create Your Explanation* page to each student and have the class record their class explanation, indicating at the top of the page that it is the Class Explanation.

☐ Assess

The class explanation should contain information such as in the example below.

> *Shape affects a location on a planet's surface temperature by affecting how much direct sunlight strikes the location. It gets cooler farther from the Equator. Light energy strikes the Equator most directly, causing the area over which a certain amount of energy is transferred to be relatively small. Because the Earth is curved, light energy strikes the Earth at smaller angles farther from the Equator, either to the north or south of the Equator. The smaller the angle at which the sunlight strikes, the more area the sunlight is spread over. Because the sunlight is spread over a larger area, it transfers heat energy over a larger area. This leaves less heat energy transferred per unit area, and results in overall lower temperatures.*

Students' explanations should be supported by evidence from personal experience, the lab, and the *My World* investigations and there must be a link between the evidence and explanation.

Update the *Project Board*

5 min.

META NOTES

Distribute *Project Board* pages as needed.

Comm...ate

Your class will meet to discuss the answers to the questions and the group explanations. Then the class will select or create a new class explanation that best explains the relationship between shape and temperature.

Update the *Project Board*

Now that you have done this investigation, you know more about how a planet's shape affects surface temperature. You are now ready to fill in the *Project Board* more completely.

Once again you are going to focus on the *What are we learning?* and *What is our evidence?* columns. You will still have questions in the *What do we need to investigate?* column. As you record what your new knowledge in the *What are we learning?* column, you will be answering some of those questions. Describe what you have determined from your investigations. Provide evidence for your new knowledge.

You will fill in the *Project Board* as a class. Make sure to record the same information on your own *Project Board* page.

△ Guide

The explanations that students have made contain a lot of new knowledge of incoming solar energy students have learned in the previous section. They should include this information on their *Project Board*.

Remind the class that the third column *(What are we learning?)* is a place to put claims and the fourth column *(What is our evidence?)* is a place to put the evidence that supports these claims. Emphasize that these two columns always go together.

Ask students what claim they would like to put in Column 3 and what evidence supports that claim. They may want to revise a claim and the evidence they have already put on the *Project Board*. Encourage students to include data trends to support their claims. Remind students to record the class's final entries on their *Project Board* pages. Record students' responses.

◇ Evaluate

Students should now have the following information on their class' *Project Board*.

Column 3 (claim): The shape of a planet affects its surface temperature.

Column 4 (evidence): Shape affects how a planet is illuminated. As a planet's surface curves away from incoming rays of light, the light energy strikes its surface indirectly. This light energy is spread out over a greater area so less light energy strikes a given location. Light can interact with the planet and transfer heat, warming the planet's surface. If less light (radiation) strikes the planet, less heat energy is transferred to warm the planet's surface. This results in lower temperatures for locations further away from where the sunlight (solar energy) strikes directly. We analyzed data the average yearly incoming solar energy per area from *My World* and found that the average yearly incoming energy decreases as you move north or south from the Equator. As you move away from the Equator, the average yearly incoming solar energy decreases from 391 units/m2 at the Equator to about 179 units/m2 at the Poles. The drop in average incoming energy is not steady (linear), the greatest change in the incoming amount of energy occurs between 40° and 60° latitude from the Equator. The smallest amount of change is between the Equator and 20° latitude away from it.

Column 3 (claim): The surface temperature of a planet depends on the incoming solar energy per area.

Column 4 (evidence): Light (electromagnetic waves emitted from a sun) can interact with a planet and transfer heat, warming the planet's surface. If less light (radiation) strikes the planet, less heat energy is transferred to warm the planet's surface. This results in lower temperatures for locations further away from where the sunlight (solar energy) strikes directly. We analyzed the average yearly incoming solar energy per area data from *My World* and found that as you move north or south from the Equator the average yearly incoming energy decreases. As you move away from the Equator the average yearly incoming solar energy decreases from 391 units/m2 at the Equator to about 179 units/m2 at the Poles. The drop in average incoming energy is not steady (linear), the greatest change in the incoming amount of energy occurs between 40° and 60° latitude from the Equator. The smallest amount of change is between the Equator and 20° latitude away from it.

△ Guide and Assess

Students should also update Column 5 *(What does it mean for the challenge or question?)*. Students may something similar to the following.

Shape affects the amount of heat energy transferred to the surface by sunlight because the sunlight is more spread out over a given area when it strikes the planet more indirectly. Because the planet is circular, the further you move from where the sun directly shines (like the Equator) the less heat energy will be transferred, and the temperature are lower. Planet X might be too hot for a colony near the Equator and too cold for a colony too far North or South from the Equator.

Teacher Reflection Questions

- What ideas did students add to their explanations and how did they support these ideas?

- How effective was the iterative process of revising their explanation?

- How did you keep students focused on task and in participating in the discussions?

NOTES

Back to the Big Challenge

Which Regions of a Newly Discovered Planet have Surface Temperatures Appropriate for a Human Colony?

◀ *1 class period*

A class period is considered to be one 40 to 50 minute class.

Overview

Students apply information from the *Learning Set* to construct temperature prediction maps for *Planet X*. Students apply the information and data about how Earth's shape affects the amount of incoming solar radiation and how this solar radiation affects the surface temperature of Earth when constructing their temperature prediction maps for *Planet X*. Students also apply what they have learned about habitability as they predict habitable regions on *Planet X* and what Earth biomes they might support. Students share their predictions during a *Solution Briefing* to communicate their solutions to the rest of the class so that students can better understand how other people approached the problem. The class then updates their *Project Board*.

Targeted Concepts, Skills, and Nature of Science	Performance Expectations
Scientists often work together and share their findings. Sharing findings makes new information available and helps scientists to refine their ideas and build on others' ideas. When another person's or group's idea is used, credit needs to be given.	Groups should work together to construct a new temperature prediction map for *Planet X* and add to it the habitable areas. Students share their results with the class.
Scientists must keep clear, accurate, and descriptive records of what they do so they can share their work with others and consider what they did, why they did it, and what they want to do next.	Students should use their previous records and need to keep accurate and detailed records of their new prediction maps to revise in the future.

Targeted Concepts, Skills, and Nature of Science	Performance Expectations
Graphs, maps, and tables are an effective way to analyze and communicate results of scientific investigation.	Students should construct prediction maps to communicate surface temperature and habitability of *Planet X* to the class.
The average amount of solar energy that strikes Earth's surface over a year is highest near the equator and the intensity of the solar energy that strikes the surface decreases as you move farther away from the Equator, whether you are moving north or south.	Students' prediction maps should support concepts of how shape affects the intensity of incoming solar radiation and surface temperature.

Materials	
1 per classroom	Computer with *My World* software and projection system
1 per group	Computer with *My World* software
1 per student	*Solution Briefing Notes* page *Project Board* page

Activity Setup and Preparation

Create a temperature prediction map showing regions of habitability prior to class. Follow the procedure in the student text. Determine where students may have difficulty and decide if you want to demonstrate how to do any of the steps.

If you do not have computers available, the students can complete this project by coloring copies of maps. The maps they create from this project will be the base for the rest of the *Big Challenge*. They will continue to progress through the program by adding to these maps of *Planet X*. As students are coloring paper copies of maps, they will need to create new versions at each point. Keep this in mind and be sure to have plenty of paper copies if you choose this method.

Homework Options

Reflection

- **Science Content:** How was the exercise with *Planet X* helpful in showing ways to meet the *Big Challenge? (Students should describe how they have found how shape influences surface temperatures and made predictions based on this. However, they still need to determine how the tilt of the planet's axis, land/water differences, and surface elevation affect the planet's surface temperature.)*

Preparation for Learning Set 3

- **Science Process:** : How do you think a planet's tilt affects its surface temperatures? *(The purpose of this question is to elicit students' initial ideas and get them thinking about how tilt might affect a planet's surface temperature.)*

NOTES

NOTES

◀ *1 class period**

Learning Set 2

Back to the Big Challenge

Which regions of a newly discovered planet have surface temperatures appropriate for a human colony?

In this *Learning Set*, you were answering the question, *How does a planet's shape affect surface temperatures?* You will now develop a map showing your predictions of the surface temperatures on *Planet X*. You will use the data you collected during the investigations you did in this *Learning Set*. You will use your predictions to identify habitable areas on *Planet X*.

You are going to paint a blank map to show what you predict the average temperature will be at each latitude on *Planet X*. You will base your predictions on the fact that this new planet is shaped just like Earth. Use what you have discovered about shape and solar energy to determine the surface temperatures of *Planet X*.

Procedure: Temperature Map for *Planet X*

1. **Open Blank *Planet X* Map**

   a) **Begin by opening *My World*.** Select "Planetary Forecaster" from the Data Library drop-down menu.

   b) **Open the "Planet X.m3vz" project file.** You will see a latitude and longitude grid for *Planet X*. You do not know much else about this planet yet.

   c) **Save your blank Planet X project** according to your teacher's directions. In the File menu, select "Save Project As." Add the names of the people in your group to the file name. For example, "Planet X Jen Tim." This will be the project you use throughout your investigation about *Planet X*.

2. **Paint Temperature Prediction Map for *Planet X*.**

   a) **Go to the Edit tab.** Click the "Zoom to All" tool ⊞ to view the full map.

PF 60

Project-Based Inquiry Science

Learning Set 2

Back to the Big Challenge
5 min.

Students create temperature maps of Planet X *and share what they have done in a* Solution Briefing.

○ Engage

Engage students by having them consider what they would apply to construct a temperature prediction map for *Planet X*. Record students responses.

TEACHER TALK

❝If you were to make a prediction map of temperatures for *Planet X*, what information would you use to help you?**❞**

*A class period is considered to be one 40 to 50 minute class.

Procedure: Temperature Map for *Planet X*

10 min.

Students create temperature prediction maps for Planet X.

META NOTES

The instructions will direct the students to save their files in a location you specify. You have a few options for this. Students can save to a portable storage device, to the computer's desktop, to a directory you specify on the hard drive, or to a directory you specify on a network (if one is available).

Students will add to and alter these electronic maps as they go.

You are going to paint a blank map to show what you predict the average temperature will be at each latitude on *Planet X*. You will base your predictions on the fact that this new planet is shaped just like Earth. Use what you have discovered about shape and solar energy to determine the surface temperatures of *Planet X*.

Procedure: Temperature Map for *Planet X*

1. **Open Blank *Planet X* Map**

    a) **Begin by opening *My World*.** Select "Planetary Forecaster" from the Data Library drop-down menu.

    b) **Open the "Planet X.m3vz" project file.** You will see a latitude and longitude grid for *Planet X*. You do not know much else about this planet yet.

    c) **Save your blank Planet X project** according to your teacher's directions. In the File menu, select "Save Project As." Add the names of the people in your group to the file name. For example, "Planet X Jen Tim." This will be the project you use throughout your investigation about *Planet X*.

2. **Paint Temperature Prediction Map for *Planet X*.**

    a) **Go to the Edit tab.** Click the "Zoom to All" tool 🔳 to view the full map.

Project-Based Inquiry Science

PF 60

△ Guide

Briefly review what students have written in Columns 3 *(What have we learned?)* and 4 *(What is our evidence?)* of the class *Project Board*.

△ Guide

Using the procedures described in the student text, show students how to open the file *Planet X.m3vz* and provide them with an example of how they should name the document.

Demonstrate for students areas you think they may have trouble with.

Let students know that they may need various records from the *Learning Set* and they should have them accessible while they are working on their prediction maps. Students should follow the *My World* instructions in their student text.

⬡ Get Going

Assign groups to computers and let them know how much time they have.

△ Guide and Assess

Monitor groups and assist them with any difficulties they may have using the software. Note any group's map that does not show temperature fluctuations similar to Earth, but do not correct them. Note prediction maps that show

b) **Select the *"Planet X"* layer in the Layer List** to open the painting tools.

c) **Select the paintbrush** ✎ **in the toolbar.**

d) **Notice the Brush Size bar.** You can adjust the size of your paintbrush by clicking on the arrow and dragging it left and right on the Brush Size bar. The smallest size you can color is one square, (or cell) on the grid at a time. If you drag the arrow to the far right side of the Brush Size bar, you can color a large square, ten cells tall and ten cells wide.

Brush Size:	1
Edit Field: Temperature Prediction ▾	Delete	Add Field...
-30 32 94	-8.9359

e) **Select a color from the color bar.** This is the bar with the range of colors showing the color key. Position the paintbrush over the color you want to select and click. In the box to the right of the color bar, you can see what value is selected and the temperature it represents.

f) **Save your *Planet X* Prediction Map.** You will use this map throughout the rest of the Unit. Since you have already saved and identified this project file with your group name, simply use "Save Project" in the File menu.

Procedure: Habitable Areas Map for *Planet X*

You have created (and saved) your prediction for the new planet based on shape. You can now identify the habitable areas based on this prediction. CSA has requested that regions with average surface temperatures of 25°F to 85°F be located. Prepare a *Habitable Areas Map* based on your *Temperature-Prediction Map.*

1. **Open your *Planet X* project file in *My World*.** Select "Open Project" in the File drop-down menu. This project file may already be open.

the greatest change in temperature between 40° and 60° latitude. This shows that students are applying the ideas and information about incoming solar energy for Earth to *Planet X.*

Once groups have created a temperature map, they will use *My World* to show habitable locations based on the temperature range given by the *CSA.*

Procedure: Habitable Areas Map for *Planet X*

10 min.

Students identify regions on Planet X *that meet the habitability criteria.*

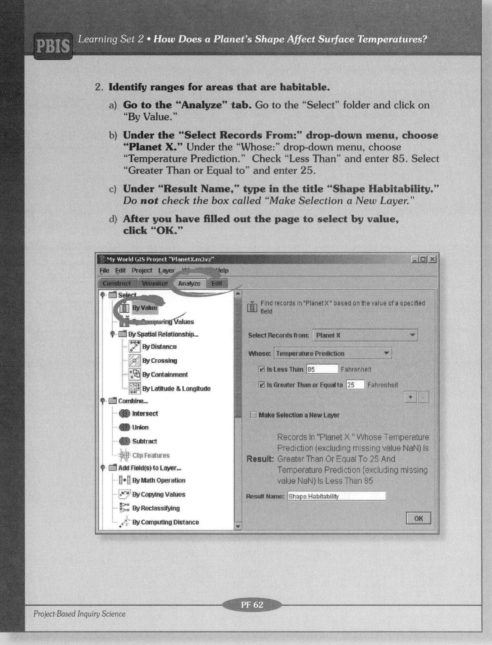

2. **Identify ranges for areas that are habitable.**

a) **Go to the "Analyze" tab.** Go to the "Select" folder and click on "By Value."

b) **Under the "Select Records From:" drop-down menu, choose "Planet X."** Under the "Whose:" drop-down menu, choose "Temperature Prediction." Check "Less Than" and enter 85. Select "Greater Than or Equal to" and enter 25.

c) **Under "Result Name," type in the title "Shape Habitability."** *Do **not** check the box called "Make Selection a New Layer."*

d) **After you have filled out the page to select by value, click "OK."**

△ Guide and Assess

Let students know that they will also be showing regions that fit the criteria for habitability according to the *CSA* on their predictions map. Ask students what the criteria are. They should note that the region must have a temperature range between 25°F and 85°F. Demonstrate for students how to shape the habitable region.

⬡ Get Going

Have groups shape their habitable regions. Let them know how much time they have.

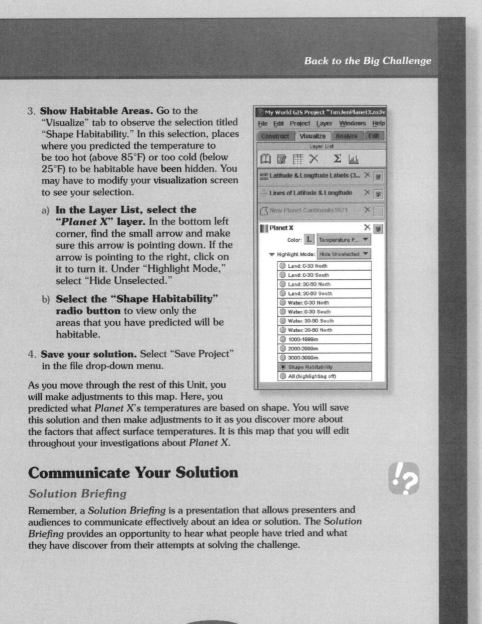

3. **Show Habitable Areas.** Go to the "Visualize" tab to observe the selection titled "Shape Habitability." In this selection, places where you predicted the temperature to be too hot (above 85°F) or too cold (below 25°F) to be habitable have been hidden. You may have to modify your visualization screen to see your selection.

   a) **In the Layer List, select the "Planet X" layer.** In the bottom left corner, find the small arrow and make sure this arrow is pointing down. If the arrow is pointing to the right, click on it to turn it. Under "Highlight Mode," select "Hide Unselected."

   b) **Select the "Shape Habitability" radio button** to view only the areas that you have predicted will be habitable.

4. **Save your solution.** Select "Save Project" in the file drop-down menu.

As you move through the rest of this Unit, you will make adjustments to this map. Here, you predicted what *Planet X's* temperatures are based on shape. You will save this solution and then make adjustments to it as you discover more about the factors that affect surface temperatures. It is this map that you will edit throughout your investigations about *Planet X*.

Communicate Your Solution

Solution Briefing

Remember, a *Solution Briefing* is a presentation that allows presenters and audiences to communicate effectively about an idea or solution. The *Solution Briefing* provides an opportunity to hear what people have tried and what they have discover from their attempts at solving the challenge.

△ Guide and Assess

Monitor students and assist them as needed if they are having difficulties with Shape Habitability. Check that students understand they will need to save this map and make revisions to it later as they learn about other factors. Consider having groups print a copy of their maps when they are done to keep posted or accessible in their science journals as they continue to explore other factors.

Communicate Your Solution:

Solution Briefing

20 min.

META NOTES

Students will need a way to project their maps (a projection of an electronic version or a printed copy.)

The goal of a *Solution Briefing* is for everyone to better understand how a particular person approached the challenge. You get the opportunity to see a variety of solutions that might work, which solutions are the most promising, and why. You can also determine what both successful and unsuccessful solutions show about the way the world works. Your presentation during this *Solution Briefing* should focus on the following points:

- Present the general look of your solution. Discuss where you observe temperature differences on your map.

- Tell others how the data you collected and science content from this *Learning Set* support the temperature predictions you have made for *Planet X*.

- Discuss how the class explanation of shape supports the solution you have developed so far. If your solution purposely does not match the class explanation, tell the class why this is so. Provide them with an explanation that better fits your idea.

As you listen, it will be important to look carefully at the solutions on each map. You should ask questions about how each map matches the ideas and knowledge of this *Learning Set*. Be prepared to ask (and answer) questions such as these:

- As the map was being developed, what changes did you make that are not visible in the final map?

- How well does the map match up with the class's explanation of how shape affects temperature?

- Are there areas that do not seem to match the explanation?

- Which areas seemed difficult to make decisions about? Which areas were easy to decide?

- Are there any changes this group might want to make on their map at this time? If so, why?

Be sure to fill out a *Solution Briefing Notes* page as you listen to everyone's presentation.

△ Guide

Remind students that the goal of a *Solution Briefing* is for everyone to hear how other students approached the challenge and to see a variety of solutions that might work. They will need to address each of the three bulleted guidelines listed. As they listen to other groups present, they will need to be able to answer each of the bulleted questions in the student text. Remind students that they will be taking notes using the *Solution Briefing Notes* page during the presentations.

Update the *Project Board*

Now that you know more about how shape affects a planet's surface temperatures, your teacher will help your class update the *Project Board*. Describe what you discovered from the investigations and the science readings in this *Learning Set*. As the class *Project Board* is updated, make sure you record the same information on your own *Project Board* page.

What's the Point?

You have just used information about shape to develop a predicted surface temperature map for *Planet X*. You also determined which regions of *Planet X* might be habitable. This is the start of your proposal to the Cooperative Space Agency. As you investigate other factors that affect surface temperatures you will continue to update your habitability predictions.

You finished studying one the four major factors responsible for surface temperature variation on *Planet X*. You still need to study tilt, land and water differences, and elevation. Your predictions for the habitable area of *Planet X* will probably change as you investigate these factors in the next *Learning Sets*.

This mountainous area of the state of Oregon sits at a latitude of approximately 45°N. Will this area receive large amounts of direct incoming solar energy?

PF 65

△ Guide and Assess

Have the groups present. As each group is presenting, check that they have addressed the three bulleted points listed in the student text.

After each presentation, encourage students to ask questions if anything was not clear or if one of the bulleted items was not addressed. Students should ask the suggested questions listed in the student text and/or other questions they may have.

Remind students to take notes as they are listening to the presentation and the responses to questions.

After each group has presented, discuss the similarities and differences between groups' ideas.

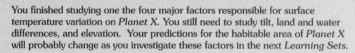

Back to the Big Challenge

Update the Project Board
10 min.

Students update the Project Board with new ideas and questions.

Update the *Project Board*

Now that you know more about how shape affects a planet's surface temperatures, your teacher will help your class update the *Project Board*. Describe what you discovered from the investigations and the science readings in this *Learning Set*. As the class *Project Board* is updated, make sure you record the same information on your own *Project Board* page.

What's the Point?

You have just used information about shape to develop a predicted surface temperature map for *Planet X*. You also determined which regions of *Planet X* might be habitable. This is the start of your proposal to the Cooperative Space Agency. As you investigate other factors that affect surface temperatures you will continue to update your habitability predictions.

You finished studying one the four major factors responsible for surface temperature variation on *Planet X*. You still need to study tilt, land and water differences, and elevation. Your predictions for the habitable area of *Planet X* will probably change as you investigate these factors in the next *Learning Sets*.

△ Guide

Have a class discussion after the *Solution Briefing* and update the *Project Board* if needed.

Teacher Reflection Questions

- What difficulties did students have in applying the information in this *Learning Set* to their temperature prediction maps for *Planet X*?

- How did the *Solution Briefing* help students' understanding of the challenge?

- What went well during the *Solution Briefing*? What would you like to do differently next time?

Learning Set 3

How Does a Planet's Tilt Affect Surface Temperatures?

◄ *6 class periods*

A class period is considered to be one 40 to 50 minute class.

Students use models to explore how the tilt of Earth's axis affects how radiation from the Sun strikes Earth's surface, affecting its surface temperatures and causing Earth's seasons.

Overview

Students use models and data to investigate how Earth's tilted axis affects its surface temperature. Students simulate how Earth rotates about its tilted axis and revolves around the Sun using a model of the Earth/Sun system. From this, students make predictions on how Earth's tilted axis affects its surface temperatures. Students use another model to investigate how the tilted axis affects incoming solar radiation for different latitudes over various months of the year. Based on their observations and their knowledge of how directness of sunlight affects surface temperature, students construct their first explanation of how Earth's tilt affects Earth's surface temperature. Using the *My World* software, students analyze data of Earth's average monthly surface temperatures at various locations for each month of the year. This leads into a discussion of how the seasons result from the tilt of Earth's axis. Students then revise their explanations for how axis tilt affects surface temperature. Students conclude this *Learning Set* by applying what they now know to constructing surface temperature prediction maps and regions of habitability for *Planet X* for the months of January and July.

Targeted Concepts, Skills, and Nature of Science	Section
Scientists often work together and share their findings. Sharing findings makes new information available and helps scientists to refine their ideas and build on others' ideas. When another person's or group's idea is used, credit needs to be given.	3.1, 3.2, 3.3, 3.4, 3.5, 3.BBC

Targeted Concepts, Skills, and Nature of Science	Section
Scientists must keep clear, accurate, and descriptive records of what they do so they can share their work with others and consider what they did, why they did it, and what they want to do next.	3.1, 3.2, 3.3, 3.4, 3.5, 3.BBC
The difference by which temperatures vary throughout the year on Earth can be linked to the latitude of the locations.	3.3, 3.4
Graphs, maps, and tables are an effective way to analyze and communicate results of scientific investigation.	3.2, 3.3, 3.BBC
Identifying factors that lead to variation is an important part of scientific investigation.	3.1
Scientists make claims (conclusions) based on evidence obtained (trends in data) from reliable investigations	3.2, 3.3
Explanations are claims supported by evidence, accepted ideas and facts.	3.2, 3.5, 3.BBC
Scientists use models to simulate processes that happen too fast, too slow, on a scale that cannot be observed directly (either too small or too large), or that are too dangerous.	3.1, 3.2
Temperatures around the Earth's surface vary widely, but can be predicted somewhat by location and season.	3.3, 3.4
The average amount of solar energy that strikes Earth's surface over a year is highest near the Equator and the intensity of the solar energy that strikes the surface decreases as you move farther away from the Equator, whether you are moving north or south.	3.4
Earth makes one complete rotation every day about its axis that is tilted with respect to the Sun. It takes a year for the planet to revolve around the Sun.	3.1
Earth's tilted axis causes differences in how solar energy strikes its surface as it moves in an orbit around the Sun.	3.2, 3.3
Seasons experienced on Earth are caused by its rotation on a tilted axis. The tilt causes either the Northern or Southern Hemisphere to have more direct sunlight and an increase in the exposure time to the Sun, creating summer conditions. The other hemisphere receives less direct sunlight and less exposure time to the Sun and experiences winter.	3.4, 3.BBC

Students' Initial Conceptions and Capabilities

Students have investigated how the shape of a planet and the directness of solar radiation affect surface temperatures. They should now realize that the more directly solar radiation hits the surface of a planet, the warmer the resulting surface temperature is. Students have only studied how the basic shape of the planet affects the variation in directness of solar energy over different parts of the planet. Students' original temperature predictions were likely to be a symmetrical yearly average. In order to understand why temperature varies with the seasons of the year, students will now explore how the tilt of the planet's axis and the planet's revolution around the Sun affects how directly the Sun's energy strikes a location over different parts of the year.

Students have several recurring misconceptions about how the Earth travels around the Sun and what causes seasons. Monitor the emergence of these misconceptions in student predictions, and try to address them directly whenever possible throughout this *Learning Set*.

- Students may have a mental picture of the Sun revolving around Earth, or they may imagine winter takes place when a face of Earth is pointing away from the Sun. A common misconception is that the seasons are caused by changing the distance between Earth and Sun (the two are closer in the summer and further apart in the winter) (Sherin, B., Edelson, D., & Brown, M., 2005, Hapkiewicz, A., 1992, Hapkiewicz, A., 1999).

- Students may believe that the Sun revolves around Earth.

- Often students think that the axis moves as Earth travels, that it is fixed with respect to the Sun rather than to Polaris. If this comes up, emphasize that the axis always points in the same direction towards a point outside our solar system (Polaris, the "North Star").

- Students should know that the Sun is so large, that its outward-radiating rays seem parallel once they reach Earth. They should recognize that the Sun is large enough to cover an entire face of the planet with light at the same time. However, some students may have the misconception that the Sun's rays only strike a small part of Earth.

- Students may think if a face of the globe is directed away from the light source, that face of Earth will not receive any solar energy at the represented time of year. Some students have interpreted the nighttime position of Earth as winter, believing that areas facing away from the Sun are in winter, while areas facing towards the Sun are in summer. This puts the Eastern and Western Hemispheres in opposite seasons, rather than the correct observation that the Northern and Southern Hemispheres have opposite seasons.

Students' Initial Conceptions and Capabilities	
	• Students may think the sun rises exactly in the east and sets exactly in the west every day.
	• Students may think the sun is always directly overhead or directly south at twelve o'clock noon.
	• Remind students that besides revolving around the Sun, Earth also rotates on its axis. Students should give the globe a few spins at each location in their investigations to see how the Sun rises and sets at each location. If you bring up this last example, be sure to talk about which direction the sun rises and sets, why this happens, and how we know. The Sun always rises in the east and sets in the west because Earth rotates counterclockwise when observed from a point looking down towards the North Pole. Be sure your students spin their globes in the correct direction.
	• Students may have a misconception regarding how Earth rotates on its axis in relation to how Earth revolves around the Sun. Be sure students can demonstrate that Earth makes a complete rotation in 24 hours and that this rotation takes place approximately 365 times in one orbit (or revolution) around the Sun, and that one complete orbit around the Sun is one year.

Understanding for Teachers

Students' original average yearly temperature predictions were likely to have been symmetrical. Because Earth along with *Planet X* is so tilted, incoming solar energy is not symmetrically distributed throughout the year. The constant tilt of Earth's axis throughout its revolution around the Sun means that the Northern Hemisphere is leaning more towards the Sun at certain times and the Southern Hemisphere is leaning more towards the Sun at other times. Sometimes neither hemisphere is leaning more towards the Sun. The tilt of the planet's axis leans along the circle of the planet's orbit instead of into or out of it.

Rotation of Earth about its Axis and Revolution of Earth about the Sun

Some students may wonder why we have leap years. This is because Earth revolves around the Sun once every 365.26 days. Because of this, every four years there is an extra day to add to the calendar. This day is added at the end of February once every four years and is called a leap year.

When we say Earth rotates counterclockwise or revolves around the Sun in a counterclockwise movement, we measure this from a vantage point of the North Pole. We have to reference this perspective because there is no absolute up or down in space. While students do not tend to have misconceptions about this, it is easy to begin thinking that there is an up and a down in space while talking about the orientation of Earth and its axis. To avoid this, be careful to use reference points when discussing the direction of Earth's movement.

Students must be sure to keep the axis leaning in the same direction because Earth's axis always points towards Polaris (the North Star). To travel north, you travel in the direction of Polaris. To measure latitude using Polaris, measure the number of degrees the North Star appears above the horizon. This is the same number of degrees as the viewer's latitude north of the Equator.

Earth's axis tilts about 23.44° on average. Earth's axis actually moves, somewhat like a wobbly top spinning around its axis. There are different wobbles that affect the spinning motion. Earth's axis varies between 22.1° and 24.5° within a 41,000-year period. Smaller wobbles, known as nutations, have an 18.6-year period.

If there was no tilt to the planet at all, any given location on the planet would receive the same amount of incoming solar energy year-round. This might sound pleasant, with comfortable temperatures all the time, but ecosystems benefit from seasonal temperature changes. Winter leaf-loss allows many tree species to have healthier spring growth. Seasonal changes also cue changes in animal behavior such as mating, migration, and hibernation.

The more extreme the tilt of a planet's axis (the larger the angle of tilt), the more extreme the seasons will be. The northern hemisphere of a planet with a higher degree of tilt will lean more towards its sun during the summer, and lean farther away from its sun during its winter. The tropics will be farther north and south, and the polar circles will be larger.

A planet with a 90° tilt is an extreme example. If Earth had this tilt, the South Pole would point directly towards the Sun in December and the North Pole would point directly towards the Sun in June. On the solstices, one entire hemisphere would be in daylight for 24 hours and the other hemisphere would be in darkness. If this was on Earth, the Sun would be directly overhead at the North Pole for a full day during the June solstice.

No matter what the angle of tilt, the latitude of the polar circles equals 90° latitude of tropical circles. The latitude of the tropical circles will always be the same as the degree of tilt. In our solar system, Mars has an axial tilt of 1°, Neptune has a tilt of nearly 30°, and Uranus tilts 98°.

Average Monthly Temperatures

Since students have just finished studying the different amounts of incoming solar energy that strike different parts of Earth in December and June, they may wonder why they are creating seasonal predictions of *Planet X* for January and July. Although December and June are the extreme months for intensity of incoming solar energy, they are not extreme months for temperature. Students should know this from experience. In the Northern Hemisphere, July is hotter than June and January is usually colder than December.

Maximum and minimum incoming solar energy does not correspond with maximum and minimum surface temperatures. The high amounts of incoming solar energy in June cause relatively rapid temperature increases. However, the same areas are still receiving solar energy in July, so they are still warming. Because they are receiving less solar energy (since it is not as direct after the solstice has passed), they are warming at a lower rate but still warming. Because of the increased temperatures at the end of June and the further, smaller increases in July, July is usually the hottest month of the year.

In the next *Learning Set*, students will learn about the rates at which land and water heat and cool. This will help them understand it takes a long period of high incoming energy to raise temperatures and a long period of no incoming energy for temperatures to decrease.

NOTES

LEARNING SET 3 IMPLEMENTATION

◄ *6 class periods**

Learning Set 3

How Does a Planet's Tilt Affect Surface Temperatures?

Do you see anything odd about the sculpture in the picture? It looks like Earth is falling over. Gilmore Clarke created this sculpture for the 1964-65 World's Fair in New York. The sculpture tilts at approximately the same 23.5° angle as Earth does when it orbits the Sun.

TO: Scientific Research Team
FROM: The Cooperative Space Agency
SUBJECT: Tilt of *Planet X's* axis

The CSA was very pleased with your research into the effects of planetary shape on surface temperatures. The data you transmitted supports your claim that shape results in temperature variations. Your initial predictions of habitable areas on *Planet X* seem right on target.

However, as you know, there are three remaining factors that could influence your temperature predictions. The CSA has discovered that the tilt of *Planet X's* axis is approximately the same as Earth's. This will make it much easier to study the effects of this factor on the new planet.

We will be expecting an updated report on *Planet X* as soon as you have completed your research into the effects of planetary tilt. Keep up the good work.

You have read that four major factors affect surface temperatures on Earth. They are shape, tilt, land and water differences, and elevation. You have data to support the claim that shape is responsible for some variations in planetary temperatures. You applied this information to *Planet X*. You were then able to identify areas on the planet that might be habitable. However, more research is needed into the remaining three factors to see how they will affect your predictions about *Planet X*. Read the bulletin on this page.

Project-Based Inquiry Science

Learning Set 3

How Does a Planet's Tilt Affect Surface Temperatures?
5 min.

Introduce the concept of tilt as a factor in determining temperatures on Planet X.

⭘ **Engage**

Ask students what they think is meant by the tilt of a planet's axis. Record students' responses.

Have students look at the image in their text book of the statue of Earth. Ask them how Earth's tilted axis is described in the text.

*A class period is considered to be one 40 to 50 minute class.

△ Guide

Have students read the introduction to *Learning Set 3*. Ask them to think about the challenge and the concept of a tilted Earth. Encourage them to visualize how tilting might affect Earth as it moves and receives energy from the Sun.

If possible, have a model of a globe that spins on an axis handy to demonstrate how Earth spins about its axis. Use a model with a tilted axis, or tilt your model so that Earth spins along at a slight tilt. Let students know this is how Earth moves.

Discuss how according to *CSA's* findings, tilt was one of the major factors responsible for temperature variations on planets and discuss the new bulletin from *CSA*.

Project the bulletin from the *CSA* or have the class look at the image of it in the student text and read it together with the class. Let students know that in order to improve their temperature predictions for the new planet, they must begin an investigation to answer the question: *How does the tilt of a planet's axis affect surface temperature?* You may also want to post this question on the wall, if your classroom layout allows.

NOTES

3.1 Understand the Challenge

What Is Earth's Tilt?

◀ $\frac{1}{2}$ *class period*

A class period is considered to be one 40 to 50 minute class.

Overview

Students make a model of Earth and simulate Earth's revolution about the Sun while spinning about its tilted axis. From this simulation, students should have a good understanding of how Earth rotates about its axis and revolves about the Sun. Students make predictions about how tilt affects surface temperature. They consider how they would respond to four ideas involving common student ideas and reasoning. The section concludes with the class updating their *Project Board* with what they think they know and what they need to investigate.

Targeted Concepts, Skills, and Nature of Science	Performance Expectations
Scientists often work together and share their findings. Sharing findings makes new information available and helps scientists to refine their ideas and build on others' ideas. When another person's or group's idea is used, credit needs to be given.	Students should work in groups to make a model and simulate how Earth rotates about its axis and revolves about the Sun. Students should then work on their own to make predictions about how tilt affects temperature. The class shares their predictions and decides on what they need to investigate.
Scientists must keep clear, accurate, and descriptive records of what they do so they can share their work with others and consider what they did, why they did it, and what they want to do next.	Students should recognize that their *Project Board* is a way to keep all the information they have organized and record what they still need to investigate.
Identifying factors that lead to variation is an important part of scientific investigation.	Students should recognize that tilt is a factor that affects surface temperature and make predictions on the relationship.

Targeted Concepts, Skills, and Nature of Science	Performance Expectations
Scientists use models to simulate processes that happen too fast, too slow, on a scale that cannot be observed directly (either too small or too large), or that are too dangerous.	Students should use a model of Earth to begin to understand its orientation and how motion affects incoming solar radiation.
Earth makes one complete rotation every day about its axis that is tilted with respect to the Sun. It takes a year for the planet to revolve around the Sun.	Students should describe how Earth rotates about its axis and how it revolves about the Sun.

Materials

1 per group	Styrene foam ball Stick or skewer Marker Large sheet of paper
1 per classroom	Star, to represent the North Star (Polaris), and tape to hang it Optional: projection of the bulletin from *CSA*
1 per student	*Project Board* page

NOTES

....

....

....

....

....

....

Activity Setup and Preparation

Make sure that your styrene foam ball and skewer are the proper sizes. You will need to be able to push the stick or skewer through the middle of the ball in order to represent the axis. The stick should be thin enough to go through the ball with little effort. Do not choose a stick or skewer with a sharp point that will be dangerous when handled. If you must use something with a sharp point, you should use duct tape or something similar to put over the point so that students do not accidentally hurt themselves while handling the model. An alternative to the styrene foam ball and skewer could be a ball of clay with a pencil pushed through it.

Choose a spot that can be used for Polaris (the North Star). The best location is the corner of the ceiling in the classroom. Do not designate Polaris to be above the light source. It will make it difficult to notice how the tilt affects the amount of light that strikes a planets' surface. All groups will be using the same reference point. Leave Polaris in its location as it will be used again later in the Unit.

Homework Options

Reflection

- **Science Content:** Describe how Earth's axis is tilted, how it revolves about its axis, and how it rotates about the Sun. (*Students' descriptions should include how Earth's axis is tilted and always points towards Polaris. They should indicate that it rotates around its axis once every 24 hours, and revolves around the sun once every 365.26 days.*)

- **Science Process:** How was using a model more helpful than reading or using other learning methods? (*Students should describe their experience with using a model.*)

Preparation for 3.2

- **Science Content:** How do you think Earth's tilt affects the amount of incoming solar energy? (*The purpose of this it to get students to begin considering the effects of axial tilt on the amount of incoming energy and to elicit their initial ideas.*)

NOTES

SECTION 3.1 IMPLEMENTATION

3.1 Understand the Challenge

What Is Earth's Tilt?

Earth, like other planets, rotates (spins) on an **axis**. An axis is an imaginary line running through the center of a planet. Earth's axis runs from the North Pole to the South Pole. The time it takes for a planet to make one full turn around its axis is called a **rotation**. Earth takes 24 hours to make one complete rotation. The time it takes for a planet to make a complete rotation defines the length of that planet's day.

view of
Earth rotating
on its axis

view over the
North Pole of Earth
rotating on its axis

axis: the imaginary line around which a planet, such as Earth, turns.

rotation: one complete turn of a planet around its axis.

revolution: the orbital motion of one heavenly body around another. Earth revolves around the Sun.

Planets orbit the Sun while they are also rotating. A planet's journey around the Sun is called a **revolution**. The time it takes for a planet to make one complete revolution around the Sun defines a year on that planet. It takes Earth 365.26 days to revolve around the Sun.

Materials

- styrene foam ball
- skewer
- marker
- large sheet of paper
- star to represent North Star

Explore

1. Make a model of a planet rotating (spinning) on its axis.

   a) Obtain a styrene foam ball and a stick or skewer. Carefully push the stick through the center of the ball. Use a marker to label the North and South Poles. Draw a line around the center. This line represents the Equator.

   b) Earth rotates in a counterclockwise direction when viewed from above the North Pole. Draw a starting point on your model and turn it in a counterclockwise direction until it makes a complete rotation.

   c) The axis about which Earth spins is not fully vertical. Earth's axis tilts at a 23.5° angle. Because Earth's axis is tilted, the Equator is not horizontal but slanted in relation to the Sun's rays. To model Earth's rotation, you will need to tilt your model the way Earth is tilted on its axis.

23.5°

view showing the tilt
of Earth's axis

PF 67

PLANETARY FORECASTER

3.1 Understand the Challenge

What is Earth's Tilt?

5 min.

Discuss Earth's rotation and revolution with students.

META NOTES

Knowing students' initial ideas will help in challenging any misconceptions they may have. Do not correct students yet. Common misconceptions will be challenged in this section and those that follow.

○ Engage

Elicit students' ideas on Earth's rotation and revolution. Have a ball or other object for students to show you what they mean.

TEACHER TALK

❝What do you think is meant by Earth's rotation?

What do you think is meant by revolution?❞

*A class period is considered to be one 40 to 50 minute class.

Use the information in the student text to describe the rotation of Earth about its axis and the revolution of Earth about the Sun.

Ask students what they think it means for the axis of rotation to be tilted. Have them show you what they think it looks like. Then ask them to show you how the Earth, on tilted axis, goes around the Sun. Ask students how the tilt of the axis will affect surface temperatures. Record students' ideas.

Explore

10 min.

Students simulate Earth's motion about its axis and the Sun using a model.

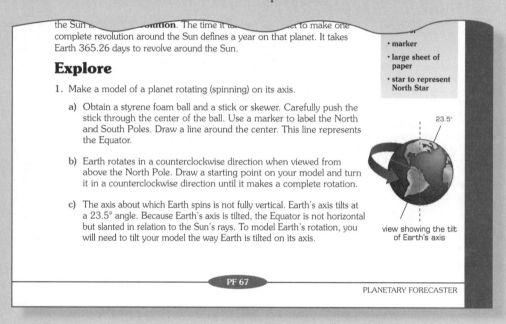

the Sun is ____ ____ **olution**. The time it ta____ ____ et to make one complete revolution around the Sun defines a year on that planet. It takes Earth 365.26 days to revolve around the Sun.

- marker
- large sheet of paper
- star to represent North Star

Explore

1. Make a model of a planet rotating (spinning) on its axis.

   a) Obtain a styrene foam ball and a stick or skewer. Carefully push the stick through the center of the ball. Use a marker to label the North and South Poles. Draw a line around the center. This line represents the Equator.

   b) Earth rotates in a counterclockwise direction when viewed from above the North Pole. Draw a starting point on your model and turn it in a counterclockwise direction until it makes a complete rotation.

   c) The axis about which Earth spins is not fully vertical. Earth's axis tilts at a 23.5° angle. Because Earth's axis is tilted, the Equator is not horizontal but slanted in relation to the Sun's rays. To model Earth's rotation, you will need to tilt your model the way Earth is tilted on its axis.

23.5°

view showing the tilt of Earth's axis

PF 67

PLANETARY FORECASTER

△ Guide

Let students know that Earth's axis always points toward Polaris. Let students know where they should consider Polaris to be in the classroom and emphasize when they run their model the axis must point in that direction.

Consider having students read through the *Explore* segment and then asking questions on points that need clarification, or going through it with them before they begin.

◯ Get Going

Let students know they will be simulating how Earth rotates about its axis and how it revolves about the Sun. Let them know that you will be observing them. Then let them know how much time they have.

△ Guide and Assess

Monitor students' progress. Check to see they simulate Earth's rotation and revolution about the Sun while keeping its axis pointed at where you have placed Polaris.

Once you have observed a group properly simulating the motion of Earth, have them answer the *Stop and Think* questions.

Hold your model upright, and tip the top of it away from you at an angle of about 23.5°. Use a protractor to help you. Spin it on its axis again.

2. Now, with your group, try to model Earth's revolution around the Sun.

   a) On a large sheet of paper, draw a large circle, and mark the center of the circle "Sun." The circle represents Earth's orbit. Place your model on this orbit.

   b) You will need to keep your Earth tilted 23.5° as it travels around the Sun. To do that, look at where in the room the North Pole of your model points when it is tilted 23.5°. Use this point as a reference. Earth's reference point is the star Polaris, also called the North Star. Earth's North Pole always points in the direction of Polaris. The North Pole on your model should always point to your reference point, just as Earth's North Pole always points to Polaris.

   c) Keeping your model tilted, revolve it around your Sun, and see if you can also spin it as you revolve it around your Sun.

Stop and Think

1. Rotation and revolution are two different movements a planet makes. Describe the movement of a planet when it rotates. Now, describe the movement of a planet when it revolves. Which of these movements is responsible for the length of a day?

2. What happens to the direction of Earth's axis as Earth revolves around the Sun?

Stop and Think
10 min.

Students have a class discussion on group responses.

△ Guide and Assess

Have a class discussion on groups' responses. Use the information below to guide and assess students' understanding.

1. Students' responses should include that a planet's rotation is the spinning movement about its axis, and a planet's revolution is its orbital motion about its sun. The rotation of Earth about its axis is responsible for the length of a day. One rotation equals one day. The Earth's revolution about the Sun is responsible for Earth's year. One revolution about the Sun equals one year.

2. Students' responses should include that Earth's axis stays pointed toward the North Star, not the Sun. The direction that Earth tilts changes with respect to the Sun as it completes an orbit.

NOTES

Predict

It is time to begin your investigation into the effects of tilt on a planet's surface temperatures. Answer the following questions. Be prepared to discuss your answers with the class.

1. Describe your prediction of how the tilt of a planet affects surface temperatures.

2. Do your best to explain why tilt may or may not affect a planet's surface temperatures.

3. Based on what you know so far, how confident are you about this prediction and explanation?

4. Below are some students' ideas about how tilt may affect a planet's surface temperatures. As you are reading, think about your response to each student's idea. What would you say to each student? What ideas would you want to investigate further?

Sasha: "The Equator is always hot, so I do not think the tilt changes surface temperatures much."

Lakiska: "Australia is hot sometimes and cold sometimes. Australia's seasons are opposite of the Northern Hemisphere. The tilt may actually be the reason for this. Sometimes, Australia is tilted toward the Sun and sometimes not."

Madison: "I do not think tilt changes anything. The North and South Poles are both cold. If tilt was a factor, one pole would be cold and the other would be warm."

Troy: "I think the tilt causes days in Alaska to be short. I heard that Alaska has days when the Sun comes up and then sets a few hours later. Less Sun means less solar energy and lower temperatures."

Update the *Project Board*

Once you have completed the questions, your teacher will lead your class in a group discussion. As the class shares their answers to the questions, update the *Project Board*. You know that Earth's axis is tilted, but you may need to investigate how this actually affects temperatures. For now, you will focus on the first two columns of the *Project Board*.

PF 69

PLANETARY FORECASTER

Predict

5 min.

Students have a class discussion on their predictions and responses.

⬡ Get Going

Let students know that they should each come up with a prediction for how a planet's tilt affects its surface temperature. Emphasize to students that there is no right or wrong when making a prediction. Ask students to answer the questions and let them know that a class discussion will follow. Let students know how much time they have.

△ Guide and Assess

Monitor students and check that they are recording their responses. These will be revisited after students have completed *Section 3.5*.

Have a class discussion on students' responses. Use the information below to guide and assess students.

1. Students' responses should clearly indicate how they think tilt will affect the surface temperature. Record students' predictions.

2. Students should be able to describe why they think the tilt will affect surface temperature as they described in their prediction. Consider asking students' how they might go about determining if their prediction is correct.

3. Students should be confident in their predictions and they should be able to describe why.

4. Students should respond to each idea presented and they should have some ideas to investigate. Record students' ideas to investigate.

Begin transitioning students by reminding them that they will need to investigate how a planet's tilt affects surface temperature in order to come up with good predictions for surface temperatures on *Planet X*.

Update the Project Board

5 min.

Students update their Project Boards *with new information and questions from earlier discussions.*

Madise .... tilt changes any..... .....and South ... are both cold. If tilt was a factor, one pole would be cold and the other would be warm."

Troy: "I think the tilt causes days in Alaska to be short. I heard that Alaska has days when the Sun comes up and then sets a few hours later. Less Sun means less solar energy and lower temperatures."

Update the *Project Board*

Once you have completed the questions, your teacher will lead your class in a group discussion. As the class shares their answers to the questions, update the *Project Board*. You know that Earth's axis is tilted, but you may need to investigate how this actually affects temperatures. For now, you will focus on the first two columns of the *Project Board*.

△ Guide

Ask students what they think they know about the tilt of a planet. Record students' responses in the first column of the *Project Board*.

Review students' predictions and what they would like to investigate further. Ask the class what they would like you to record in Column 2 (*What do we need to investigate?*) of their class *Project Board*. Record students' investigative questions.

What's the Point?

Planets move in two ways. They rotate on an axis. One full rotation of a planet on its axis is one day. Planets rotate at different speeds, so days are different lengths on different planets. Days on Earth are 24-hours long because it takes that long for Earth to rotate on its axis. Planets also revolve. They move around the Sun. Each planet revolves at a different speed, too. The time it takes for a planet to move around its star determines the length of a year. Earth takes about 365 days to revolve around its star, the Sun.

Earth is tilted at an angle of 23.5°. You can't detect that by simply living on Earth, but you have been told that tilt is a factor that influences the surface temperatures of planets. Your job is to discover how and why tilt affects temperatures. You need to understand the basics of this concept to develop questions and ideas about how it might affect surface temperatures on the new planet.

You and your classmates may have some ideas about how tilt affects planetary surface temperatures. Your initial prediction helped to make you aware of your understanding of this as a factor. The class was able to share ideas and questions about tilt's effects during the *Project Board* group discussion. Your classmates may have had different opinions and different questions. Now that these differences are out in the open, your class can pursue investigations to learn more. You'll have a chance at the end of this *Learning Set* to revisit and revise your predictions.

NOTES

Assessment Options

Targeted Concepts, Skills, and Nature of Science	How do I know if students got it?
Earth makes one complete rotation every day about its axis that is tilted with respect to the Sun. It takes a year for the planet to revolve around the Sun.	**ASK:** Define what is meant by a planet's rotation, revolution, and tilt of the axis and provide an example of this using Earth. **LISTEN:** Students should describe how Earth rotates about its axis once a day, how it revolves about the Sun once a year, and how its axis is tilted so that it always points towards Polaris.

Teacher Reflection Question

- How did the simulation help students' understanding of Earth's motion? Did any students make connections between the axial tilt and the directness of incoming radiation?

- How did the sample student ideas about tilt help students to understand tilt?

- What issues arose when running the model? How could these be handled in the future?

NOTES

3.2 Investigate

How Does Tilt Affect the Amount of Incoming Solar Energy?

◀ $1\frac{1}{2}$ *class periods*

A class period is considered to be one 40 to 50 minute class.

Overview

Students simulate how sunlight strikes Earth's surface using a globe and flashlight. The class runs a participatory model in which each student passes around a globe on a tilted axis along a circle that has a light source at its center. By carefully keeping the axis pointed toward one location (Polaris), students observe how the light shines on the globes' surface. They infer the directness of incoming sunlight is different on different parts of Earth because of its tilt and the amount of time that light strikes Earth's surface in various regions changes because of Earth's tilt. Students use a globe and light source to model how a tilted axis affects the amount of incoming solar energy that strikes Earth's surface.

Targeted Concepts, Skills, and Nature of Science	Performance Expectations
Scientists often work together and share their findings. Sharing findings makes new information available and helps scientists to refine their ideas and build on others' ideas. When another person's or group's idea is used, credit needs to be given.	Students should work together as a class to run the simulation. They should construct explanations for how axial tilt affects surface temperatures individually, with their groups, and with the class.
Scientists must keep clear, accurate, and descriptive records of what they do so they can share their work with others and consider what they did, why they did it, and what they want to do next.	Students should keep records of their observations to refer to later.
Graphs, maps, and tables are an effective way to analyze and communicate results of scientific investigation.	Students should record their data in a table and use this data table in analyzing their results.

Targeted Concepts, Skills, and Nature of Science	Performance Expectations
Scientists make claims (conclusions) based on evidence obtained (trends in data) from reliable investigations	Students should make claims based on their observations of the simulation of Earth revolving about the Sun.
Explanations are claims supported by evidence, accepted ideas and facts.	Students should construct explanations for how Earth's axial tilt affects incoming sunlight striking Earth and how this affects the surface energy. Claims should be supported by observations from simulations run in this and the previous sections and information from previous *Learning Sets*.
Scientists use models to simulate processes that happen too fast, too slow, on a scale that cannot be observed directly (either too small or too large), or that are too dangerous.	Students should describe the usefulness of models in studying phenomena on a scale difficult to observe or not safe to observe.
Earth's tilted axis causes differences in how solar energy strikes its surface as it moves in an orbit around the Sun.	Students should simulate how Earth's tilted axis and revolution about the Sun causes sunlight to strike its surface differently depending on its orbital location.

Materials

1 per classroom	Lamp Tilt-mounted globe Piece of cardboard Set of markers Masking tape Set of labels: December, March, June, and September Star, to represent the North Star (Polaris)
1 per class	Paper and easel
2 per student and 1 per group	*Create Your Explanation* page

Activity Setup and Preparation

You will need to clear out space in your classroom to accommodate a circle of students sitting on the floor. You can keep the North Star in its position from the previous section to use in this investigation.

Make sure that the lamp you use gives off enough light to observe on the globe from several feet away. You may need to dim the lights and close the shades in order to effectively observe how the light strikes the globe. Make sure that the light from the lamp shines on each part of the circle with equal intensity.

Label the index cards:

- December (December Solstice)
- March (Vernal Equinox)
- June (June Solstice)
- September (Autumnal Equinox)

Determine where the four months of the year should be before class. Students will determine this during their investigation.

When Earth's axis points toward Polaris, the Northern Hemisphere is tilted toward the Sun and the South Pole is dark, it is June. When the Southern Hemisphere is lit and the North Pole is dark, it is December. Use the images in *Section 3.4* of the student text to guide you. The months should be placed similar to what is shown below. The placement of students is shown in a view from above.

[Student]
March

[Student] June   December [Student]

September
[Student]

Homework Options

Reflection

- **Science Process:** How does using models help scientists to learn? *(Students' response should include that models are used to observe phenomena in systems that cannot be easily observed directly due to size or safety.)*

- **Science Content:** How does changing the position of how a planet's tilt affect how light shines on it? *(Students responses should include how changing the position of a curved surface causes some parts of the surface to be more directly exposed to the Sun, while causing other parts to be less directly exposed.)*

Preparation for 3.3

- **Science Process:** How do you think Earth's tilt affects temperatures at different latitudes? *(The purpose of this question is to elicit students' initial ideas about how tilt affects temperature. Students' responses should indicate that the less direct the sunlight is, the lower the average temperatures will be.)*

NOTES

....

....

....

....

....

....

....

....

....

....

SECTION 3.2 IMPLEMENTATION

3.2 Investigate

How Does Tilt Affect the Amount of Incoming Solar Energy?

In this investigation, you are going to observe the effects of Earth's tilt on incoming solar energy. You will see how tilt affects the amount of incoming solar energy that reaches different parts of the planet during different times of the year. You will be able to answer these questions:

- What happens to the directness of incoming solar energy on different parts of the planet as Earth, tilted at 23.5°, revolves around the Sun?

- What happens to the number of daylight hours on different parts of the planet as Earth, tilted at 23.5°, revolves around the Sun?

You will use a model of Earth revolving around the Sun to investigate tilt.

These pictures were taken on the same day (January 20) in the Northern and Southern Hemispheres. It is winter in Montana, but the kangaroos are experiencing summer in Australia! You will investigate to find out what is responsible for the differences in seasons.

PF 71

PLANETARY FORECASTER

3.2 Investigate

How Does Tilt Affect the Amount of Incoming Solar Energy?

5 min.

Elicit students' initial ideas.

◯ Engage

Elicit students' ideas about how the axial tilt affects the directness of incoming sunlight and the number of daylight hours. Record students' responses.

*A class period is considered to be one 40 to 50 minute class.

META NOTES

Observations students make in this section support ideas of how tilt causes seasonal changes in temperature by affecting the angle and intensity of incoming solar energy.

TEACHER TALK

"In the last section you made a model to help understand what axial tilt is and the motion of Earth about its axis and about the Sun. In this section, you will be running a model to determine how the tilt affects the amount of incoming solar energy.

What do you think happens to the directness of incoming sunlight on different parts of Earth, tilted at 23.5°, as it revolves about the Sun? (*Record students' ideas.*)

What do you think happens to the number of daylight hours on different parts of Earth, tilted at 23.5°, as it revolves around the Sun? (*Record students' ideas.*)"

Let students know that they will look at how the tilt of a planet's axis affects incoming solar energy using a model.

NOTES

Predict

Predictions are sometimes written as "If …then…" statements.
Complete these "If…then…" statements.

- If the North Pole is tilted away from the Sun, then the Northern Hemisphere will receive incoming solar energy that is (*more direct than, equally direct as, less direct than*) the Southern Hemisphere.

- If the North Pole is tilted away from the Sun, then the Northern Hemisphere will have (*more, the same, fewer*) daylight hours than the Southern Hemisphere.

Record your predictions.

Build and Run Your Participatory Model

1. Use the *Participatory Model Data* page to record data from the model. Assign one person to be the recorder for the class.

2. Build a **participatory model** of Earth orbiting the Sun. With your classmates, sit in a large circle. One student will sit in the middle of the circle near the lamp. The lamp will represent the Sun. Make a sign or star that says "North Star," and tape it as high as possible on a wall. This will represent Polaris, or the North Star.

3. Place the globe inside the circle in front of the person sitting closest to the North Star. The tilted axis must be pointed toward the North Star. Consider the following:

- Is the Northern Hemisphere pointed toward or away from the Sun?

- What latitudes are receiving the most direct solar energy?

- What latitudes are receiving the least solar energy?

- What latitudes are receiving no direct solar energy?

- What month would it most likely be? Have the student closest to this point hold the label with the name of that month.

As a class, fill in the first two columns of the data table for the month you decided on.

Materials
- lamp
- tilt-mounted globe
- cardboard
- markers
- masking tape
- paper and easel
- four labels: December, March, June, and September
- star to represent North Star

participatory model/ simulation: model or simulation in which you play a role.

Predict

5 min.

Students predict how tilt affects the directness of incoming solar radiation and the number of daylight hours.

⚠ Guide

Let students know that sometimes predictions consist of "If...then..." statements. For this Predict segment there are two If...then... statements to complete. Remind students to record their responses.

Build and Run Your Participatory Model

20 min.

Students build a model and run a simulation to observe how solar energy strikes Earth as it rotates and orbits around the Sun on its tilted axis.

META NOTES

Make sure that the North Star is placed in a position in the classroom where it is relatively far from the students and high above them. An ideal location would be the corner of the ceiling. Although the students are asked to keep the axis pointing at the North Star, Earth's axis does not always point directly at it due to wobbling about the axis.

...plete these "If..." ...s.

- If the North Pole is tilted away from the Sun, then the Northern Hemisphere will receive incoming solar energy that is (*more direct than, equally direct as, less direct than*) the Southern Hemisphere.

- If the North Pole is tilted away from the Sun, then the Northern Hemisphere will have (*more, the same, fewer*) daylight hours than the Southern Hemisphere.

Record your predictions.

Build and Run Your Participatory Model

1. Use the *Participatory Model Data* page to record data from the model. Assign one person to be the recorder for the class.

2. Build a **participatory model** of Earth orbiting the Sun. With your classmates, sit in a large circle. One student will sit in the middle of the circle near the lamp. The lamp will represent the Sun. Make a sign or star that says "North Star," and tape it as high as possible on a wall. This will represent Polaris, or the North Star.

3. Place the globe inside the circle in front of the person sitting closest to the North Star. The tilted axis must be pointed toward the North Star. Consider the following:

   - Is the Northern Hemisphere pointed toward or away from the Sun?

   - What latitudes are receiving the most direct solar energy?

   - What latitudes are receiving the least solar energy?

   - What latitudes are receiving no direct solar energy?

   - What month would it most likely be? Have the student closest to this point hold the label with the name of that month.

As a class, fill in the first two columns of the data table for the month you decided on.

Materials
- lamp
- tilt-mounted globe
- cardboard
- markers
- masking tape
- paper and easel
- four labels: December, March, June, and September
- star to represent North Star

participatory model/ simulation: model or simulation in which you play a role.

PF 72

Project-Based Inquiry Science

△ Guide

Have the students sit in a circle around the room, with the light in the middle of the circle and explain the model.

NOTES

....

....

....

....

"Each of you represent a place on Earth's orbit around the Sun. The light in the middle represents the Sun. You will pass the globe from one person to another during this simulation. It is important to keep Earth's axis pointing toward Polaris, the North Star. As you pass the globe around, each person will rotate the globe around Earth's axis so we can see how the sunlight is shining on all parts of Earth during a day for that particular position in Earth's orbit. You will try to figure out where these four months are located in Earth's orbit: December, March, June, and September. Remember that it takes one Earth year for Earth to go around the Sun."

Show students the labels for the four months. Let students know they will be figuring out who in the circle should hold each card.

Let students know one person will be the recorder for the class and all students will copy the data table in the student text because they will need the data and will copy the data table later. Alternatively, you could have each student fill out the data table during the simulation.

Demonstrate for students how they should hold the globe, with the axis always pointing toward Polaris. Place the globe in front of the person closest to the North Star, with the axis tilted toward the North Star.

Ask students the five bulleted items in the student text under Step 3. Emphasize the last item asking students what month they think is at this location in Earth's orbit and have the student at this location hold the label of that month. Have the recorder fill in the information for the selected month on the data table.

META NOTES

Students may change their minds about what month it is after collecting more information. The month that represents this location is December.

NOTES

....

....

....

....

....

META NOTES

When we say that Earth rotates counterclockwise or revolves around the Sun in a counterclockwise movement, we measure this from a vantage point above the North Pole. We have to reference this perspective because there is no absolute up or down in space. While students do not tend to have misconceptions about this, it is easy to begin thinking that there is an up or down in space while talking about the orientation of the Earth and its axis. To avoid this, be careful to use reference points when discussing the direction of Earth's movement.

4. Keeping the globe in place, rotate (spin) the globe counterclockwise. The parts of the globe facing away from the Sun represent night. The parts of the globe facing the Sun represent day.

   - What ranges of latitude receive no solar energy (no sunlight) in a day at this time of year?

   - What ranges of latitudes receive solar energy (sunlight) all day?

   As a class, fill in the last two columns of the data table for the same month you decided on, in the last step.

5. Keeping the North Pole pointed at the North Star, move the globe around the circle in a counterclockwise direction. This represents Earth orbiting the Sun. Stop moving Earth around the Sun when Earth's North Pole is tilted toward the Sun.

   - Is the Northern Hemisphere pointed toward or away from the Sun?

   - What month would it most likely be? Have the student closest to this point hold the label with the name of that month.

   As a class, identify latitudes receiving the most and least direct solar energy, and fill in the data table for the month you decided on.

6. Rotate the globe counterclockwise several times. Each time the globe makes one complete rotation, it represents a 24-hour day.

   - What ranges of latitude receive no solar energy in a day at this time of year?

   - What ranges of latitudes receive solar energy all day?

   As a class, identify latitudes receiving no light or sunlight all day, and fill in the data table for the month you decided on.

7. Move the globe around the circle counterclockwise, keeping the North Pole pointed at the North Star the entire time.

Participatory Model Data				
Name:			Date:	
Month	Latitudes receiving most direct solar energy	Latitudes receiving least direct solar energy	Latitudes receiving no solar energy at all	Latitudes receiving 24 hours of solar energy
December				
March				
June				
September				

PF 73

PLANETARY FORECASTER

Have the student closest to Polaris rotate the globe counterclockwise (when looking from above). Describe to students that the parts of the globe facing away from the Sun represent night and the parts facing the Sun represent day. Have a discussion on the two bulleted points under Step 4 in the student text and fill out the information in the data table. Check if students still want to keep the same label for the month they selected.

Have the student with the globe pass it to the person on their left. This will move the globe in a counterclockwise position. For each position of the globe, the student should spin the globe counterclockwise. When the globe reaches the point where Earth's North Pole is tilted toward the Sun, have a discussion on the bulleted points under Step 5. Then, fill in the class data table.

Where the North Pole is pointing toward the Sun, have the student sitting behind the globe rotate the globe counterclockwise several times. Discuss the bulleted points under Step 6 and fill out the class data table.

Continue passing the globe around. After they have completed one orbit, ask students where they think March is represented and have them move the globe to this location. After the class has decided where they think March is located in the orbit, have them fill out the data table.

Have the class decide where September is in Earth's orbit and have them complete the data table. As a class, summarize the results and have each student fill out their data table.

NOTES

Analyze Your Data

15 min.

Students have a discussion on responses to the analysis questions.

- What does it represent when the globe is moved around the circle one complete time?

8. Again, keeping the North Pole pointed toward the North Star, move the globe counterclockwise around the circle again. Stop at the point you think represents March. Give the "March" label to the student closest to this point.

  - Describe the tilt of Earth's axis in relation to the Sun.

As a class, identify latitudes receiving the most and least direct solar energy, no sunlight, or sunlight all day, and fill in the data table for March.

9. Repeat Step 8 for September.

Analyze Your Data

1. Draw a diagram of Earth's orbit around the Sun. Label the position of Earth in December, June, September, and March. (Remember that Earth's North Pole is always pointing to the North Star.)

2. When Earth's North Pole is tilted away from the Sun, the Northern Hemisphere receives less direct solar energy at any time of day than locations in the Southern Hemisphere. Describe how this affects surface temperatures. What would you expect to see on a temperature map for December?

3. When Earth's North Pole is tilted toward the Sun, the Northern Hemisphere receives more direct solar energy at any time of day than locations in the Southern Hemisphere. Describe how this affects surface temperatures. What would you expect to see on a temperature map for June?

4. Geoconda lives in Quito, Ecuador. It is near the Equator. Geoconda says: "The amount of solar energy we receive is pretty much the same all year. It is fairly constant because the amount of direct sunlight striking this area does not change much throughout the year." Do you agree with Geoconda? Support your reasoning.

PF 74

Project-Based Inquiry Science

⬡ Get Going

Let students know they will now answer the questions and a class discussion will follow. Let students know how much time they have.

△ Guide and Assess

Monitor students' progress and assist them as needed. Determine who you want to start the discussion of a question or to bring out certain points.

Have a class discussion on students' responses. Assess students' responses and guide the discussion using the following information.

5. Helmut lives in Reykjavik, Iceland. It is in the North Atlantic at about 64° North latitude. Helmut says: "The amount of solar energy we receive varies a lot throughout the year. There are times when we are getting more direct sunlight, and other times we are receiving less direct sunlight. In December, we get about 4 hours of sunlight, and in June we get about 21 hours of sunlight. The amount of direct sunlight changes throughout the year." Do you agree with Helmut? Give evidence for your reasoning.

6. Oana lives in Melbourne, Australia, at about 34° South latitude. Oana wrote that the amount of solar energy remains fairly constant there. "We get about the same amount of sunlight each day throughout the year." Do you agree with Oana? Support your reasoning.

7. *Planet Y* is round like Earth but not tilted. Describe the surface temperatures of *Planet Y* throughout the year.

8. *Planet Z* is round like Earth and tilted like Earth. Describe the surface temperatures of *Planet Z* throughout the year.

9. How does tilt influence the surface temperatures of Earth?

Explain

Your challenge is to determine the effects of tilt on the surface temperatures of a planet. Using a model to represent Earth orbiting the Sun, you were able to observe how tilt affects the directness of sunlight striking a planet's surface. From previous experience, you know that the directness of incoming solar energy affects temperature. Based on your background knowledge and your investigation, you can now create an explanation about the relationship between tilt and temperature.

Remember that the purpose of a scientific explanation is to help others understand the results from an investigation and how you reached your conclusions. Scientists use the results of an investigation to make a claim. This is a statement summarizing what you understand or the conclusion you reached based on an investigation. Using the *Create Your Explanation* page, write an explanation of your own. Be sure to include evidence from your investigation and your own knowledge. Share your completed explanation with your group. After everyone has had a turn speaking and listening, your group will work together to develop a group explanation.

1. Students should diagram Earth's orbit around the Sun and where Polaris is. Students should include a drawing of Earth indicating its axis for the positions on its orbit that represent March, June, September, and December. Students should be able to support their diagram with observations from the simulation done in class.

2. Students' descriptions should include how less direct solar energy results in lower temperatures. Surface temperatures in the Northern Hemisphere are less than those in the Southern

Hemisphere when the North Pole is tilted away from the Sun. Students should describe how the average temperatures might vary on Earth for the month of December. Students may not recognize that during December it is much cooler in the Northern Hemisphere (winter) than in the Southern Hemisphere (summer). They should recognize that the Northern Hemisphere on the average has cooler temperatures in December (resulting in snow in some regions) and that there are warmer temperatures in the Southern Hemisphere.

META NOTES

How Earth's tilted axis affects global temperatures and causes the seasons is further developed during the next two Sections.

3. Students' descriptions should include how more direct solar energy results in higher temperatures. Surface temperatures in the Northern Hemisphere are higher than those in the Southern Hemisphere when the North Pole is tilted toward the Sun. Students should describe how the average temperatures might vary on Earth for the month of June. Students may not recognize that during June it is much cooler in the Southern Hemisphere (winter) than in the Northern Hemisphere (summer). They should recognize that the Northern Hemisphere on the average has warm temperatures in June and that there are cooler temperatures in the Southern Hemisphere (resulting in snow in some regions).

4. Point out where Ecuador is on a globe or map, or have a student do so. Students should realize that locations near the Equator are not affected by Earth's tilt as much as locations further from the Equator. Locations near the poles are tilted closer to the Sun in relation to the Equator. Students should support their responses with their reasoning.

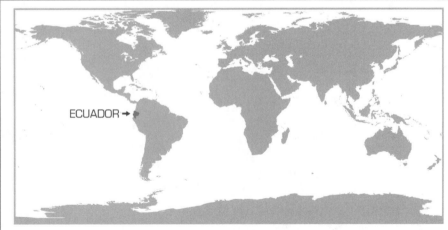

5. Point out where Iceland is on a globe or world map, or have a student do so. Students should realize that Iceland is farther north from the Equator and is greatly affected by Earth's tilt. Students should recognize that because it is so far north and because of Earth's tilt, it receives more sunlight during June and less in December. Consequently, when it is facing less directly from the Sun, it experiences daylight for only a brief portion of its rotation. Students' descriptions should include that the less sunlight striking the location, the lower the temperature. This would result in low average temperatures in December and high average temperatures in June. Have students model this if they do not understand.

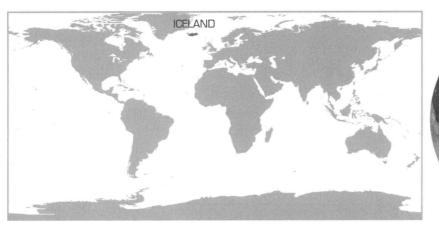

6. Help students find the location of Australia on a globe or world map, or have them locate it. Students should realize that Melbourne is south of the Equator. Students may disagree with Oana because they may think the location of Melbourne is very close to the South Pole. Melbourne should experience more direct sunlight as it is tilted toward the Sun in December than it would in June when it is tilted away from the Sun. Consider relating this latitude south of the Equator to a similar latitude north of the Equator. Melbourne has about the same latitude as Georgia, Alabama, and Mississippi in the United States. This should give students a rough idea of how the average temperatures might vary in Melbourne. Consider reminding students how the amount of direct sunlight in these locations is different in June and December.

233

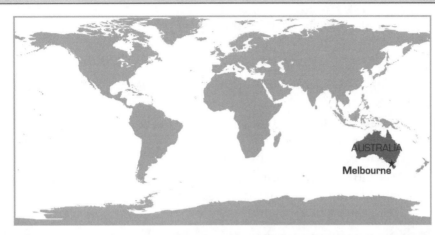 

7. Students should realize that a planet does not necessarily have to rotate on a tilted axis. Students should make connections with their investigations from *Learning Set 2.* Students may ask if *Planet Y's* sun is located the same distance away from it as Earth's sun. This means students have made the connection realizing how far away the Sun is will affect the amount of sunlight that strikes the planet. If necessary, you can model a round planet that rotates on an axis that is straight up and down. Students should see the amount of energy from the sun should be fairly constant for different latitudes and the average temperatures will be about the same all year.

8. Students should apply the conditions on Earth with a fictional *Planet Z* which is round and tilted as Earth is. Students may realize the connection between how far away the Sun is affects the amount of sunlight that strikes the planet and ask if *Planet Z's* sun is located the same distance away from it as Earth's sun. If *Planet Z's* sun is the same distance from it as Earth's sun is, *Planet Z* should experience differences in temperature and daylight the same way that Earth does.

9. Students should provide a summary of the effects of a tilted axis on surface temperatures. Locations that are tilted toward the Sun receive more direct sunlight and are warmer. Locations that are tilted away from the Sun receive less direct sunlight and are colder. The movement of Earth in an orbit and rotation around its axis results in changes in position for locations on the surface, most dramatically at the poles.

temper... ...Planet Z throughout the ye...

9. How does tilt influence the surface temperatures of Earth?

Explain

Your challenge is to determine the effects of tilt on the surface temperatures of a planet. Using a model to represent Earth orbiting the Sun, you were able to observe how tilt affects the directness of sunlight striking a planet's surface. From previous experience, you know that the directness of incoming solar energy affects temperature. Based on your background knowledge and your investigation, you can now create an explanation about the relationship between tilt and temperature.

Remember that the purpose of a scientific explanation is to help others understand the results from an investigation and how you reached your conclusions. Scientists use the results of an investigation to make a claim. This is a statement summarizing what you understand or the conclusion you reached based on an investigation. Using the *Create Your Explanation* page, write an explanation of your own. Be sure to include evidence from your investigation and your own knowledge. Share your completed explanation with your group. After everyone has had a turn speaking and listening, your group will work together to develop a group explanation.

PF 75

Explain
10 min.

Students individually construct an explanation, share with their groups, and together revise and create another explanation.

⬡ Get Going

Let students know that each student should construct an explanation on the relationship between tilt and temperature. Let students know they will share their explanation with their group members and then, as a group, they will come up with an explanation for how tilt affects temperature.

Distribute one *Create Your Explanation* page to each student and let students know how much time they have.

△ Guide and Assess

Monitor students. Check to see if students are supporting their claims with evidence from the observations they made from running the participatory model from this section and previous section.

When students complete their explanations have groups meet. Distribute one *Create Your Explanation* page to each group and have them write Group Explanation on the top of their page. Monitor groups for participation and progress. Guide students as needed.

Communicate

15 min.

Groups present their explanations and form a class explanation for how tilt affects temperature.

Communicate

Finally, your class will meet to share and discuss each group explanation. Your class will select and develop an explanation that best explains the relationship between tilt and temperature.

If you are not completely satisfied with your explanation, do not worry. Remember that learning is a process. This explanation is based on what you have discovered up to this point. As you gain more knowledge, you will have the opportunity to refine your explanation later.

What's the Point?

You began this investigation by making predictions about the effect of tilt on incoming solar energy and the number of daylight hours. The data you collected in the investigation and the trends identified in that data provide evidence to support the claim that tilt does affect incoming solar energy. By modeling the tilt of Earth as it orbits the Sun, you were able to observe these effects.

You now have a better idea of how tilt influences temperature variation throughout the year on a planet. In the next section, you will use *My World* to examine real data showing the ways Earth's tilt influences its surface temperatures. Soon you will be able to apply all your new knowledge to your *Big Challenge* on *Planet X*.

△ Guide

Let students know each group will be presenting.

"Each group has constructed an explanation for how tilt affects temperature. Now each group will present their explanation to the class and then we will construct a class explanation. It is important that when you present your explanation, you point out the information that supports your claim. It is also important that if something is not clear to you, that you ask questions."

△ Guide and Assess

Have each group present their group explanation. Discuss each explanation. Encourage students to ask questions and discuss the supporting evidence. Discuss misconceptions and correct them as needed.

After all groups have presented, have a class discussion on the explanations.

"We've heard explanations from all groups. Think about the similarities between the explanations and the differences. The things that were similar between all groups are things we probably want to keep in our class explanation. The things that are different should be discussed. You will need to determine what is best to put in the class explanation."

Make a list of similarities and differences in the explanations. Have a class discussion on these and begin to construct the class explanation. Edit the class explanation throughout the discussion. When it is complete, distribute another *Create Your Explanation* page for students to record the class explanation.

◇ Evaluate

Students should understand that Earth's tilt is responsible for changes in the amount of sunlight that strikes Earth (or length of day) and Earth's temperature. Students may or may not connect these changes to Earth's seasons as the planet moves in its orbit around the Sun. This concept will be more fully explored in *Learning Set 4*.

Assessment Options

Targeted Concepts, Skills, and Nature of Science	How do I know if students got it?
Explanations are claims supported by evidence, accepted ideas and facts.	**ASK:** What are the parts of an explanation? What parts of the class explanation state how tilt affects temperature? **LISTEN:** Students should describe that explanations are claims supported by evidence from observations and science knowledge. Students should describe these parts for their class explanation.
Scientists use models to simulate processes that happen too fast, too slow, on a scale that cannot be observed directly (either too small or too large), or that are too dangerous.	**ASK:** What was the model we used and how was it useful? **LISTEN:** Students should describe the participatory model and how the globe represented Earth, the lamp represented the Sun, and a point on the corner of the wall or ceiling represented Polaris. Students should describe how the model is useful in studying how Earth's tilt affects temperature on a much smaller scale so they could observe how the tilt affected the sunlight striking the surface. Students should describe the usefulness of this model for studying something that is too big to study directly.
Earth's tilted axis causes differences in how solar energy strikes its surface as it moves in an orbit around the Sun.	**ASK:** How does Earth's tilted axis cause differences in how solar energy strikes Earth's surface? **LISTEN:** Students should describe how Earth's tilted axis causes the Northern Hemisphere to receive more light energy during parts of Earth's orbit than the Southern Hemisphere, and conversely for other parts of Earth's orbit around the Sun. The amount of solar energy reaching Earth's surface affects the surface temperature of Earth. The more solar energy striking the surface, the greater the surface temperature.

Teacher Reflection Questions

- What difficulties did students have in running the model with the tilted globe?

- How did explanations change during the iterations between individual, group, and class explanations?

- What did you do to keep everyone involved in the discussions? What would you try next time?

NOTES

NOTES

3.3 Investigate

How Does Earth's Tilt Affect Surface Temperatures at Different Latitudes?

◀ *1 class period*

A class period is considered to be one 40 to 50 minute class.

Overview

Students analyze data to find a relationship between Earth's temperatures and Earth's tilt. Using *My World,* students analyze surface temperatures for eight different locations on Earth for each month of the year. For various latitudes in each hemisphere of Earth, students find the temperature ranges and obtain evidence for seasonal trends.

Targeted Concepts, Skills, and Nature of Science	Performance Expectations
Scientists often work together and share their findings. Sharing findings makes new information available and helps scientists to refine their ideas and build on others' ideas. When another person's or group's idea is used, credit needs to be given.	Students should work in groups analyzing data to help them understand the relationship between planet tilt, solar energy, and temperature.
Scientists must keep clear, accurate, and descriptive records of what they do so they can share their work with others and consider what they did, why they did it, and what they want to do next.	Students should keep clear notes of their data and conclusions to use later when revising their explanations.
Graphs, maps, and tables are an effective way to analyze and communicate results of scientific investigation.	Students should keep their data in tables and use maps in *My World* to obtain the data they need.

Targeted Concepts, Skills, and Nature of Science	Performance Expectations
Scientists make claims (conclusions) based on evidence obtained (trends in data) from reliable investigations	Students should make claims based on their data analysis. Students' claims should connect how Earth's tilt affects the amount of incoming solar radiation and the temperatures on Earth. Students may begin to make claims about how tilt causes the seasons.
Temperatures around the Earth's surface vary widely, but can be predicted somewhat by location and season.	Students should describe how temperatures vary across Earth and describe how they think Earth's tilt affects the temperature across Earth based on the quantitative data they gather in this section and the qualitative data they obtained from the previous section. They should note the change in temperatures in the tropics, in the mid-latitudes for the Northern and Southern Hemispheres, and the poles.
Earth's tilted axis causes differences in how solar energy strikes its surface as it moves in an orbit around the Sun.	Students may begin to describe how Earth's tilt affects the incoming solar radiation.

Materials

1 per group	Computer with *My World* software
1 per classroom	Computer with *My World* software and a projection system

NOTES

....

....

....

....

....

....

Activity Setup and Preparation

Using the information in the student text and the *Implementation* portion that follows, go through the procedure using the *My World* software. Determine where your class may have difficulties and what you should emphasize in the demonstration.

Homework Options

Reflection

- **Science Process:** How does finding patterns when using data or making observations help scientists learn about something? *(Students' descriptions should include how patterns or trends in data help scientists understand the relationship between two variables.)*

- **Science Content:** Describe how data about temperature averages is collected. *(Students' descriptions should include that temperatures are taken in locations with a thermometer throughout a time period. Those temperatures are added together and then divided by the total number of temperatures in order to come up with the average temperature.)*

Preparation for 3.4

- **Science Content:** Is there a relationship between Earth's tilt and its seasons? Why or Why not? *(The purpose of this question is to see how much students have connected on their own about the relationship between tilt and seasons.)*

NOTES

NOTES

SECTION 3.3 IMPLEMENTATION

◀ *1 class period* *

3.3 Investigate

How Does Earth's Tilt Affect Surface Temperatures at Different Latitudes?

In this investigation, you will look at how Earth's surface temperatures vary throughout the year. You have seen that the tilt of Earth affects the amount of incoming solar energy that reaches different parts of the planet during different times of the year. In this investigation, you will look at how temperature varies throughout the year as a result of that tilt. Keep this question in mind as you proceed with the investigation.

How much does temperature vary throughout the year in each of these locations as a result of Earth's tilt?

- The Equator
- Mid-latitudes
- The poles

You will look at one year of average monthly temperature maps to determine how much the average temperature varies throughout the year.

Predict

Write a prediction by completing the following sentences.

If tilt is a factor affecting Earth's temperature, then

- temperatures near the Equator will vary (*a lot, a little, or some*).
- temperatures at mid-latitudes will vary (*a lot, a little, or some*).
- temperatures at the poles will vary (*a lot, a little, or some*).

PF 77

PLANETARY FORECASTER

3.3 Investigate

How Does Earth's Tilt Affect Surface Temperatures at Different Latitudes?

< 5 Min.

Introduce the investigation

META NOTES

Scientists use quantitative and qualitative data to learn about phenomena and the relationship between to factors.

⚠ Guide

Remind students of the models they have run to explore how Earth's tilt affects the amount of sunlight that reaches different locations on Earth's surface. Let students know they will be using *My World* to gather average monthly temperature data from various latitudes around Earth for a year. Then they will be analyzing this data to find trends and relationships between tilt and temperature. Describe how the information they gather in this investigation will be quantitative and how the information they gathered in running the models was qualitative.

*A class period is considered to be one 40 to 50 minute class.

Predict

5 min.

Students complete the three prediction statements.

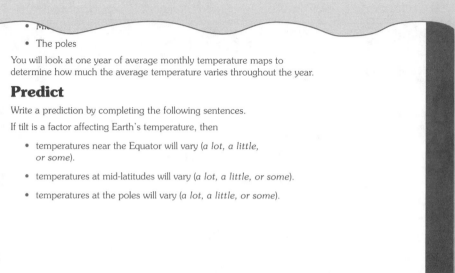

- The poles

You will look at one year of average monthly temperature maps to determine how much the average temperature varies throughout the year.

Predict

Write a prediction by completing the following sentences.

If tilt is a factor affecting Earth's temperature, then

- temperatures near the Equator will vary (*a lot, a little, or some*).

- temperatures at mid-latitudes will vary (*a lot, a little, or some*).

- temperatures at the poles will vary (*a lot, a little, or some*).

PF 77

PLANETARY FORECASTER

△ **Guide**

Let students know that they will be considering how the temperature varies throughout the year at the Equator, mid-latitudes, and the poles.

TEACHER TALK

❝Think about locations near the Equator, in the mid-latitudes, and near the poles. You have considered how the average temperature varies for different latitudes for the months of January and July. How do you think the average monthly temperatures vary over the entire year? Do you think they will vary a lot, a little, or some?❞

Ask students to copy and complete the prediction statements. Ask them how Earth's tilt is related to temperature variation.

TEACHER TALK

❝What role do you think Earth's tilt plays in this? What information would help you determine if the variation in temperature is due to Earth's tilt?❞

Let students know that the investigation will provide them with data that may or may not support their predictions.

Learning Set 3 • How Does a Planet's Tilt Affect Surface Temperatures?

Procedure:

1. **Open the Monthly Average Temperature Visualization.**

   a) **Open *My World* and select "Planetary Forecaster"** from the Data Library drop-down menu.

   b) **Open the "PF Monthly Average Temperature" project file.** The default will open an "Average Surface Temperature" Map for January. The "Average Surface Temperature" layer has fields for each month of the year.

   c) **Fit your map in the window using "Zoom to All" tool** . Select the "PF Monthly Average Temperature" data layer.

2. **Collect Monthly Temperature Data for locations at different latitudes.**

   a) **Select the "Average Surface Temperature" layer.** You will see a yellow box around the layer and the layer will turn from gray to white.

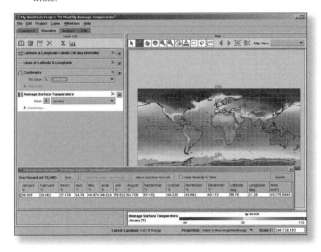

Procedure
20 min.

Each group collects temperature data from My World *for various latitudes.*

META NOTES

After clicking on the *Get Information* tool and then clicking on the desired latitude and longitude on the map, all **12** months of data should appear in a new window.

△ Guide

Demonstrate for students opening the file *PF Monthly Average Temperature* in *My World*. Then describe to the class the procedures on how to collect temperature data while demonstrating to the class how to do it.

Let students know that they should put a circle around the yearly high temperature and a square around the yearly low temperature for each location.

b) **Select the "Get Information" tool.** This tool can give you information about the data layer selected.

c) **Choose a location from the table.** Move the cursor over the visualization. The latitude and longitude are being tracked in the lower left corner. Match the latitude and longitude as closely as you can to the location you have chosen.

d) **Select a cell to get information.** A small window will open when you click on a cell on a map. This window has a chart including the average temperature for each month for that location, as well as the latitude and longitude for that cell.

e) **View the average temperatures for each month.** You can also use the field drop-down menu in the "Average Surface Temperature" layer to view the temperature visualization for each month.

Monthly Temperature Data

Name: _____ Date: _____

Location	Jan.	Feb.	Mar.	Apr.	May	June	July	Aug.	Sep.	Oct.	Nov.	Dec.
Peary Land, Greenland (81°N, 36°W) polar												
Helsinki, Finland (60°N, 24°E) mid-latitude north												
Atlanta, GA, USA (33°N, 84°W) mid-latitude north												
Quito, Ecuador (0°, 78°W) tropic												
Darwin, Australia (14°S, 131°E) tropic												
Buenos Aires, Argentina (34°S, 58°W) mid-latitude south												
Sydney, Australia (34°S, 150°E) mid-latitude south												
Mount Seeling, Antarctica (82°S, 104°E) polar												

Recording Your Data

Collect average monthly temperature data for each of these locations. Record the temperature to the nearest degree on your *Monthly Temperature Data* page.

Put a circle around the yearly high temperature for each location.

Put a square around the yearly low temperature for each location.

⬡ Get Going

Have groups begin collecting data. Let students know how much time they have.

△ Guide and Assess

Monitor students' progress as they are collecting data and guide them as needed. Check their progress and have them begin the *Analyze Your Data* segment as soon as they are done collecting data.

Students' data should be similar to the data shown below.

Monthly Temperature Data   3.3.1

Name: _____ Date: _____

Location	Jan.	Feb.	Mar.	Apr.	May	June	July	Aug.	Sep.	Oct.	Nov.	Dec.
Peary Land, Greenland (81°N, 36°W) *polar*	-45°F	-28°F	-38°F	-12°F	15°F	29°F	31°F	27°F	10°F	-10°F	-22°F	-35°F
Helsinki, Finland (60°N, 24°E) *mid-latitude north*	22°F	4°F	23°F	35°F	41°F	52°F	63°F	60°F	52°F	41°F	32°F	30°F
Atlanta, GA, USA (33°N, 84°W) *mid-latitude north*	32°F	43°F	50°F	60°F	63°F	72°F	72°F	72°F	71°F	66°F	57°F	42°F
Quito, Ecuador (0°, 78°W) *tropic*	75°F	75°F	73°F	73°F	75°F	74°F	72°F	72°F	72°F	74°F	73°F	74°F
Darwin, Australia (14°S, 131°E) *tropic*	84°F	84°F	83°F	82°F	82°F	79°F	77°F	77°F	81°F	84°F	86°F	85°F
Buenos Aires, Argentina (34°S, 58°W) *mid-latitude south*	75°F	71°F	69°F	62°F	70°F	53°F	49°F	53°F	62°F	66°F	71°F	80°F
Sydney, Australia (34°S, 150°E) *mid-latitude south*	75°F	72°F	62°F	61°F	52°F	48°F	46°F	47°F	52°F	61°F	67°F	73°F
Mount Seeling, Antarctica (82°S, 104°E) *polar*	-13°F	-45°F	-77°F	-89°F	-94°F	-81°F	-89°F	-82°F	-79°F	-62°F	-31°F	-14°F

Analyze
Your Data

15 min.

Students analyze their data.

Analyze Your Data

Calculate the temperature range for each location using your *Temperature Range Data* page.

| | Temperature Range Data | | | | | |

Answer these questions to help you summarize the results of your investigation. Remember, you were attempting to determine how the tilt of a planet affects the temperature at different latitudes.

1. Which latitudes have the smallest change in temperature throughout the year? Why do you think that happens?

2. Which latitudes have the largest change in temperature throughout the year? Why do you think that happens?

3. In which months are the temperatures in the Northern Hemisphere the highest? The lowest?

4. In which months are the temperatures in the Southern Hemisphere the highest? The lowest?

PF 80

Project-Based Inquiry Science

⚠ Guide

Have each student fill out the *Temperature Range Data* page table using the average monthly temperature data they collected.

Consider having students construct graphs. They could construct graphs for each question. For Questions 1 and 2, students could graph temperature change versus latitude. For Questions 3 and 4, they could graph average monthly temperature for each location.

Let students know they should answer all the questions and a class discussion will follow.

△ Guide and Assess

Have a class discussion on students' responses. Use the information below to guide and assess students. Ask students to consider how their predictions were supported or not supported by the data.

1. Students should have observed that the smallest change in temperature throughout the year occurs around the Equator with a high of 75°F occurring in January, February, and May and a low temperature of 72°F occurring in July, August, and September. The yearly temperatures change is 3°F. Record students' ideas of why this happens. Students should try to make connections between incoming sunlight and temperature. The more the amount of incoming sunlight varies, the greater the variation in temperature.

2. Students should have observed that the greatest change in temperature throughout the year occurs around Mount Seeling, Antarctica with a high of -13°F occurring in January, and a low temperature of -94°F occurring in May. The yearly temperature change is 81°F. Record students' ideas of why this happens. Students should try to make connections between incoming sunlight and temperature. The more the amount of incoming sunlight varies, the greater the variation in temperature.

3. Students should have data showing that the highest temperatures in the Northern Hemisphere occur in July and the lowest occur in January and February.

4. Students should have data showing that the highest temperatures in the Southern Hemisphere occur in December and January and the lowest temperatures occur in July and May.

Ask students why they think the highest temperatures in the Northern Hemisphere are around the same month as the lowest temperatures in the Southern Hemisphere. Record students' ideas.

What's the Point?

Your investigation should have provided each group with a trend in the data collected. This trend in the data provides you with some evidence to understand the relationships between planet tilt, solar energy, and temperature. The discussions you had within your group and with other groups should have focused on this trend. You probably noticed that the tropics (areas around the Equator) had the smallest change in temperatures during the year. The poles had very large changes in temperature. You should have also noticed that temperatures in the Northern Hemisphere were highest in July and August.

Why do the tropics have small changes in temperature compared to the poles?

PF 81

PLANETARY FORECASTER

Assessment Options

Targeted Concepts, Skills, and Nature of Science	How do I know if students got it?
Scientists make claims (conclusions) based on evidence obtained (trends in data) from reliable investigations	**ASK:** What claims can you make about how the temperature changes on Earth based on your data? What role do you think Earth's tilt plays in this? **LISTEN:** Students' claims should connect how Earth's tilt affects the amount of incoming solar radiation and the temperatures on Earth. Students may begin to make claims about how tilt causes the seasons.
Temperatures around the Earth's surface vary widely, but can be predicted somewhat by location and season.	**ASK:** Describe the trend in data showing how location affects temperature on Earth and how Earth's tilt may affect these? **LISTEN:** Students should describe how temperatures vary across Earth and how Earth's tilt affects these temperatures. They should note the change in temperatures in the tropics, in the mid-latitudes for the Northern and Southern Hemispheres, and the poles.

Teacher Reflection Questions

- What inferences did students make about how tilt affects temperature based on the data they analyzed and running their models in the previous sections?

- How did the use of technology (*My World*) help students?

- What management issues arose with the use of the computers? What ideas do you have for next time?

NOTES

3.4 Read

What Is the Relationship Between a Planet's Tilt and its Seasons?

◀ *1 class period*

*A class period is considered to be one 40 to 50 minute class.

Overview

Students consider how a planet's tilt affects temperature. Students read about how Earth's tilt affects the directness of incoming sunlight and the amount of time the sunlight strikes. Students are introduced to solstices and equinoxes. Students should make connections between tilt and temperature and provide a reason for Earth's seasons.

Targeted Concepts, Skills, and Nature of Science	Performance Expectations
Scientists often work together and share their findings. Sharing findings makes new information available and helps scientists to refine their ideas and build on others' ideas. When another person's or group's idea is used, credit needs to be given.	Students should share their thoughts on how tilt causes the seasons and affects temperature.
Scientists must keep clear, accurate, and descriptive records of what they do so they can share their work with others and consider what they did, why they did it, and what they want to do next.	Students should use previous records of data and information along with the information provided in the student text to answer questions about how tilt causes the seasons. The class should update their *Project Board*.
Temperatures around the Earth's surface vary widely, but can be predicted somewhat by location and season.	Students should describe how tilt affects the incoming sunlight and temperatures, and how the tilt causes seasons.
The average amount of solar energy that strikes Earth's surface over a year is highest near the Equator and the intensity of the solar energy that strikes the surface decreases as you move farther away from the Equator, whether you are moving North or South.	Students should describe how Earth's temperature varies more further away from the Equator because of shape and tilt.

Targeted Concepts, Skills, and Nature of Science	Performance Expectations
Seasons experienced on Earth are caused by its rotation on a tilted axis. The tilt causes either the Northern or Southern Hemisphere to have more direct sunlight and an increase in the exposure time to the Sun, creating summer conditions. The other hemisphere receives less direct sunlight and less exposure time to the Sun and experiences winter.	Students should describe how seasons are caused by the axial tilt, the equinoxes, the solstices, and when each season occurs in each hemisphere.

Materials	
1 per student	*Project Board* page
1 per class	Class *Project Board*

Activity Setup and Preparation

This section contains expository reading. Determine if students should read on their own, aloud, with their groups, or if it will just be discussed in class.

Homework Options

Reflection

- **Science Content:** Describe how Earth's tilt affects the amount of incoming sunlight. *(Students should include how tilt affects the directness of sunlight and the amount of time sunlight strikes Earth.)*

Preparation for 3.5

- **Science Content:** Go over your earlier explanation about tilt as a factor in surface temperatures. Is there anything that needs to be revised? *(Students should revise their explanations, which they will also do in the next section.)*

SECTION 3.4 IMPLEMENTATION

3.4 Read

What Is the Relationship Between a Planet's Tilt and its Seasons?

This is an image of the night sky falling over Earth. As you know from your investigation, the length of daylight is not the same across the planet. This is due to Earth's tilt. The tilt of Earth's axis is also the cause for the change of seasons throughout the year.

ellipse: a circle or flattened circle; the shape of planetary orbits.

It is about to get dark in Italy.

You have modeled how Earth revolves around the Sun. Earth travels around the Sun in an orbit that is almost circular, called an **ellipse**. As Earth revolves around the Sun, its North Pole always points towards the North Star. This is true no matter where Earth is in its orbit. This constant tilt means that different regions of Earth lean toward the Sun at different times of the year.

PF 82

Project-Based Inquiry Science

3.4 Read

What Is the Relationship Between a Planet's Tilt and its Seasons?
10 min.

Students have a class discussion on how a planet's tilt affects the incoming sunlight and are introduced to solstices.

○ Engage

Elicit and record students' ideas about the solstices and equinoxes.

> **TEACHER TALK**
>
> **"**You now know about the first day of summer and the first day of winter. The first day of summer is called the summer solstice. The first day of winter is called the winter solstice. What do you think is special about these days besides the beginning of a new season? What about the first day of spring called the vernal equinox and the first day of fall called the autumnal equinox?**"**

257

In June, the Northern Hemisphere leans toward the Sun, and the Southern Hemisphere leans away from the Sun. In December, the Northern Hemisphere leans away from the Sun, and the Southern Hemisphere leans toward the Sun. The hemisphere leaning toward the Sun receives more direct sunlight and also has more daylight hours. This combination of more direct sunlight and more daylight hours results in more heat energy from the Sun. The hemisphere leaning away from the Sun receives less direct sunlight and has shorter days. The combination of less direct sunlight and fewer daylight hours results in less heat energy from the Sun.

summer solstice: the day with the greatest number of daylight hours.

winter solstice: the day with the least number of daylight hours.

As Earth revolves around the Sun, each hemisphere cycles through times when there is more heat energy and times when there is less heat energy. These changes create the seasons. Mid-latitudes and the poles experience large variations in the amount of incoming solar energy throughout the year. They have large variations in their seasons. Latitudes near the Equator experience very little variation in the amount of incoming solar energy throughout the year. They have little variation in their seasons.

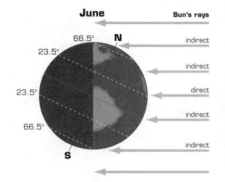

When you think about summer, you think about sunshine and hot temperatures. The Northern Hemisphere experiences the greatest number of daylight hours on or around June 20. This day is called the **summer solstice**. After the summer solstice, the number of daylight hours decreases each day until the **winter solstice**. In the Northern Hemisphere, the winter solstice is on or around December 21. The winter solstice is the day with the least number of daylight hours. After the winter solstice, the number of daylight hours increases each day until the summer solstice arrives again.

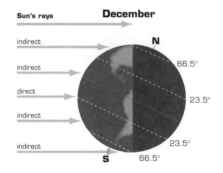

PF 83

PLANETARY FORECASTER

△ Guide

Review what students have learned from the simulations they ran and the data they analyzed in the previous section. Ask students how the amount of sunlight shining on Earth changed for the different locations in Earth's orbit and how this affected the Northern and Southern Hemispheres. Emphasize how it affected the amount of daylight at the poles. Review how this information is related to the average monthly temperatures they obtained in *My World*.

Let students know Earth's orbit is an ellipse. Remind students that Earth is almost circular and its tilted axis always points to the North Star.

Ask students which way the Northern Hemisphere tilts, toward or away, from the Sun in June. Then ask which way the Northern Hemisphere tilts in December. Describe how the amount of sunlight striking Earth changes using the images in the student text.

Describe the summer solstice for the Northern Hemisphere. Emphasize that on this day, locations in the Northern Hemisphere have the greatest number of daylight hours. Consider demonstrating this with a globe and a flashlight and reminding students of the simulations they already ran.

Ask students if the first day of summer in the Southern Hemisphere is around June 20th and ask them to support their answers with evidence they have gathered from the previous sections. Consider demonstrating with a globe and a flashlight. Discuss how this day has the least number of daylight hours in the Southern Hemisphere, and that it is called the winter solstice in the Southern Hemisphere.

Have students look at the image of Earth in December in the student text. Ask students to describe how the Northern and Southern Hemispheres are affected at this location in the orbit on the winter solstice.

◇ **Evaluate**

Students should recognize that the winter solstice represents the day with the least daylight hours and the summer solstice represents the day with the most sunlight hours.

NOTES

Monthly Average Hours of Daylight

5 min.

Students have a class discussion on equinoxes and how the number of daylight hours affects temperature.

META NOTES

You may wish to have students figure out the latitude and longitude of their location and then find the daylight hours as the seasons change.

Monthly Average Hours of Daylight

Between the summer solstice, when the number of daylight hours is greatest, and the winter solstice, when the number of daylight hours is smallest, the number of daylight hours gets smaller each day. If you look at the *Monthly Average Hours of Daylight* chart below, you can see that pattern. There's another pattern you might be able to see in that chart. Look for columns where the average number of daylight hours is close to 12 in each location.

equinox: a day when the number of daylight hours equals the number of nighttime hours.

Did You Know?

We use the solstices and equinox days to mark the beginnings and ends of the seasons on the calendar.

There is one day in each of those months, March and September, when the number of daylight hours and nighttime hours is equal. When the number of daylight hours equals the number of nighttime hours, it is called an **equinox** (similar to the word "equal"). The equinox in the spring is called the spring equinox. The one in the fall is called the fall equinox. In the Northern Hemisphere, the spring equinox occurs on or around March 20, and the fall equinox is on or around September 21.

Look again at the table of monthly average hours of daylight. Notice the pattern of daylight hours and when different places experience their summer solstice and winter solstice.

Monthly Average Hours of Daylight												
Location	Jan	Feb.	Mar.	Apr.	May	June	July	Aug.	Sep.	Oct.	Nov.	Dec.
Helsinki, Finland (60°N, 24°E)	6.8	9.1	11.9	14.7	17.3	18.8	18	15.6	12.8	10.1	7.5	6
Atlanta, USA (33°N, 84°W)	9.69	10.7	11.7	12.9	13.8	14.3	14.1	13.3	12.2	11.1	10.1	9.7
Quito, Ecuador (0°, 78°W)	12.1	12.1	12.1	12.1	12.1	12.1	12.1	12.1	12.1	12.1	12.1	12.1
Buenos Aires, Argentina (34°S, 58°W)	14.1	13.3	12.3	11.1	10.2	9.7	9.9	10.7	11.8	12.9	13.9	14.3

△ Guide

Ask the class to look at the table of monthly average hours of daylight to determine what is meant by the term equinox, which occurs on the first day of spring and the first day of autumn.

As a class, discuss how on these days the number of hours of daylight equals the number of hours of no daylight.

Have students briefly compare the data with the temperature data they obtained in the previous section and ask them for the trends they find. This emphasizes the fact that as the number of daylight hours decreases, the temperature decreases.

NOTES

Stop and Think

15 min.

Students have a class discussion on students' responses to the questions.

Stop and Think

1. The Northern Hemisphere experiences summer solstice in June. When do you think the Southern Hemisphere experiences summer solstice?

2. The Northern Hemisphere experiences winter solstice in December. When do you think the Southern Hemisphere experiences winter solstice?

3. When does Helsinki, Finland experience the summer solstice (greatest number of daylight hours)? Winter solstice (least number of daylight hours)?

4. When does Buenos Aires, Argentina experience the summer solstice? Winter solstice?

5. Which city in the table has the most variation in day length?

6. Which city in the table has the least variation in day length?

7. If the Northern Hemisphere experiences the spring equinox in March, when does the Southern Hemisphere experience the spring equinox?

8. When does the Southern Hemisphere experience the fall equinox?

9. When does Quito, Ecuador experience equinox?

Earth at the spring equinox ...

2004 Mar 20 9:00:00 pm UT

the fall equinox ...

2004 Sep 22 9:00:00 pm UT

the summer solstice ...

2004 Jun 21 9:00:00 pm UT

and the winter solstice.

2004 Dec 22 9:00:00 pm UT

PF 85

PLANETARY FORECASTER

◯ Get Going

Let students know that they should use the information from the student text and class discussions to answer the *Stop and Think* questions. A class discussion will follow.

△ Guide and Assess

Have a brief class discussion on students' responses.

1. Students' responses should be December.

2. Students' responses should be June.

3. Students' responses should be June for the summer solstice and December for the winter solstice.

4. Students' responses should be December for the summer solstice and June for the winter solstice.

5. Students' responses should be Helsinki. Discuss how this location in the table is furthest from the Equator.

6. Students' responses should be Quito. Discuss how this location in the table is at Equator.

7. Students' responses should be September.

8. Students' responses should be March.

9. Students should explain that according to the table, locations at the Equator experience equinox constantly, since they average approximately 12 hours of daylight throughout the year.

10. Students' responses should state that because the Northern Hemisphere is tilted toward the Sun in summer, there are fewer hours that locations on that hemisphere are facing away from the Sun. Therefore, there are more hours of daylight as the hemisphere is exposed to the Sun for a majority of its rotation.

11. Students' responses should state that because Quito is on the Equator. It is not affected much by the tilt of Earth's axis and does not experience the four seasons. However, Chicago is in the Northern Hemisphere and is affected much more by the tilted axis.

12. Encourage students to support their responses. Make sure to address the common misconception described. Earth is not closer to the Sun in the summer. Earth is actually closest to the Sun in January and farthest from the Sun in July. There is a slight temperature effect from this, making winters in the Northern Hemisphere a little warmer than they would be otherwise, but the effect of distance is much less significant than the effect tilt has on the amount of sunlight reaching a location.

As a class, discuss the four images of Earth in the student text. Point out how the poles are illuminated on the solstices.

Consider asking students how the seasons would be different if Earth was tilted even farther than it is.

Remind students that *Planet X* has the same tilt as Earth and ask them how they think the tilt will affect the temperatures.

> **META NOTES**
>
> There is a slight variation of daylight hours at the Equator, but it is slight.

> **META NOTES**
>
> The more extreme the tilt of a planet's axis (the larger the angle of tilt), the more extreme the seasons will be. The northern hemisphere of a planet with a higher degree of tilt will lean more towards its sun during the summer, and farther away from its sun during its winter. The tropics will be farther north and south, and the polar circles will be larger.

Update the Project Board

10 min.

Have the class update their Project Board.

10. Why are the hours of daylight the greatest during the summer?

11. Quito, Ecuador experiences warm tropical weather and about 12 hours of daylight all year. Chicago, Illinois experiences cold winters, hot summers, and warm spring and fall temperatures. Chicago's longest daytime is about 15 hours, and its shortest is about 9 hours. Why are these two places different?

12. Cindy thinks it is hot in summer because Earth is closer to the Sun in the summer. Do you agree with Cindy? What would you say to Cindy?

Update the *Project Board*

You began this *Learning Set* by exploring if and how tilt affects a planet's temperatures. You have modeled Earth's tilt as it orbits the Sun and have collected data to support your claim that there is an effect. You gathered more information as you read about Earth's tilt and its effect on seasons and number of daylight hours. You can now focus on the next two columns of the *Project Board*, *What are we learning?* and *What is our evidence?* You and your classmates should describe your new knowledge from the investigation and the science readings. Evidence includes data from investigations, as well as knowledge gained from other sources, such as reading, talking to experts, or media. As the class *Project Board* is updated, make sure you record the same information on your own *Project Board* page.

Which regions of a newly discovered planet have surface temperatures appropriate for a human colony?				
What do we think we know?	What do we need to investigate?	What are we learning?	What is our evidence?	What does it mean for the challenge or question?

PF 86

△ Guide

Remind students that the *Project Board* is a means of organizing ideas and questions and keeping track of how their ideas have changed.

❝You should now have a lot of information to include on your class *Project Board.* The *Project Board* is a tool that helps to organize the information you have and the ideas you want to investigate. Focus on the third and fourth columns in particular: *What are we learning?* and *What is our evidence?*❞

Ask students what they would like to include in Columns 1 and 2.

Ask the class what their ideas are and the evidence that supports those ideas. As a class, edit these before recording them on the *Project Board.*

◇ Evaluate

Make sure the following concepts are included on the *Project Board.*

Column 3 (claim): Earth's tilt causes a variation in the amount of light that reaches a location on Earth's surface and results in Earth's seasons.

Column 4 (evidence): Earth's tilt causes the Northern and Southern Hemispheres to vary the hours of daylight depending on whether or not the axis is tilted toward the Sun or away from it. This changes the amount of incoming solar energy and the temperatures causing the seasons. We observed this qualitatively in models we ran using a globe to represent Earth and a light source to represent the Sun. These showed that the amount of time light shined on locations of Earth and the intensity of light varied depending on Earth's axis being tilted toward or away from the Sun as it went around its orbit. The hemisphere that tilted toward the Sun received more incoming light. The more incoming light there is, the greater the temperature. This was quantitatively supported by data from *My World* on monthly average temperatures around the world and from the data table in the text showing average hours of daylight for each month at various locations.

Information about the solstices, the equinoxes, and the lack of seasons at the Equator should also be included either as separate claims or within the claim above.

Students are often too focused on filling in information that they have learned and tend to neglect the questions that prompt them to think ahead and come up with new ideas. The purpose of the *Project Board* is to organize students' ideas, questions, and answers, and focus and draw out the ideas and questions that drive the *Big Challenge.*

Assessment Options

Targeted Concepts, Skills, and Nature of Science	How do I know if students got it?
Seasons experienced on Earth are caused by its rotation on a tilted axis. The tilt causes either the Northern or Southern Hemisphere to have more direct sunlight and an increase in the exposure time to the Sun, creating summer conditions. The other hemisphere receives less direct sunlight and less exposure time to the Sun and experiences winter.	**ASK:** What causes the seasons and what does the first day of each season signify? **LISTEN:** Students should describe how seasons are caused by Earth's tilt. The hemisphere leaning toward the Sun receives more hours of daylight and more solar energy. This increases the temperature in that hemisphere. The first day of winter is known as the winter solstice and signifies when the hemisphere is receiving the least amount of daylight hours. During the first day of summer, or the Summer Solstice, the hemisphere receives the greatest number of daylight hours. During the first day of spring and fall (the vernal and autumnal equinoxes), there are equal hours of light and dark.

Teacher Reflection Questions

- What misconceptions did your students have about the cause of the seasons?

- How did filling Columns 3 and 4 in the *Project Board* help the class understand how tilt affects Earth's temperature?

- How did you choose the method of reading?

SECTION 3.5 INTRODUCTION

3.5 Revise Your Explanation

Tilt and Temperature

◀ *1 class period*

*A class period is considered to be one 40 to 50 minute class.

Overview

Students revise their explanation of how a planet's tilt affects its surface temperatures. Students begin by reviewing their previous explanation and then answering questions designed to guide them to revise their explanation using their observations, analysis, and the information presented during this *Learning Set*. Students use an iterative process much like scientists do to come up with an explanation the class agrees on. Groups share their explanations with the class and the class constructs an explanation. The class updates their *Project Board* to include what they are learning and the evidence that supports it.

Targeted Concepts, Skills, and Nature of Science	Performance Expectations
Scientists often work together and share their findings. Sharing findings makes new information available and helps scientists to refine their ideas and build on others' ideas. When another person's or group's idea is used, credit needs to be given.	Students should share their revised explanation for how tilt affects temperature with their group members and decide upon an explanation for the group. Then groups should share their explanations with the class and the class should decide upon an explanation.
Scientists must keep clear, accurate, and descriptive records of what they do so they can share their work with others and consider what they did, why they did it, and what they want to do next.	Students should use their records to revise their explanations.
Explanations are claims supported by evidence, accepted ideas and facts.	Students should construct an explanation for why, how, and how much tilt affects surface temperatures. Their claims should be supported by evidence from their investigations and science knowledge.

Materials	
3 per student	*Create Your Explanation* page
1 per student	*Project Board* page
1 per class	Class *Project Board*

Homework Options

Reflection

- **Science Content:** What new information caused you to change one of the ways you thought about the way Earth's tilt affected surface temperatures? *(Students should describe something they learned that caused them to revise their thinking.)*

Preparation for **Back to the Big Challenge**

- **Science Content:** *Planet X* has the same tilt as Earth. What do you think the temperature ranges will be like in the northern and southern hemispheres of *Planet X? (The purpose of this is to get students started with their predictions. In the next section, students will create temperature prediction maps for* Planet X *for January and July.)*

SECTION 3.5 IMPLEMENTATION

3.5 Revise Your Explanation

Tilt and Temperature

You have studied tilt and its effects on incoming solar energy, temperatures, and seasons. You are ready to revise your explanation about tilt as a factor in predicting surface temperatures. Soon you will revise your predictions for *Planet X.*

Look at your original prediction on tilt. Think about how you originally thought tilt affected temperature. Think about what you now know about tilt and how it relates to seasons and the number of daylight hours. You also saw how much the temperature varies at higher latitudes compared to the Equator because of tilt. The revised explanation you write now will show your new knowledge about tilt. It will also be useful as you revise your predictions for *Planet X.*

Review Your Explanation

Earlier, your class wrote an explanation of how tilt affects surface temperatures. Review the explanation using the results from this last investigation. Use the following *Stop and Think* questions as a guide.

Stop and Think

These questions will help you analyze and refine the class explanation. Answer these questions on your own.

1. Describe your current understanding of how the tilt of a planet **affects** surface temperatures. Use evidence from your investigations to support your claim.

2. How has your claim changed since your earlier prediction? What have you learned that made you change it?

3. How has your understanding of why tilt affects surface temperatures changed since you started? What information made you change your explanation?

4. Write a statement that combines the answers to *how*, *why*, and *how much* tilt affects surface temperatures. Make sure to use evidence from your investigations in your statement.

PF 87

3.5 Revise Your Explanation

Tilt and Temperature

< 5 min.

Introduce the section.

Review Your Explanation

5 min.

Students review the class explanation, adding new science knowledge.

△ Guide

Let students know that in this section they will each revise the class explanation they constructed previously to include the new information they have about how tilt affects surface temperatures.

*A class period is considered to be one 40 to 50 minute class.

⬡ Get Going

Let students know that the *Stop and Think* questions should help them revise their explanations and that they should answer these first. Like last time, they will be sharing their explanations with their group and then the class.

Distribute a *Create Your Explanation* page and let students know how much time they have.

△ Guide and Assess

Monitor students. Check that students are answering the questions. They should be referring to their initial prediction from *Section 3.1,* their data, the claims they made earlier in the *Learning Set,* and the class explanation from *Section 3.2.*

Stop and Think

10 min.

Students answer questions and revise their explanation.

temperatu... ...w the explanation using th... ...om this last investigation. Use the following *Stop and Think* questions as a guide.

Stop and Think

These questions will help you analyze and refine the class explanation. Answer these questions on your own.

1. Describe your current understanding of how the tilt of a planet affects surface temperatures. Use evidence from your investigations to support your claim.

2. How has your claim changed since your earlier prediction? What have you learned that made you change it?

3. How has your understanding of why tilt affects surface temperatures changed since you started? What information made you change your explanation?

4. Write a statement that combines the answers to *how, why,* and *how much* tilt affects surface temperatures. Make sure to use evidence from your investigations in your statement.

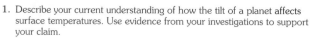

PF 87

PLANETARY FORECASTER

△ Guide and Assess

Have the students read through the *Stop and Think* questions and write down their answers. These questions should stimulate their thought processes and guide them as they use a *Create Your Explanation* page to write an explanation.

Monitor students' progress.

1. Students should describe how tilt affects temperature and support their claims using evidence from their investigations. Encourage students to draw pictures and use labels to help describe the concepts.

2. Students should describe how their claim has changed since the prediction they made in *Section 3.1*. They should include information from running their models, their analysis using data from *My World*, and from the reading in which they discussed the number of daylight hours and the seasons.

3. Students should describe their thought process and the changes that occurred since they began the *Learning Set*. Students have not yet written their revised explanations, but are about to.

4. Students should describe how, why, and how much tilt affects surface temperatures and they should support their claims with evidence and science knowledge. This is their explanation.

NOTES

Explain

10 min.

Students record their explanations and meet with their groups to discuss their explanations and construct a group explanation.

Explain

Use the *Create Your Explanation* page to rewrite the explanation on your own. Then share it with your group. Your group will then consider everyone's explanation and create a group explanation.

Communicate

Your class will meet to discuss the answers to these questions and the group explanations. Your class will also select or create a new class explanation. Remember that learning is a process, and this explanation is based on the information you have up to this point.

At latitudes north of the Arctic Circle and south of the Antarctic Circle, the Sun can remain visible for a continuous six-month period.

○ Get Going

Distribute a *Create Your Explanation* page to each student and ask students to record their explanation on it. Let students know how much time they have.

△ Guide

Let groups know that they will be meeting to share their explanations and to create a group explanation. Emphasize that they should begin by having each student present their responses to the questions and their explanation to the group. After everyone has presented, they should discuss the similarities and differences between their explanations. Where they have differences, they should look at the data supporting the parts of the explanations to help them determine what their best explanation will be.

⬡ Get Going

Distribute a *Create Your Explanation* page to each student and ask students to write Group Explanation on it. Let students know how much time they have.

△ Guide and Assess

Monitor groups and assist them as needed. Model appropriate language as needed.

TEACHER TALK

"I don't understand how the science knowledge backs up your explanation. Could you walk me through it?

I don't see how ... is supported by your data. Could you show me?

This statement doesn't make sense to me. Could you state it another way?

I'm not sure if I understand this. Do you mean: ... "

△ Guide

Let students know each group will be presenting their explanation. Emphasize that after each presentation, if anything was not clear, students should ask questions to the presenting group to make sure they understand the explanation and how the evidence and science knowledge supports the claim. When needed, model appropriate language.

Consider having the class point out the claim, the evidence, and the science knowledge if the presenting group is not getting many questions. Encourage the presenting group to answer the person asking the question.

After all groups have presented, guide the class to discussing the similarities and differences between all the explanations. Record the points the class agrees on. Discuss why differences arise and what the class thinks would be best to include in the explanation.

Have the class construct a class explanation. Once the class explanation is completed, distribute another *Create Your Explanation* page and have students record their class explanation, indicating on their pages that this is the class explanation.

Communicate
15 min.

Students have a class discussion on groups' explanations and then create a class explanation.

◇ Evaluate

The final class explanation should contain information about how a planet's tilt affects the amount of sunlight and the amount of time the sunlight shines on a location. A description of how the tilt causes one hemisphere of the planet to be closer to the Sun or further with results of more or less sunlight received. It should make a connection between how the sunlight transfers heat by radiation to the planet's surface and how more sunlight means a higher surface temperature.

Students' evidence should include their observations from models they ran which showed that the amount of time light shined on locations of Earth and the intensity of light varied if Earth's axis tilted toward or away from the Sun as it went around its orbit. Students should also include evidence from their analysis of data using *My World* and science knowledge presented throughout the *Learning Set*.

Students should understand that if there were no tilt, there would be no seasons. Some students should grasp the concept that if the tilt were more extreme, the change in seasons would be more dramatic.

An example of an explanation is shown below.

A planet's tilt affects the angle sunlight strikes the surface and the amount of time the sunlight shines on the surface. Earth's tilt is always pointed in the same direction and causes the Northern Hemisphere to lean towards the Sun in July, so it receives more direct solar energy over a longer amount of time during a day, making it warmer. This is summer. Since the Southern Hemisphere leans away from the Sun in July, it receives less energy for less amount of time each day. The Southern Hemisphere is colder in July and experiences winter during this time. When the Earth is on the other side of the Sun in January, the Southern Hemisphere is leaning towards the Sun and experiences more direct sunlight for longer amounts of time per day, and is experiencing summer. The Northern Hemisphere is tilted away from the Sun and receives less direct sunlight for shorter amounts of time each day and is experiencing winter.

This is supported by our observations. We observed this qualitatively in models we ran using a globe to represent Earth and a light source to represent the Sun. These showed how the amount of time light shined on locations of Earth and the intensity of light varied depending on Earth's axis tilt toward or away from the Sun as it went around its orbit. The hemisphere that tilted toward the Sun received more incoming light. The more incoming light there was, the greater the temperature. This was quantitatively supported by data from My World showing monthly average temperatures around the world and from the data table in the text showing average hours of daylight for each month at various locations.

3.5 *Revise Your Explanation*

Update the *Project Board*

You have now reviewed and revised your class explanation about how tilt affects surface temperatures.

Once again, you will focus on the two columns, *What are we learning?* and *What is our evidence?* When you record what you are learning in the third column, you will be answering a question or set of questions from the *What do we need to investigate?* column. You should describe your new knowledge from the investigation you just did. You should also provide evidence to support this knowledge.

As the class fills in the *Project Board*, make sure to record the same information on your own *Project Board* page.

Which regions of a newly discovered planet have surface temperatures appropriate for a human colony?				
What do we think we know?	What do we need to investigate?	What are we learning?	What is our evidence?	What does it mean for the challenge or question?

Update the *Project Board*
5 min.

The class updates their Project Boards.

META NOTES

Distribute *Project Board* pages as needed.

△ Guide

Review the *Project Board* with the class and ask if they would like to add or revise. Record students' responses.

Ask students what they would like to enter in Column 5: *What does it mean for the challenge or question?* Remind them that the challenge is to determine which regions of *Planet X* have appropriate temperatures for a human colony. Remind them that *Planet X* has the same tilt as Earth.

Students should include information about how tilt must be taken into account since it affects the range of temperatures a planet experiences and how it affects the temperature.

Teacher Reflection Questions

- What ideas did students add to their explanations and how did they support these ideas?

- How effective was the iterative process of revising their explanation?

- How did you keep students focused on the task and participating in the discussions?

NOTES

Back to the Big Challenge

Which Regions of a Newly Discovered Planet have Surface Temperatures Appropriate for a Human Colony?

◀ *1 class period*

A class period is considered to be one 40 to 50 minute class.

Overview

Groups construct their average monthly temperature prediction maps for *Planet X* for the months of January and July based on the knowledge that *Planet X* has the same tilt as Earth. They begin by copying and revising their previous average-yearly temperature prediction map for January and the month of July. Students share their predictions during a *Solution Briefing* to communicate their solutions to the rest of the class so that students can better understand how other people approached the problem.

Targeted Concepts, Skills, and Nature of Science	Performance Expectations
Scientists often work together and share their findings. Sharing findings makes new information available and helps scientists to refine their ideas and build on others' ideas. When another person's or group's idea is used, credit needs to be given.	Groups should work together to construct prediction maps for average monthly temperatures in January and July and a habitability map for *Planet X*. Groups should share their solutions with the class.
Scientists must keep clear, accurate, and descriptive records of what they do so they can share their work with others and consider what they did, why they did it, and what they want to do next.	Students should use records created during this Unit to construct their maps. During the *Solution Briefing*, students should take notes of other presentations on what they did and ideas on how they want to change their own prediction maps.

Targeted Concepts, Skills, and Nature of Science	Performance Expectations
Graphs, maps, and tables are an effective way to analyze and communicate results of scientific investigation.	Students should construct prediction maps of the average monthly temperatures for July and January for *Planet X*, and a habitability map based on these. These maps are used to convey students' ideas during the *Solution Briefing*.
Explanations are claims supported by evidence, accepted ideas and facts.	Students should discuss how the class explanation supports their maps.
Seasons experienced on Earth are caused by its rotation on a tilted axis. The tilt causes either the Northern or Southern Hemisphere to have more direct sunlight and an increase in the exposure time to the Sun, creating summer conditions. The other hemisphere receives less direct sunlight and less exposure time to the Sun and experiences winter.	Students should recognize that the seasons on *Planet X* will be like Earth's seasons since the planets have the same tilt and are the same distance from the Sun.

Materials

1 per classroom	Computer with *My World* software and projection system
1 per group	Computer with *My World* software
1 per student	*Solution-Briefing Notes* page *Project Board* page
1 per class	Class *Project Board*

Activity Setup and Preparation

Create a temperature prediction map for January and July and a prediction map showing regions of habitability prior to class. Use the instructions in the student text. Determine where your students may have difficulty and decide if you want to demonstrate to them how to do any of the steps.

If you do not have computers available, the students can complete this project by coloring printed copies of maps.

Decide how students will present their ideas during the *Solution Briefing*. You could have students present their ideas using a computer projection system, or they could use printouts that are projected.

Homework Options

Reflection

- **Science Content:** Why are data for January and July used to create the habitability map? *(Students' responses should include that the two months occur at a particularly cold and particularly warm period during the year. By ruling out temperatures that do not fit into both periods, it is more likely that the temperature range reflects that of the average year.)*

- **Science Content:** How has the exercise with *Planet X* gotten you closer to meeting the *Big Challenge?* *(Students should describe how they have found how tilt influences surface temperatures and made predictions based on this. However, they still need to determine how land/water differences, and surface elevation affect the planet's surface temperature.)*

Preparation for Learning Set 4

- **Science Process:** How do you think the land and water of a planet affects its surface temperatures? *(The purpose of this question is to elicit students' initial ideas and get them thinking about how land and water might affect a planet's surface temperature.)*

NOTES

◀ *1 class periods**

Learning Set 3

Back to the Big Challenge

Which regions of a newly discovered planet have appropriate surface temperatures for a human colony?

It is time for you to revise your prediction about habitable areas of *Planet X* based on what you have discovered about tilt. The *Planet X* temperature prediction that you have so far is an average over the whole year. *Planet X*'s axis is tilted at 23.5°, the same as Earth's axis. Temperatures vary throughout the year because of a planet's tilt. Modify your predictions to show how tilt affects surface temperatures on *Planet X* in January and July. You will then use these temperature predictions to revise your map of habitable areas on *Planet X*.

Procedure: Prepare the January Fields

1. **Open your *Planet X* project file in *My World*.** Select "Open Project" in the File drop-down menu.

2. **Show habitable and non-habitable areas.** In the "Visualize" tab, turn off the "Shape Habitability" selection by selecting the "All (highlighting off)" radio button in the *Planet X* layer. This will display your prediction for the whole planet, including both habitable and non-habitable areas.

3. **Duplicate the *Planet X* Temperature Field.**

   a) **Go to the "Edit" tab.** Double-click the *Planet X* layer to edit that layer. Be sure "Temperature Prediction" is selected from the Edit Field drop-down menu.

   b) **Click "Add Field..."** in the bottom right corner of the screen.

   c) **Select "Duplicate an Existing Field"** as shown on the next page.

   d) **Create a duplicate of "Temperature Prediction."** Name the new field "Tilt January." Click OK. You now have a new field to edit called "Tilt January."

PF 90

Learning Set 3

Back to the Big Challenge

< 5 min.

Review what students have done and introduce the section.

○ **Engage**

Engage students by having them consider what they would apply to construct an average July temperature prediction map for *Planet X*. Record students' responses.

❝If you were to make a prediction map of average July temperatures for *Planet X* what information would you use to help you?❞

*A class period is considered to be one 40 to 50 minute class.

Ask students if a July map would be sufficient or if they would need to consider any other months. Ask them to identify which ones and why.

TEACHER TALK

❝Would a July temperature map for *Planet X* be sufficient to determine the habitability of the planet or do we need to consider other months? Which months would need to be considered and why?❞

△ Guide

Briefly review what students have written in Columns 3 (*What are we learning?*), 4 (*What is our evidence?*), and 5 (*What does it mean for the challenge or question?*) of the class *Project Board*. Let students know they will be revising the temperature prediction maps they created after studying how shape affects surface temperature.

TEACHER TALK

❝Based on what is on your *Project Board* about tilt, you should update your previous surface temperature maps of *Planet X* which were based only on the shape of the planet. You are asked to construct a surface temperature prediction map for the months of January and July. Why are we picking January and July?

From these two maps, you will construct a habitability map for *Planet X.*❞

META NOTES

Students should apply what they know about Earth's tilt and temperature patterns to select the months of January and July as representatives for extreme temperatures in habitable regions.

Procedure: Prepare the January Fields

10 min.

Students create a January surface temperature map for Planet X.

Temperatures vary throughout the year because of a planet's tilt. Modify your predictions to show how tilt affects surface temperatures on *Planet X* in January and July. You will then use these temperature predictions to revise your map of habitable areas on *Planet X*.

Procedure: Prepare the January Fields

1. **Open your *Planet X* project file in *My World*.** Select "Open Project" in the File drop-down menu.

2. **Show habitable and non-habitable areas.** In the "Visualize" tab, turn off the "Shape Habitability" selection by selecting the "All (highlighting off)" radio button in the *Planet X* layer. This will display your prediction for the whole planet, including both habitable and non-habitable areas.

3. **Duplicate the *Planet X* Temperature Field.**

   a) **Go to the "Edit" tab.** Double-click the *Planet X* layer to edit that layer. Be sure "Temperature Prediction" is selected from the Edit Field drop-down menu.

   b) **Click "Add Field..."** in the bottom right corner of the screen.

   c) **Select "Duplicate an Existing Field"** as shown on the next page.

   d) **Create a duplicate of "Temperature Prediction."** Name the new field "Tilt January." Click OK. You now have a new field to edit called "Tilt January."

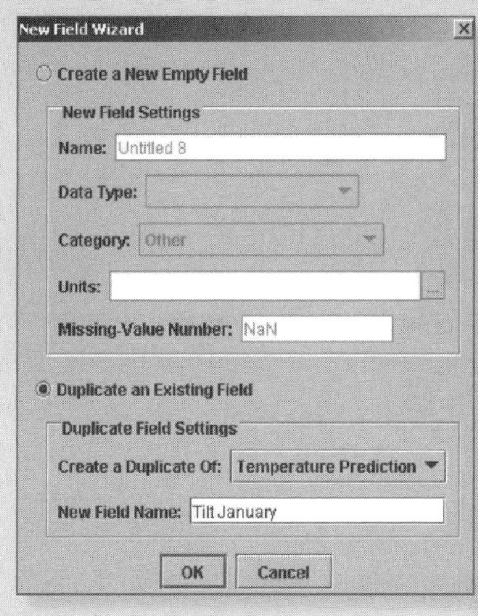

4. **Paint the *Planet X* temperature map for January.** While still in the "Edit" tab, select the *Planet X* layer to open the paintbrush tools. Under the Edit Field drop-down menu, be sure you have selected "Tilt January." Use the paintbrush tools to change the map to show your prediction for what temperatures will be like in January on *Planet X*.

5. **Save your changes.** Select "Save Project" in the File menu.

6. **Record your observations.** Describe changes you made to your *Planet X* prediction map to represent surface temperatures in January.

Procedure: Prepare the July Fields

1. **Open your *Planet X* project file in *My World*.** Select "Open Project" in the File drop-down menu. If you have not closed your project file after creating the "Tilt January" field, simply change the edit field to "Temperature Prediction."

2. **Show habitable and non-habitable areas.** In the "Visualize" tab, turn off the "Shape Habitability" selection by selecting the "All (highlighting off)" radio button in the *Planet X* layer. This will display your prediction for the whole planet, including both habitable and non-habitable areas.

3. **Duplicate the Planet X Temperature Field.**

   a) **Go to the "Edit" tab.** Double-click the *Planet X* layer to edit that layer. Be sure "Temperature Prediction" is selected from the Edit Field drop-down menu.

   b) **Click "Add Field …"** in the bottom right corner of the screen.

   c) **Select "Duplicate an Existing Field"** as shown above.

New Field Wizard

○ Create a New Empty Field

New Field Settings
Name: Untitled 8
Data Type:
Category: Other
Units:
Missing-Value Number: NaN

● Duplicate an Existing Field

Duplicate Field Settings
Create a Duplicate Of: Temperature Prediction
New Field Name: Tilt January

OK   Cancel

META NOTES

If you do not have computers available, the students can complete this project by coloring printed copies of maps of *Planet X*.

△ Guide

Use the procedures described in the student text to demonstrate for students how to complete Steps 1 and 2.

Once you have brought students to the Visualize tab, show students how to duplicate and rename the file by demonstrating Step 3. After following the procedures for Step 3, your screen should look like the one on the next page.

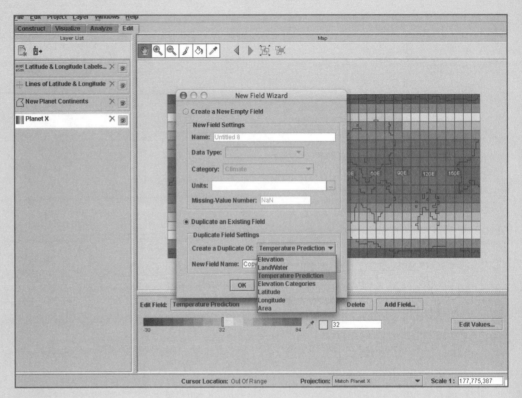

Students should call the new field Tilt January. This is not a new file, but a new file in an old file. When students have added their January and July temperature fields the fields available to them in their file will look like that shown below.

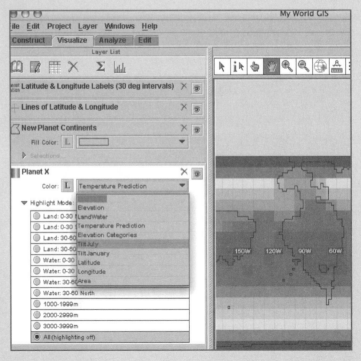

Then briefly remind students how to change the color and save their data as described in Steps 4 and 5.

Emphasize to students that they should record their observations in Step 6.

Let students know that the next procedure follows the same steps as those that were demonstrated. Once they have finished their January fields, they should continue on with their July fields.

Emphasize that they will need to record their observations, describing any changes they made to their map.

○ Get Going

Students should use the same computer they previously used if their files are stored on the computer. Let groups know how much time they have.

△ Guide and Assess

Monitor students' progress. Check each group to assure that they understand and are following the procedures. Check that all members of the group are participating and guide groups as needed. Make sure students are recording the changes they make.

As groups complete their January temperature maps have them continue on to complete their July temperature maps and let them know how much time they will have.

META NOTES

It is important that students are monitored early on to assure that they understand the procedure.

NOTES

Procedure: Prepare the July Fields

10 min.

Students create field average surface temperature maps for July for Planet X.

changes you made to your *Planet X* prediction map to represent surface temperatures in January.

| Create a Duplicate Of: | Temperature Prediction ▼ |
| New Field Name: | Tilt January |

OK   Cancel

Procedure: Prepare the July Fields

1. **Open your *Planet X* project file in *My World*.** Select "Open Project" in the File drop-down menu. If you have not closed your project file after creating the "Tilt January" field, simply change the edit field to "Temperature Prediction."

2. **Show habitable and non-habitable areas.** In the "Visualize" tab, turn off the "Shape Habitability" selection by selecting the "All (highlighting off)" radio button in the *Planet X* layer. This will display your prediction for the whole planet, including both habitable and non-habitable areas.

3. **Duplicate the Planet X Temperature Field.**

   a) **Go to the "Edit" tab.** Double-click the *Planet X* layer to edit that layer. Be sure "Temperature Prediction" is selected from the Edit Field drop-down menu.

   b) **Click "Add Field ..."** in the bottom right corner of the screen.

   c) **Select "Duplicate an Existing Field"** as shown above.

PF 91

PLANETARY FORECASTER

△ Guide and Assess

As students begin creating their maps for the average surface temperature of July, assist them as needed with the procedures. Remind them that the name of the map should be called Tilt July.

Check that all members of the group are participating and guide groups as needed. Make sure students are recording the changes they make.

NOTES

PBIS *Learning Set 3 • How Does a Planet's Tilt Affect Surface Temperatures?*

d) **Create a duplicate of "Temperature Prediction."** Name the new field "Tilt July." Click OK. You now have a new field to edit called "Tilt July."

4. **Paint the *Planet X* temperature map for July.** While still in the "Edit" tab, select the *Planet X* layer to open the paintbrush tools, if not done already. Under the Edit Field drop-down menu, be sure you have selected "Tilt July." Use the paintbrush tools to change the map to show your prediction for what the temperatures will be like in July on *Planet X*.

5. **Save your changes.** Select "Save Project" in the File menu.

6. **Record your observations.** Describe the changes you made to your *Planet X* prediction map to represent surface temperatures in July.

Habitable Areas of *Planet X*

You have created (and saved) a January and a July prediction map for *Planet X*. Some places may be habitable in July but not in January. The Cooperative Space Agency wants to know the places on *Planet X* that are habitable all year. Use the January and July temperature-prediction maps to create a new habitability map.

Procedure: Create a habitability map

1. **Open your *Planet X* project file in *My World*.** Select "Open Project" in the File drop-down menu. This project file may already be open after creating the Tilt January and July fields.

2. **Identify ranges for areas that are habitable in both January and July.**

   a) **Go to the Analyze tab.** Go to the "Select" folder and click on "By Value."

   b) **Under the "Select Records From:" drop-down menu, choose *Planet X*.**

   c) **Under the "Whose" drop-down menu, choose "Tilt July."** Check "Less Than" and enter 85. Check "Greater Than or Equal to" and enter 25.

Habitable Areas of Planet X

5 min.

Demonstrate for students how to construct a habitability map.

Procedure: Create a habitability map

5 min.

Students create their habitability maps.

△ Guide

Remind students that the *CSA* is interested in the habitable regions of *Planet X*, which are determined by regions that are between 25°F and 85°F.

△ Guide

Demonstrate for students how to construct their habitability map using the steps given in the procedure. Use the student text to check that you have followed the instructions correctly.

d) **Click the button marked with a small plus sign** to the right of the screen. This will allow you to add a second set of requirements for your selection.

e) **Under the second "Whose" drop-down menu, choose "Tilt January."** Check "Less Than" and enter 85. Check "Greater Than or Equal to" and enter 25.

f) **Under "Result Name," type in the title "Tilt Habitability."** *Do **not** check the box called "Make Selection a New Layer."*

g) **After you have filled out the page to select by value, click OK.**

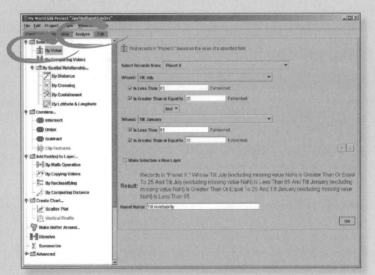

3. **Show habitable areas.** Go to the "Visualize" tab to observe the selection titled "Tilt Habitability." In this selection, places where you predicted the temperature to be too hot (above 85°F) or too cold (below 25°F) to be habitable in either January or July have been hidden.

PLANETARY FORECASTER

Once OK is selected, *My World* should automatically show the tilt habitability. If it does not, follow Step 3 and 4 as needed. The window should look like the one below.

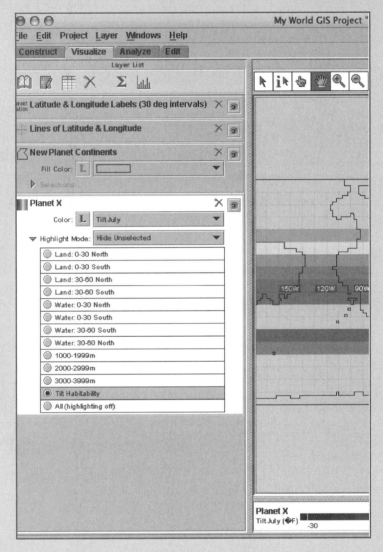

Remind students to save their work, and then let them begin.

○ Get Going
Let students know how much time they have and let them begin.

△ Guide and Assess
Monitor groups. Check that they understand the procedures and that all group members are participating.

Remind students to save their work.

Communicate Your Solution *Solution Briefing*

15 min.

Students have a class discussion on groups' ideas on temperature predictions and habitability for Planet X.

4. **You may have to modify your visualization screen to see your selection.**

   a) **In the Layer list, click on the "Planet X" layer.** In the bottom left corner, find the small arrow and be sure this arrow is pointing down. If the arrow is pointing to the right, click on it to turn it. Under "Highlight Mode," select "Hide Unselected."

   b) **Select the "Tilt Habitability" radio button** to view only the areas that you have predicted will be habitable.

5. **Save your solution.** Select "Save Project" in the File drop-down menu. Remember that this will be the project you use throughout your investigations about *Planet X*.

Communicate Your Solution

Solution Briefing

After everyone has developed their maps of *Planet X*, some of you will present your ideas to the class in a *Solution Briefing*.

Your *Solution Briefing* should focus on these points:

- Present the general look of your solution. Point out where the temperature differences are that appear on your map.

- Tell others how the data you collected and science concepts from this *Learning Set* support your decisions about habitability on *Planet X*.

- Discuss how the class explanation of "shape" supports the solution you have developed so far. If your decisions purposely do not match the explanation, tell your audience why this is so.

As you listen, it will be important to carefully look at each map that is presented. You should ask questions about how the decisions on each map match up with the ideas and knowledge from this *Learning Set*. Be prepared to ask and answer questions such as these:

- As the map was being developed, what changes did you make that we do not see in the final map?

- How well does the map match the explanation developed by the class as to how tilt affects surface temperatures?

△ Guide

Remind students that the goal of a *Solution Briefing* is for everyone to hear how other students approached the challenge and to see a variety of solutions that might work.

- Are there areas that do not seem to match the explanation?
- Which areas were difficult to choose? Which areas were easy to choose?
- Are there any changes you might want to make on your map at this time? If so, why?

Be sure to fill out a *Solution Briefing* page as you listen to everyone's presentation.

What's the Point?

You have just used your knowledge about tilt to improve your original proposal to the Cooperative Space Agency. There are probably some areas you thought were habitable that you now know are not. There may also be areas that you originally thought were not habitable but that actually are. As you investigate the other factors that affect surface temperature, you will continue to update your habitability predictions. Scientists do this all the time.

You have finished studying two of the four major factors that affect surface temperature. You still have to study the differences between land and water, and the effects of elevation. Your predictions for the habitable areas of *Planet X* will probably change as you investigate these factors in the next *Learning Sets*.

Snow melting in the Tundra in summer.

PF 95

PLANETARY FORECASTER

Emphasize to the class that they will need to address each of the three bullets listed in the student text and that as they listen to other groups present they will need to be able to answer each of the bulleted questions below. Remind students that they will be taking notes using the *Solution-Briefing Notes* page as they listen to presentations.

Point out to the class that as they listen they will need to look at each map and consider if the maps fit with what they understand about how a planet's tilt affects temperature. Emphasize to the class they should be prepared to ask and answer the five bulleted items in the student text.

META NOTES

Students will need a way to project their maps (either a projection of an electronic version or a printed copy.)

⬭ Get Going

Distribute the *Solution-Briefing Notes* page and let groups know how much time they have to prepare their presentations and how much time they have for their presentations.

△ Guide and Assess

Have groups present. As each group is presenting, check that they have addressed the three bulleted points listed in the student text.

After each presentation, encourage students to ask questions if anything was not clear or if one of the bulleted items was not addressed. Students should ask the suggested questions listed in the student text and/or other questions they may have.

Remind students to take notes as they are listening to the presentation and the responses to questions.

After each group has presented discuss the similarities and differences between groups' ideas.

Teacher Reflection Questions

- What difficulties did students have in applying the information in this *Learning Set* to their temperature prediction maps for *Planet X?*

- How did the *Solution Briefing* help students' understanding of the challenge?

- What went well during the *Solution Briefing?* What would you like to do differently next time?

LEARNING SET 4 INTRODUCTION

Learning Set 4

How Do Land and Water Affect Surface Temperatures?

◀ $8\frac{1}{2}$ *class periods*

A class period is considered to be one 40 to 50 minute class.

Students explore how land and water differences affect surface temperature by investigating factors that affect how much heat energy is transferred to different materials and analyzing Earth's surface temperature data using My World.

Overview

Students investigate how land and water affect surface temperature. Students begin by considering the differences between how warm or cool materials feel in their everyday experiences. Students investigate the time it takes water and sand to warm up and to cool down. From their observations and analysis, students conclude that different materials have different rates of warming and cooling. Students then read about the specific heat capacity and how the absorption or reflection of sunlight affect the overall heat transferred from the Sun. With this information, students construct their first explanation of how land and water differences affect surface temperature. Students predict how land and water temperatures vary for different latitudes around Earth. Quantitative evidence is provided when students analyze data from *My World* of how Earth's temperatures over land and sea vary. Students revise their explanations of how land and water differences affect surface temperature. Students then modify their temperature prediction and habitability maps of *Planet X* and share their ideas with the class during a *Solution Briefing*.

Targeted Concepts, Skills, and Nature of Science	Section
Scientists often work together and share their findings. Sharing findings makes new information available and helps scientists to refine their ideas and build on others' ideas. When another person's or group's idea is used, credit needs to be given.	4.1, 4.2, 4.3, 4.5, BBC

Targeted Concepts, Skills, and Nature of Science	Section
Scientists must keep clear, accurate, and descriptive records of what they do so they can share their work with others and consider what they did, why they did it, and what they want to do next.	4.1, 4.2, 4.3, 4.4, 4.5, BBC
Graphs, maps, and tables are an effective way to analyze and communicate results of scientific investigation.	4.2, 4.4, 4.5, BBC
Identifying factors that lead to variation is an important part of scientific investigation.	4.1, 4.2
Scientists make claims (conclusions) based on evidence obtained (trends in data) from reliable investigations	4.2, 4.4, 4.5
Explanations are claims supported by evidence, accepted ideas and facts.	4.3, 4.5, BBC
Heat energy may be transferred through conduction, radiation, or convection.	4.2
Temperatures around Earth's surface vary widely, but can be predicted somewhat by location and season.	4.4
Different substances (such as soil and water) transfer heat energy at different rates and require different amounts of energy to raise their temperatures. The amount of energy needed to raise the temperature of a substance is described by its specific heat capacity.	4.2, 4.3, BBC

Students' Initial Conceptions and Capabilities

In studies of student learning about Earth Science topics, students have several recurring misconceptions about the relative temperatures of water and land, and heat transfer. Below are common misconceptions and concerns that should be addressed as they arise.

- Water is always colder than land. Students often believe this is true because they have seen water freeze and become ice, while the land appears the same as it gets colder.

- Land is always colder than water.

- When land is near water students may believe that the land or the water is warmer because sunlight bounces off one surface to heat the other.

Students' Initial Conceptions and Capabilities	• Students may not realize that in an investigation of temperature change, it is important to keep the mass of materials heated the same. This variable must be controlled in order to validate the data. • Students may not realize that the transfer of heat is not spontaneous (Kesidou, 1990; Wiser, 1986). • Students may still have difficulty distinguishing between heat and temperature (Kesidou & Duit, 1993; Tiberghien, 1983; Wiser, 1988). • Students may think that some substances cannot heat up (Tiberghien, 1985), and others get warm quickly because they attract heat, suck heat in, or hold heat well (Erickson, 1985).

Understanding for Teachers

This *Learning Set* focuses on how differences between land and water affect temperature. Specific heat capacity and absorption of electromagnetic radiation are two important factors that affect how heat energy is transferred to or away from an object.

Specific Heat Capacity

The amount of energy needed to increase the temperature of one gram of substance by 1°C is called the specific heat capacity of the substance.

Absorption, Reflection, and Transmission

When the Sun's light (electromagnetic waves) shines on a substance, it can absorb, reflect, or transmit some of the radiation. For a substance to absorb radiation, the electromagnetic wave must be at the right frequency. This frequency is called the natural frequency or resonances of the atom/molecule. Consider using an example of swinging on a swing. If you pump your legs at the wrong time (with the wrong frequency) then the swing will not go higher. The process here is similar. When the frequency is just right, the atom/molecule can absorb the incoming radiation and it can cause the atoms/molecules to move more, increasing their average kinetic energy and temperature. This is what happens when heat is transferred by radiation. This energy can then be transferred between atoms/molecules during collisions.

Reflection occurs when the incoming light bounces off the surface of the substance. The incoming light is not at the right frequency of the atoms/molecules. Like pumping your legs at the wrong time, the incoming radiation vibrates the atoms/molecules briefly but does not increase the amplitudes of their vibrations. The light is re-emitted outward or bounces off as a reflected light wave.

Transmission occurs when incoming light is not near natural frequencies of the atoms/molecules making up the substance and goes through the substance without disturbing it. The light is transferred from one atom/molecule to another through the substance.

Water can be very reflective and very absorptive due to its changing surface from waves and other properties. The amount of light water reflects is very dependent on the angle of the incoming light. For incoming light that is nearly skimming the surface, such as during sunrise or sunset, very little light is absorbed. Incoming light more perpendicular to the surface, such as at around noon time, is mostly absorbed.

Albedo

Albedo is a term often used and means the amount of light reflected off a surface, typically a planet or moon or a part of a planets' surface such as its oceans.

Latent heat

When a substance is changing phase, it absorbs or releases more energy than the specific heat that defines it.

At low temperatures, the phase difference between liquid water and solid land contributes to the dramatic difference in temperature. This difference in phase causes the temperature differences closer to the poles to be significantly greater than the temperature differences closer to the Equator, particularly during the winter season. For example, the Gulf of Alaska remains in the high 30°s (-1.1°C) and low 40°s (4.4°C) during the winter months while the surrounding land masses in Alaska and Canada drop far below 0°F.

Learning Set 4

How Do Land and Water Affect Surface Temperatures?

Based on your experience, which of the two slides in the pictures, metal or plastic, would you rather go down on a very hot day?

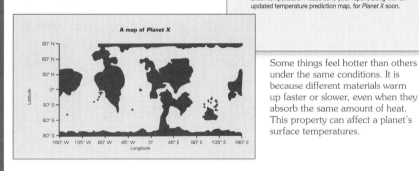

A map of *Planet X*

Some things feel hotter than others under the same conditions. It is because different materials warm up faster or slower, even when they absorb the same amount of heat. This property can affect a planet's surface temperatures.

Project-Based Inquiry Science

PF 96

Learning Set 4

How Do Land and Water Affect Surface Temperatures?

5 min.

Introduce the Learning Set *to the class.*

◯ Engage

Introduce the *CSA* bulletin and elicit students' initial ideas about land water differences and how they might affect temperature. Record students' ideas.

*A class period is considered to be one 40 to 50 minute class.

TEACHER TALK

"This *Learning Set* focuses on land water differences and how they affect surface temperature. The *CSA* has sent another bulletin showing a map of the continents and oceans of *Planet X* and has determined that the soil is similar to Earth.

How do you think land and water might affect surface temperature and why?"

After listing students' ideas about land and water, ask them to look in the student text at the images of the slides and elicit their ideas about which slide they would want to use on a hot day and why. Record their ideas for the plastic slide and the metal slide.

Ask them which feels warmer, walking on tile or walking on wood.

△ Guide

Introduce the idea of the rate at which heat energy is transferred.

TEACHER TALK

"Some things feel warmer than other things under the same conditions, even if they are the same temperature (such as a tile floor versus a wood floor). This is because different materials warm up faster or slower, even when they absorb the same amount of heat energy transferred to them. For example, metal warms up faster than plastic or wood and it cools down faster too. If you touch a piece of metal at room temperature and a piece of wood at room temperature, the metal feels cooler. This is because it absorbs the heat energy transferred to it from your hand at a faster rate.

The fact that different materials absorb and transfer heat energy at different rates can affect a planet's surface temperature."

SECTION 4.1 INTRODUCTION

4.1 Understand the Challenge

Predicting the Effects of Land and Water on Surface Temperatures

◀ $\frac{1}{2}$ *class period*

A class period is considered to be one 40 to 50 minute class.

Overview

Students consider some common ideas about how land and water might affect surface temperature and have a discussion about these ideas. Students predict how they think land and water can influence surface temperature and share their ideas with the class. The class updates their *Project Board,* recording what they think they know and what they need to investigate.

Targeted Concepts, Skills, and Nature of Science	Performance Expectations
Scientists often work together and share their findings. Sharing findings makes new information available and helps scientists to refine their ideas and build on others' ideas. When another person's or group's idea is used, credit needs to be given.	Students should share their predictions about how land and water can influence temperature on a planet. The class should discuss what they think they know and what they need to investigate.
Scientists must keep clear, accurate, and descriptive records of what they do so they can share their work with others and consider what they did, why they did it, and what they want to do next.	The class should update their *Project Board,* recording what they think they know and what they need to investigate.
Identifying factors that lead to variation is an important part of scientific investigation.	Students should consider what factors they think they should investigate to see how land and water differences affect surface temperature.

Materials	
1 per classroom	Optional - projection of the *CSA* bulletin

Materials	
1 per class	Class *Project Board*
1 per student	*Project Board* page

Homework Options

Reflection

- **Science Content & Process:** Write an experiment to test one of the investigative questions listed in the class *Project Board*. *(Students should create the process of the experiment, explain expected results, and describe one or more experiences in which they noticed temperature differences.)*

Preparation for 3.2

- **Science Content:** Do you think locations on the coast are warmer or cooler than locations inland? Why? Is this true for all times of the year? *(The purpose of this is to get students to apply their initial ideas about land and water differences and prepare them for the next section.)*

SECTION 4.1 IMPLEMENTATION

◀ $\frac{1}{2}$ *class period**

4.1 Understand the Challenge

Predicting the Effects of Land and Water on Surface Temperatures

To predict the temperatures on *Planet X*, you will need to have a very good understanding of how and why different substances warm up differently. You will be conducting an investigation to help you explore this. However, you can begin by thinking about your own experiences. Have you ever been to the beach on a hot day and walked barefoot in the sand? The sand can get so hot that you run into the water to cool off your feet! The same thing happens when you walk in bare feet on an asphalt driveway. All you want to do is run for the grass. But why do the water and the grass feel cooler than the sand or the asphalt? How does this affect temperatures on Earth's surface? This is the challenge before you.

Get Started

Below are some student ideas about how land and water differences might affect surface temperatures. As you are reading, think about each student's idea. Compare their ideas to your own.

Rashad: "I do not think that land and water make a difference. The Sun hits all surfaces the same. The differences in temperature are caused by something else."

Katy: "I think the land and water on Earth's surface do matter. Earth is made of different substances, and each will react differently to the Sun's solar energy."

Camille: "I think land and water will be different. Water is clear, so it will warm up easier than trees, plants, and rocks."

Spencer: "The land and water will both heat up the same as long as they are at the same latitude, just as we have learned so far."

Have you ever walked barefoot on the sand on a hot day?

PF 97

PLANETARY FORECASTER

4.1 Understand the Challenge

Predicting the Effects of Land and Water on Surface Temperatures
5 min.

Students start to make predictions for Planet X *and update the* Project Board *with their ideas.*

○ Engage

Ask students to imagine a hot summer day at the beach or in an area with paved surfaces and grass. Ask students to describe the beach scene in terms of how their bare feet feel in the sand and the water. Ask them how grass or pavement feel in this weather.

Let students know they will need to consider these things as they investigate how the land and water differences affect surface temperatures.

*A class period is considered to be one 40 to 50 minute class.

your feet. ~~~ning happens when you
bare feet on an asphalt driveway. All you want to do is
run for the grass. But why do the water and the grass
feel cooler than the sand or the asphalt? How does
this affect temperatures on Earth's surface? This is the
challenge before you.

Get Started

Below are some student ideas about how land and
water differences might affect surface temperatures.
As you are reading, think about each student's idea.
Compare their ideas to your own.

Rashad: "I do not think that land and water make a
difference. The Sun hits all surfaces the same. The
differences in temperature are caused by something
else."

Katy: "I think the land and water on Earth's surface do
matter. Earth is made of different substances, and each
will react differently to the Sun's solar energy."

Camille: "I think land and water will be different. Water is clear, so it will
warm up easier than trees, plants, and rocks."

Spencer: "The land and water will both heat up the same as long as they
are at the same latitude, just as we have learned so far."

*Have you ever walked
barefoot on the sand
on a hot day?*

PF 97

PLANETARY FORECASTER

Get Started

10 min.

*Students have
a discussion on
their ideas.*

⬡ Get Going

Ask the class to read through each of the four ideas provided in the student
text and to consider their own.

△ Guide

Begin a class discussion eliciting students' thoughts on each statement and
their reasoning. Encourage students by asking them what they agreed with,
what they disagreed with, and how they might correct the statement or
change it.

Predict

Record your prediction about how land and water can influence temperatures on a planet. Based on what you know so far, how sure are you about this prediction?

Update the *Project Board*

As your class shares their predictions, your teacher will help you update the *Project Board*. From your discussion, you may have new questions or new ideas about how land and water might influence the temperatures of a planet. Record these ideas, predictions, and reasons in the column *What do we think we know?* Record questions under *What do we need to investigate?*

Which regions of a newly discovered planet have surface temperatures appropriate for a human colony?				
What do we think we know?	What do we need to investigate?	What are we learning?	What is our evidence?	What does it mean for the challenge or question?

What's the Point?

You and your classmates probably have a lot of ideas about how land and water might affect the temperatures of *Planet X*. Some of you may have some experience or knowledge of how different substances warm up differently. Your initial prediction should help you become aware of how much you do know and how much you need to learn. Sharing your ideas and questions on the *Project Board* helps everyone understand what to focus on as you investigate the differences in how land and water warm up.

Predict

5 min.

Students make predictions about how the land and water surfaces affect temperatures.

⬡ Get Going

Ask the students to record their predictions about how land and water can influence temperatures on a planet. They will need to keep these predictions handy so they can refer to them at the end of the *Learning Set*.

△ Guide

Ask students to share their predictions. Let students know they will be conducting an investigation over the next several days. At the end of their investigation, they will revise their predictions based on what they learn.

Update the *Project Board*

5 min.

Have the class update their Project Boards *with any new questions and knowledge.*

Record your prediction about how land and water can influence temperatures on a planet. Based on what you know so far, how sure are you about this prediction?

Update the *Project Board*

As your class shares their predictions, your teacher will help you update the *Project Board*. From your discussion, you may have new questions or new ideas about how land and water might influence the temperatures of a planet. Record these ideas, predictions, and reasons in the column *What do we think we know?* Record questions under *What do we need to investigate?*

Which regions of a newly discovered planet have surface temperatures appropriate for a human colony?				
What do we think we know?	What do we need to investigate?	What are we learning?	What is our evidence?	What does it mean for the challenge or question?

What's the Point?

You and your classmates probably have a lot of ideas about how land and water might affect the temperatures of *Planet X*. Some of you may have some experience or knowledge of how different substances warm up differently. Your initial prediction should help you become aware of how much you do know and how much you need to learn. Sharing your ideas and questions on the *Project Board* helps everyone understand what to

△ Guide

Ask students what they think they know about land and water differences and how these differences might affect the temperature of a planet. Record students' responses in the first column of the class *Project Board*.

Review predictions and what they would like to investigate further with the class. Ask what they would like you to record in Column 2 (*What do we need to investigate?*) of their class *Project Board*. Record students' investigative questions and remind them that these are the questions they will need to answer to help make their prediction map for *Planet X*.

Teacher Reflection Questions

- Did students' questions to investigate correlate well with their predictions? How varied were students' predictions.

- How did the four ideas presented in the student text impact students' predictions?

- How did you encourage students to participate in class discussions?

SECTION 4.2 INTRODUCTION

4.2 Investigate

Heating and Cooling of Land and Water

◀ **2 class periods**

A class period is considered to be one 40 to 50 minute class.

Overview

Students investigate the rate at which heat energy is received and transferred from sand and water. Students measure the temperature of identical masses of sand and water every three minutes for twelve minutes while they are warmed. Then students measure the temperature of these substances every three minutes for twelve minutes as the substances cool down. Students graph and analyze their data. Students determine how the coastal water and land temperatures compare for the Northern and Southern Hemisphere in June. Groups prepare posters and share their results with the class in an *Investigation Expo*.

Targeted Concepts, Skills, and Nature of Science	Performance Expectations
Scientists often work together and share their findings. Sharing findings makes new information available and helps scientists to refine their ideas and build on others' ideas. When another person's or group's idea is used, credit needs to be given.	Students should work in groups to measure the rate at which sand and water change temperature. Students should analyze the results, consider what the results imply for land and water temperatures on Earth, and discuss their ideas. Groups should then share their results with the class.
Scientists must keep clear, accurate, and descriptive records of what they do so they can share their work with others and consider what they did, why they did it, and what they want to do next.	Students should keep records of their measurements and analysis to share with others and to refer to in later sections.
Graphs, maps, and tables are an effective way to analyze and communicate results of scientific investigation.	Students should construct a table and graph of their data to use when presenting their results.

305

Targeted Concepts, Skills, and Nature of Science	Performance Expectations
Identifying factors that lead to variation is an important part of scientific investigation.	Students should identify material type (e.g. land and water) as a factor that affects surface temperatures of a planet.
Scientists make claims (conclusions) based on evidence obtained (trends in data) from reliable investigations	Students should make claims based on their measurements and analysis of how material type affects the rate at which heat is transferred to or from a material and how this causes differences in planet temperatures.
Heat energy may be transferred through conduction, radiation, or convection.	Students should describe the heat energy transferred from the lamp to the sand and water primarily through radiation and conduction.
Different substances (such as soil and water) transfer heat energy at different rates and require different amounts of energy to raise their temperatures. The amount of energy needed to raise the temperature of a substance is described by its specific heat capacity.	Students should observe that sand and water change temperatures at different rates.

Materials

1 per group	Metric ruler
	Lamp with 25 W heat lamp bulb
	Stand and clamp
	Cup stand
	Fine, dry sand, 200 g
	Water, 200 g
	Tape or modeling clay
2 per group	Clear plastic cups
	Plastic lids with holes in the center
	Black paper liners for lids
	Thermometers

306

Materials	
1 per class or group	Clock with second hand
1 per class	Scale for measuring sand and water
1 per student	*Land and Water Temperature Data* page

Activity Setup and Preparation

Conduct the experiment prior to class to see where your students may have difficulties. Have a set of equipment ready to demonstrate to students the setup. Make sure to weigh out equal amounts of soil and water and allow them to reach room temperature before students begin the lab.

Pair samples together with similarly calibrated thermometers. For example, if two thermometers read too high, try to put those two thermometers together in a pair of soil and water samples.

Homework Options

Reflection

- **Science Process:** Why is it important to use samples that have the same mass or weight when measuring temperature changes? *(Students should understand that using samples with different masses might cause temperature differences since it takes more heat energy to heat a larger sample. They should recognize that this would not be not a fair test for the experiment.)*

- **Science Content:** How is the rate of heating or cooling represented on a graph? *(Students should describe how the rate of heating or cooling is represented by the slope of the line. A steep line represents rapid heating or cooling, while a flat line represents slow change.)*

Preparation for 4.3

- **Science Content:** From the experiment you conducted, you observed that some materials warm up faster than others. What do think causes this? *(The purpose of this is to elicit students' initial ideas.)*

NOTES

4.2 Investigate

Heating and Cooling of Land and Water

In this investigation, you and your group will take temperature measurements of land (sand) and water as they are exposed to heat and as they cool. You will answer the following questions:

- Which material heats faster, and which heats more slowly?
- Which material cools faster, and which cools more slowly?

Predict

Predictions are sometimes written as "If …then…" statements. Complete these "If…then…" statements.

- If a sample of sand and water receive the same amount of incoming heat energy, then sand will heat up (*faster or slower*) than water.
- If the source of energy is removed, then the sand will cool (*faster or slower*) than water.

Record your predictions on the *Land & Water Temperature Data* page.

Procedure

1. Label the two cups *water* and *sand*.
   - Measure and carefully pour 200 g of water into one cup.
   - Measure and place 200 g of sand into the second cup.
2. Place a lid with a black liner on each cup.
3. Carefully push a thermometer through the hole in each lid. The bulb of the thermometer should be placed so that the red near the bulb is just covered by the sand or the water. Secure the thermometer in place with tape or modeling clay.

Materials
- lamp with 250-W heat lamp bulb
- stand and clamp
- 2 clear plastic cups
- 2 plastic lids with holes in center
- 2 black paper liners for lids
- cup stand (optional)
- 200 g fine, dry sand
- 200 g water
- 2 thermometers
- tape or modeling clay
- clock with second hand
- scale for measuring sand and water

PF 99

PLANETARY FORECASTER

4.2 Investigate

Heating and Cooling of Land and Water

< 5 min.

Students conduct an investigation into the effects of land and water temperature on surface temperatures.

○ Engage

Let students know they will be conducting an experiment in which they investigate equal masses of sand and water and how their temperature changes over time. Show them the setup they will be using and ask if they think the sand or water will heat up or cool down differently.

*A class period is considered to be one 40 to 50 minute class.

Predict

< 5 min.

Students record their predictions.

measure ...., and water as .... to heat
and as they cool. You will answer the following questions:

- Which material heats faster, and which heats more slowly?
- Which material cools faster, and which cools more slowly?

Predict

Predictions are sometimes written as "If ...then..." statements.
Complete these "If...then..." statements.

- If a sample of sand and water receive the same amount of incoming heat energy, then sand will heat up (*faster or slower*) than water.
- If the source of energy is removed, then the sand will cool (*faster or slower*) than water.

Record your predictions on the *Land & Water Temperature Data* page.

Procedure

- lamp with 250-W heat lamp bulb
- stand and clamp
- 2 clear plastic cups
- 2 plastic lids with holes in center
- 2 black paper liners for lids
- cup stand (optional)
- 200 g fine, dry sand
- 200 g water
- 2 thermometers
- tape or

△ Guide

Let students know they should record their predictions on the Land and *Water Temperature Data* page. Let them know that if they think the sand and water will cool at the same rate, they should put "at the same rate" in their prediction.

................, than water.

Record your predictions on the *Land & Water Temperature Data* page.

Procedure

1. Label the two cups *water* and *sand*.

   - Measure and carefully pour 200 g of water into one cup.
   - Measure and place 200 g of sand into the second cup.

2. Place a lid with a black liner on each cup.

3. Carefully push a thermometer through the hole in each lid. The bulb of the thermometer should be placed so that the red near the bulb is just covered by the sand or the water. Secure the thermometer in place with tape or modeling clay.

...sand

- 200 g water
- 2 thermometers
- tape or modeling clay
- clock with second hand
- scale for measuring sand and water

Procedure

35 min.

Students run the experiment.

△ Guide

Discuss the setup and procedures with the students. Emphasize that the mass of water is the same as the mass of sand. Ask why. Students should describe it as a variable that should be controlled to make the experiment a fair test. If needed, discuss fair tests with students.

Ask students why the black liner is placed on the lids. Record students' responses. Ask students how it feels on a sunny day when they are wearing a black shirt or a white shirt. Students should describe how the black shirt makes them feel warmer.

Describe how heat is transferred in this system.

"Dark colors absorb more light energy than lighter colors. That is why you feel warmer wearing a black shirt rather than a white shirt on a sunny day. The heat lamp is modeling the Sun and is emitting electromagnetic energy to the surroundings. To make the system more efficient, we have a black liner on top of the lids of the two cups holding the sand and water. The black lids absorb more of the electromagnetic energy emitted by the lamp and have heat energy transferred to them primarily by radiation, although heat energy is also transferred by conduction."

Discuss the differences between heat energy transferred by conduction and radiation. Emphasize that in a conduction interaction, two atoms or molecules collide resulting in the atoms/molecules transferring kinetic energy. In a radiation interaction, the atoms/molecules absorb electromagnetic radiation moving through space resulting in increased motion or kinetic energy.

NOTES

4. Place the cups next to each other. Clamp the lamp so the light is about 30 cm above the top of the cups. Adjust the stand to position the light as shown in the picture. Use tape to fix the thermometers to the lamp as shown.

5. Use the *Land & Water Temperature Data* page to record data during this investigation.

6. Record the temperature in each cup.

7. Turn on the lamp and record the temperature in each cup every 3 minutes for 12 minutes total. Use extreme caution with the light bulb, as it can get very hot. Do not look directly at the light bulb at any time.

8. Turn off the lamp and record the temperature in each cup every 3 minutes for another 12 minutes.

9. Return all equipment to its proper place and clean up your work area.

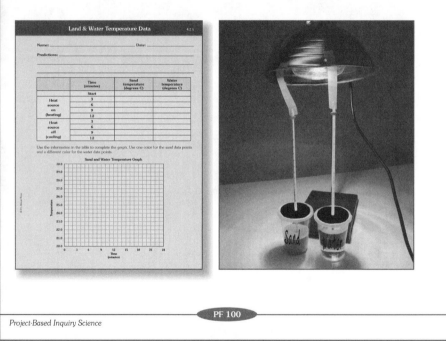

⬡ Get Going

Distribute materials and let students know how much time they have.

△ Guide and Assess

Make sure to have the students record the temperatures every three minutes as they take readings. Groups may function more efficiently if the students are each responsible for one task. One student should each be responsible for reading the temperature, recording the temperature, and timing.

After turning off the heat source, it is likely that a small increase in temperature occurs for a minute or two. Students often believe this is because it takes a while for the energy from the heat source to turn into heat in the sample. Correct students by explaining that even though the heat source has been turned off, its temperature is still higher than the ambient temperature of the room so heat is still being transferred from the heat source to the surrounding environment. This will continue to happen until the heat source's temperature matches the temperature of its immediate surroundings. As heat in that area begins to spread to other areas of the room, the immediate area around the heat source and samples will begin to lose heat. This is when students will begin to see a drop in temperature.

As groups finish collecting data, have them begin the *Analyze Your Data* segment.

NOTES

4.2 Investigate

Analyze Your Data

1. Draw a graph to show how the two materials heated and cooled. Plot time along the *x*-axis. Plot the temperature in half-degrees along the *y*-axis.

2. What trends do you see here?

   a) What differences do you see in how much the sand and water heated?

   b) What differences do you see in the time it took for the sand and water to heat?

   c) What differences do you see in how much the sand and water cooled?

   d) What differences do you see in the time it took the sand and water to cool?

3. Write a statement comparing the heating and cooling of sand and water.

4. Compare the results of your investigation with the prediction you made. Describe how the results are the same or different from your prediction.

5. Apply your results from this investigation. Based on your data, which heats up more quickly during the day—land or water? Which cools more quickly at night—land or water?

Why do you think the sand is warmer than the grass on a hot summer day?

⬡ Get Going

Let students know they should work on this segment on their own and then briefly discuss them with their group members.

△ Guide and Assess

Monitor students. Assist students with graphing if needed.

Analyze Your Data

10 min.

Students graph and analyze their data using their observations from this experiment.

While students are graphing their data, ask groups various questions to see if they are interpreting their data correctly. Once students recognize that their sand sample increased in temperature more quickly than water, ask them to think about what would happen if they put the samples outside on a hot summer day. Once students recognize that their sand sample decreased in temperature more quickly than water, ask them to think about what would happen if they put the samples outside on a very cold winter day. What temperature changes would they see?

1. Students should create a graph using the temperature data they recorded. The first 12 minutes corresponds with the measurements while the heat source is on. The last 12 minutes (from 12 to 24 minutes on the graph) corresponds with the measurements while the heat source is off.

2. Students should describe the observations they made over time for the sand and water samples. By comparing the change in temperature and change in time, students are considering the slope, or the rate, at which temperature changes. The steeper the slope, greater changes in temperature over the same amount of time, and the greater the rate at which heat is transferred. Students should observe that the sand warms up and cools down more rapidly than the water sample, however they may not observe lower temperatures for the sand while cooling down.

3. Students should write a conclusion based on their observations comparing the rate at which sand and water change temperatures as heat energy is transferred to and from them. They should include their data to back up their conclusion.

4. Students should compare their results with their predictions and describe how the results support or do not support their predictions.

5. Students should infer that land warms and cools faster than water.

Reflect

10 min.

Students answer the questions and then share with the class.

Reflect

Look at the world map below and imagine it is June. Use the map to answer the following questions. Be prepared to share your answers with the class.

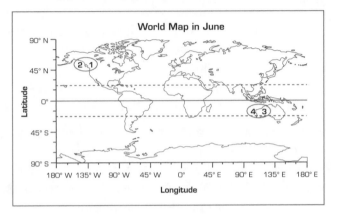

1. In June, what season is it at locations 1 and 2 on the map?

2. Based on the results of this investigation, would you expect the temperature at location 1 to be warmer or cooler than the temperature at location 2? Why?

3. In June, what season is it at locations 3 and 4?

4. Based on the results of this investigation, would you expect the temperature at location 3 to be warmer or cooler than the temperature at location 4? Why?

Communicate

Investigation Expo

Your group will share the results and analysis of your investigation with other groups in an *Investigation Expo*. You will make a poster to display the results of your investigation and some of your answers from the *Analyze*

◯ Get Going

Let students know they will be sharing their answers to these questions with the class.

△ Guide

Determine if you want students to discuss these now or during the *Investigation Expo.* During the discussion, guide and assess students' responses using the information below.

1. Students' responses should indicate that locations 1 and 2 are in the Northern Hemisphere which experiences summer in June.

2. Students should describe location 1 as warmer than location 2 and include the reasoning that location 1 is over land, which warms quicker than water.

3. Students' responses should indicate that locations 3 and 4 are in the Southern Hemisphere which experiences winter in June.

4. Students should describe location 4 as warmer than location 3 and include the reasoning that location 4 is over water, which cools slower than land.

NOTES

Communicate: *Investigation Expo*

20 mins.

Students answer the questions and then share with the class.

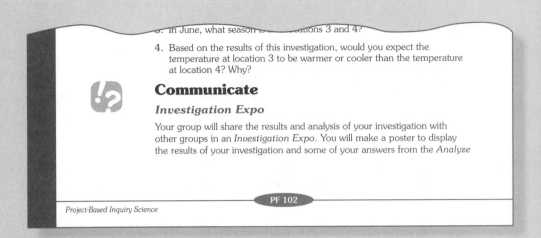

3. In June, what season is ~~~ ~~~ations 3 and 4?

4. Based on the results of this investigation, would you expect the temperature at location 3 to be warmer or cooler than the temperature at location 4? Why?

Communicate

Investigation Expo

Your group will share the results and analysis of your investigation with other groups in an *Investigation Expo*. You will make a poster to display the results of your investigation and some of your answers from the *Analyze*

PF 102

Project-Based Inquiry Science

⬡ Get Going

Have each group create a poster that displays the results they obtained. Have the students follow the directions in the student text and follow the specifications for the poster. Let students know if you want them to include their responses to the *Reflect* questions on the poster or in their presentations.

△ Guide and Assess

Monitor groups as they are constructing their posters. Check that they have included their diagram of the experimental setup, a list of variables (independent, dependent, and controlled), their graph, a summary of their results, and how their results may be applied to a planet's surface temperature. Assist groups as needed.

△ Guide

When students are done with their posters, display them around the room. Allow each group to visit each poster for a minute or so. Have each group present their results.

Guide the class discussion during presentations, if needed. Encourage groups to discuss similarities and differences with other results presented.

Discuss potential experimental errors if data is very different. If the heat source is closer to one cup than the other, the data they collected may not be accurate. If the materials started out at different temperatures, the data may be difficult to analyze. All of the variables, except for the type of material, should be constant.

Students may find that the soil temperature never actually drops below water temperature during the time they are measuring, even though it is dropping in temperature faster than water. If students are not convinced that soil cools faster, have them think about how much time it takes each sample to decrease by one degree, and point out the temperatures of the water and sand before they began decreasing in temperature.

4.2 Investigate

Your Data questions. On one-third of the poster, draw a diagram of your experimental setup. List the independent variable, dependent variable, and controls. Remember that the independent or manipulated variable is the one you intend to vary in the experiment. The dependent or responding variables are the ones that change as a result of the procedure you are carrying out. They are the ones you measure. The controlled variables are the ones you make sure remain the same each time you carry out the procedure. In the middle section, present the graphs of your data. In the third section, summarize your results and decide how they may be applied to a planet's surface temperature.

Once every group has completed their poster, your teacher will display each poster in the classroom. As a class, review and discuss the answers to the *Analyze Your Data* questions. You may want to refer to the posters during your discussion.

What's the Point?

Your investigation should have shown a trend in the data collected. This trend in the data provides you with some evidence to understand the different effects solar energy has on land and on water bodies. The discussions you had within your group and with other groups should have focused on this trend. During the *Investigation Expo*, you probably were able to spot this trend. The *Investigation Expo* posters allowed you to compare data and procedures. Even though every group completed the same procedure, you might have noticed differences in some data collected.

The data you collected in this investigation provides evidence that water and soil heat up and cool down at different rates. The sand represents the land. It heated up more quickly than water. It also cooled down faster than water. These data are important to understanding that different materials heat and cool at different rates. However, they do not explain to you why this happens. You will explore this question in the next section.

META NOTES

Students may not realize surface area is a variable that has an effect on energy absorption. Water in a flat, wide dish will increase in temperature faster than the same amount of water in a tall, narrow dish because it has more surface area to absorb incoming energy. If the cups used in the experiment vary in diameter than the sand and water do not have the same surface area.

Assessment Options

Targeted Concepts, Skills, and Nature of Science	How do I know if students got it?
Graphs, maps, and tables are an effective way to analyze and communicate results of scientific investigation.	**ASK:** How did the graph assist in communicating results? **LISTEN:** Students should describe how the steepness, or slope, of the graph shows the rate at which the temperature is changing.
Identifying factors that lead to variation is an important part of scientific investigation.	**ASK:** What factor affects the rate at which temperature changes? **LISTEN:** Students should describe that material type affects the rate at which temperature changes.
Heat energy may be transferred through conduction, radiation, or convection.	**ASK:** How was heat energy transferred to the materials during the experiment? **LISTEN:** Students should describe the heat energy transferred from the lamp to the sand and from the lamp to the water primarily through radiation and conduction.
Different substances (such as soil and water) transfer heat energy at different rates and require different amounts of energy to raise their temperatures. The amount of energy needed to raise the temperature of a substance is described by its specific heat capacity.	**ASK:** What is your evidence that material type affects the rate at which temperature changes? **LISTEN:** Students should recognize the experiment with sand and water supports the claim that material type affects the rate at which temperature changes. Sand changed temperature at a faster rate when warming up and cooling down than the water did.

Teacher Reflection Questions

- What difficulties did students have applying the results from their investigation to the *Reflect* questions?

- How did you guide students during the *Investigation Expo?*

- What management issues arose during the investigation? What would you do differently next time?

4.3 Read

Why Do Some Substances Warm Up Faster Than Others?

◀ *2 class periods*

A class period is considered to be one 40 to 50 minute class.

Overview

Students explore the factors that affect how a material changes temperature. Students are introduced to specific heat capacity (the energy required to raise one gram of a substance by one degree Celsius) and how this property affects the rate at which heat energy is transferred to or away from a substance. They read about how reflectivity and absorption of a material affects how a substance increases in temperature. Students apply what they have learned to specific situations and the class discusses them. Students construct an explanation using the science knowledge from the student text and data from the previous section. Students share their explanations with their group members to come up with an explanation their group agrees on. Groups share their explanations with the class and the class constructs an explanation. The class updates the *Project Board* to include what they are learning and the evidence that supports it.

Targeted Concepts, Skills, and Nature of Science	Performance Expectations
Scientists often work together and share their findings. Sharing findings makes new information available and helps scientists to refine their ideas and build on others' ideas. When another person's or group's idea is used, credit needs to be given.	Students should share their initial explanations of how differences between land and water affect surface temperature with their group. The group comes up with an explanation they agree upon and then share their explanations with the class. Together, the class constructs an explanation.
Scientists must keep clear, accurate, and descriptive records of what they do so they can share their work with others and consider what they did, why they did it, and what they want to do next.	Students should refer to previous records to write their explanations. They should keep records of their explanations to revise later and update their class *Project Board*.

Targeted Concepts, Skills, and Nature of Science	Performance Expectations
Explanations are claims supported by evidence, accepted ideas, and facts.	Students should discuss their initial explanations of how differences between land and water affect surface temperature with their group and the group should construct an explanation. Groups should share their explanations with the class and the class should construct an explanation they agree on. These explanations should be supported by evidence from the experiment students conducted and information presented in the student text.
Different substances (such as soil and water) transfer heat energy at different rates and require different amounts of energy to raise their temperatures. The amount of energy needed to raise the temperature of a substance is described by its specific heat capacity.	Students should explain how different materials affect the temperature due to rates of warming and cooling. Students should include how they are affected by how much light energy a substance can absorb and its specific heat capacity.

Materials	
1 per class	Class *Project Board*
1 per student	*Project Board* page
3 per student	*Create Your Explanation* page
1 per classroom (Optional, for demonstration)	Flashlight Piece of glass Mirror Paper Black felt

Activity Setup and Preparation

Decide on the method classes will use for reading. Consider demonstrating reflection, transmission, and absorption by shining light on a piece of glass, a mirror, paper, and black felt.

Homework Options

Reflection

- **Science Content:** Describe two factors of a material that affect how much heat energy is needed to change its temperature? *(Students should describe the specific heat capacity and the amount of light energy absorbed. The specific heat capacity is the amount of heat energy needed to increase one gram of substance by one degree Celsius. The amount of absorbed light is the light that is not reflected away or transmitted through the material.)*

- **Science Content:** What does a calorie measure? *(Students' responses should describe a calorie as the amount of energy required to raise the temperature of one gram of a substance by 1°C.)*

NOTES

NOTES

SECTION 4.3 IMPLEMENTATION

4.3 Read

Why Do Some Substances Warm up Faster Than Others?

Which will warm up faster, the water or the sand in this coastal area?

Consider what you have just discovered about the differences in soil and water as you think about this question. Do all parts of Earth absorb incoming solar energy equally? As you discovered in your investigation, the answer is no. Land areas warm up faster than bodies of water. Because the energy absorbed by Earth's surface heats the surrounding air, these differences result in differences in surface air temperatures.

Heat Transfer

Why did the sand heat faster than the water? The amount of heat energy needed to increase the temperature differs from substance to substance. Scientists compare the way different substances heat up. They measure the amount of heat energy it takes to raise 1 gram of a substance 1° Celsius. This is called the **specific heat capacity** of a substance. Heat energy is measured in calories (cal).

PF 104

Project-Based Inquiry Science

4.3 Read

Why Do Some Substances Warm Up Faster Than Others?

< 5 min.

Students read about heat transfer and reflected light to further understand surface temperature in order to formulate resolutions to the Big Challenge.

△ Guide

Ask students if all parts of Earth absorb incoming solar energy equally. Students should realize that land and water do not absorb solar energy the same way and they should use their data from the previous section to support this. Ask students to describe how land and water compare when transferring heat energy away. Students should describe that the water transfers heat away more slowly.

*A class period is considered to be one 40 to 50 minute class.

Let students know that because the energy absorbed by Earth's surface heats the surrounding air, these differences result in differences in surface air temperatures.

Heat Transfer

10 min.

Students have a class discussion on specific heat capacity and the calorie.

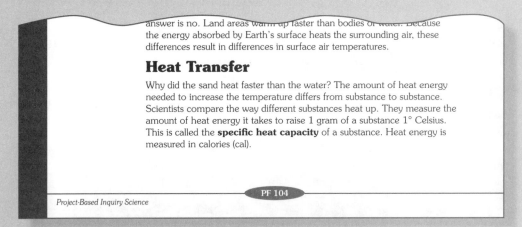

answer is no. Land areas warm up faster than bodies of water. Because the energy absorbed by Earth's surface heats the surrounding air, these differences result in differences in surface air temperatures.

Heat Transfer

Why did the sand heat faster than the water? The amount of heat energy needed to increase the temperature differs from substance to substance. Scientists compare the way different substances heat up. They measure the amount of heat energy it takes to raise 1 gram of a substance 1° Celsius. This is called the **specific heat capacity** of a substance. Heat energy is measured in calories (cal).

PF 104

Project-Based Inquiry Science

△ Guide

Consider having students read this segment on their own and then discussing it with them, or guiding them as a class through the material.

Emphasize that the specific heat capacity is a characteristic property of a material that defines how much heat energy is needed to raise one gram of the substance by one degree Celsius.

Define how scientists measure heat energy.

TEACHER TALK

❝The specific heat capacity is a measure of how much heat energy is required to raise one gram of a substance by one degree Celsius. Scientists usually use the units of calories when describing heat energy. One calorie is defined as the amount of energy required to raise one gram of water by one degree Celsius.

Based on this definition, do you think the amount of heat energy needed to raise one gram of sand by one degree Celsius is greater than or less than one calorie?❞

Students should recognize that the amount of energy required to raise one gram of sand by one degree Celsius is less than that of water so the amount of energy needed is less than a calorie. They should base this on their experiment results. If they are looking at the student text, ask them how their experiment supports this.

Draw students' attention to the table in the student text and discuss what this implies for the surface temperature.

Water is unique. Compared to other materials, a huge amount of energy is needed to raise the temperature of water. You probably already know this if you have ever waited a long time for a pot of water to boil. It takes 1 calorie of heat energy to raise the temperature of one gram of water 1°C (or 1.8°F) but it takes only 0.19 calorie (approximately $\frac{1}{5}$ of a calorie) to raise the temperature of 1 gram of dry sand the same amount. That is why it took longer for the temperature of the water to increase in the investigation. Since less energy is needed to heat the sand, the temperature of the sand will increase faster than the temperature of the water when the same amount of heat energy is transferred. This is why the sand feels hotter to your feet than the water on a hot day at the beach.

Material	Heat energy required to raise 1g of material 1°C (calories/gram)
water (liquid)	1.000
air	0.239
concert	0.214
dry sand	0.190
iron	0.106
silver	0.057
gold	0.031

Why did the sand cool faster than the water? Sand changes temperature with a small amount of energy transfer. When 1 gram of sand loses 0.19 calories of energy, its temperature will drop 1°C, but the same amount of water needs to lose 1 calorie of energy to drop 1°C. Think about that day at the beach again. After it gets dark, the sand does not stay warm for very long. This is because sand has a low specific heat capacity.

Reflected Light

The amount of heat energy that needs to be transferred to and away from a substance to change its temperature is important. But it is only one factor that helps determine how long it will take for a substance to heat or cool. The amount of light **reflected** by a surface is also important. To reflect light means to bounce it back. A substance does not absorb light that is reflected. Different materials reflect different amounts of incoming light.

specific heat capacity: the amount of energy required to raise the temperature of 1 gram of a substance by 1° Celsius.

reflected: bounced back.

Did You Know

The calorie used to measure heat is almost the same calorie used as a measure of food. When food is "burned," it releases heat energy. Your body uses this energy to carry out daily activities. However, food calories are actually kilocalories. One food calorie is equal to 1000 of the calories used to describe the amount of energy needed to raise the temperature of a substance.

NOTES

....

....

....

TEACHER TALK

❝Dry sand has a specific heat capacity of 0.19 calories, which means that during a hot summer day each gram of sand only needs 0.19 calories of heat energy to increase by one degree Celsius as compared to one calorie for water. When the Sun goes down, each gram of warmer sand will transfer only 0.19 calories of heat energy to the cooler air, but each gram of warmer water will transfer one calorie of heat energy to the cooler air. Where will the air be warmer in the evening, near the water or the land?**❞**

Reflected Light

10 min.

Students read the section in pairs or small groups.

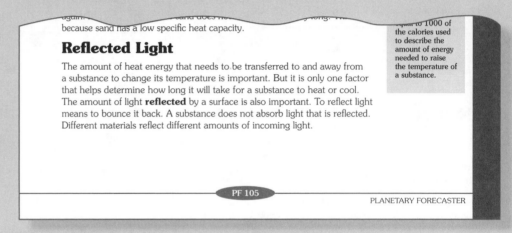

again. .... .sand does no........y long. ...
because sand has a low specific heat capacity.

Reflected Light

The amount of heat energy that needs to be transferred to and away from a substance to change its temperature is important. But it is only one factor that helps determine how long it will take for a substance to heat or cool. The amount of light **reflected** by a surface is also important. To reflect light means to bounce it back. A substance does not absorb light that is reflected. Different materials reflect different amounts of incoming light.

...qual to 1000 of the calories used to describe the amount of energy needed to raise the temperature of a substance.

PF 105

PLANETARY FORECASTER

⃝ Engage

Ask the students to describe their own experiences with reflected light and absorption. You may want to ask students which shirt they would rather wear, a white t-shirt or a black t-shirt, on a hot summer day.

Ask students what they think happens to light when it shines on an object. Record their responses and discuss how light can be absorbed by the object, transmitted through the object, or reflected from the object.

NOTES

....

....

....

....

Smooth, sweaty skin reflects light more easily. This can cause sunlight to glare into the eyes of athletes. Many athletes put black paint under their eyes because it absorbs light instead of reflecting it.

Think about a fresh winter snow. The glare is so bright that you sometimes squint or need sunglasses to see. This is because the snow reflects most (80% to 90%) of the light energy it receives from the Sun. White and light materials reflect more light from their surfaces than dark materials. A blacktop road reflects 5% to 10% of the light energy it receives. This means it absorbs 90% to 95% of the energy it receives. Snow reflects 80% to 90% of the light it receives. This means it absorbs only 10% to 20% of that energy. The more energy a surface reflects, the less energy it absorbs. A blacktop road or driveway absorbs most of the light energy it receives. It gets hot more quickly than a light-colored pavement that reflects back more light energy than it absorbs.

Surface	Percentage of light energy reflected
snow, fresh	80-90%
clouds (average)	50-55%
snow, old	45-70%
white sand	30-60%
concrete	17-27%
green crops and grass	5-25%
soil, dark	5-15%
water	8-98%
blacktop road	5-10%

Overall, Earth reflects about 30% of the light it receives. It absorbs about 70%. The table shows the percentage of light reflected by some common materials.

If you look at *water* in the table, you will see that the percentage of light reflected has a wide range. Sometimes it reflects a lot of light, sometimes very little.

Have you ever been fishing early in the morning or watched the sunset at the beach? If you have, you might have noticed a lot of light reflecting off the water. The amount of light reflected and absorbed by water varies with the direction of the light from the Sun. If the Sun is directly overhead, most

PF 106

NOTES

"When light shines on an object, some of it could be reflected from the object. Some of the light could go through the object, the same way light goes through a glass window. This is called transmission. Light can also be absorbed. When light is absorbed it is usually transformed to kinetic energy of the atoms and molecules of the object. Remember the average kinetic energy of an object is the temperature of the object. The absorbed light increases the temperature of the object. This is known as heat transfer by radiation.

We don't talk about the light being transmitted through Earth's land and water very much because any light that gets transmitted is eventually absorbed or reflected by something else. Light might be transmitted through the water, some of it might get absorbed by an object in the water, reflected off the object in the water, or reflected back out of the water."

Consider demonstrating for students how light is absorbed, reflected, and transmitted by using a flashlight and a mirror, a piece of glass, a piece of paper, and a piece of black felt. Shine the light on the mirror to show how light is reflected off of it onto a nearby wall. Then shine the light through the glass and show how light shines on a nearby wall. Show students that the black felt absorbs a lot of light because it reflects and transmits little.

Discuss the examples in the student text, including the items listed in the table, and emphasize that the substance cannot absorb energy from the light reflected away from it.

Discuss the wide range of reflectance that water has (from 8% to 98%) and emphasize that water's reflectivity increases with the indirectness of the incoming light. Point out that in the early morning and evening more light is reflected off water than at noon time.

Emphasize that Earth reflects about 30% of its energy and absorbs about 70%. Let students know that astronomers call the portion of light reflected the albedo.

Consider asking students to choose two materials from the table and to imagine them on a sunny day. Have the students compare the amount of light reflected and absorbed by each surface. Have students predict how the temperatures of each surface would compare.

4.3 **Read**

of the sunlight is absorbed, and little is reflected. If the Sun is low on the horizon, it strikes the water indirectly. When the Sun's light is indirect, the water reflects most of the sunlight, and little is absorbed.

These two factors together result in water taking a longer time to heat up and cool down than most other materials. Water needs to absorb a lot of energy to heat up. Water also needs to transfer a lot of energy to cool down. And the amount of energy absorbed and reflected during each day can also cause water to take longer to heat up than other materials.

Stop and Think

1. It takes 0.214 calorie to raise the temperature of 1 gram of concrete 1°C. It takes 0.108 calorie to raise the temperature of 1 gram of iron 1°C. Which substance would cool down faster, concrete or iron?

2. Describe why the air over land is warmer during the day than the air over water.

3. Cities are made of bricks and cement. How do you think this affects the way cities heat and cool compared to country areas where there are not many buildings?

4. Which reflects more sunlight—dark soil or white sand?

5. Which substances listed in the table on the previous page absorb the most energy?

6. Describe why people who would like to stay cool on a hot summer day prefer to wear white clothing.

7. You are at the beach early in the morning, and the Sun glare makes you squint. What is happening to the light energy?

8. What Earth surfaces do you suppose reflect the greatest amount of light?

Explain

Your challenge is to determine how the differences between land and bodies of water might affect the planet's temperature. You have read something about how heat energy is transferred to and from different surfaces differently. You also read about how different surfaces reflect light differently. Now you need to create an explanation of how land and water bodies affect a planet's surface temperatures.

PF 107

PLANETARY FORECASTER

Stop and Think

15 min.

Students have a class discussion on their responses.

◯ Get Going

Let students know that they should each answer the questions and a class discussion will follow. Let students know how much time they have.

△ Guide and Assess

Have a class discussion using the information below to guide and assess students' responses.

1. Students should state that iron would cool faster than concrete because it has a lower specific heat capacity which means that it would transfer heat energy away from it at a faster rate.

2. Students' responses should include that the water has a high reflectivity when the sunlight is less direct, which means that it will not absorb much energy until later in the day. The water also requires more energy to warm up because of its higher specific heat capacity. The land warms up more quickly because it absorbs more energy early in the day and has a lower specific heat capacity. The land will reach a higher temperature than the air quicker and will then transfer energy to the air above it at a faster rate.

3. Students' responses should include that concrete and brick, prominent in cities, warms up quickly and retains heat. As a result, cities are often much warmer than country areas.

4. Students should state white sand reflects more sunlight based on information in the table.

5. Students should state that the substances listed in the table that absorb the most energy are those that have the lowest percentage of reflected light. These are blacktop, dark soil, plants, and water when the sunlight is direct.

6. Students should note that white clothing reflects more light energy than dark clothing and stays cooler.

7. Students should state that the light is being reflected from the sand and water, causing more light energy to strike your eyes. Point out that light is most reflective off water during the early morning and late evening.

8. Students should state that arctic areas covered with snow reflect the most amount of light.

6. Describe why people who would like to stay cool on a hot summer day prefer to wear white clothing.

7. You are at the beach early in the morning, and the Sun glare makes you squint. What is happening to the light energy?

8. What Earth surfaces do you suppose reflect the greatest amount of light?

Explain

Your challenge is to determine how the differences between land and bodies of water might affect the planet's temperature. You have read something about how heat energy is transferred to and from different surfaces differently. You also read about how different surfaces reflect light differently. Now you need to create an explanation of how land and water bodies affect a planet's surface temperatures.

PF 107

Explain

15 min.

Students individually construct an explanation and then construct explanations with their groups based on their common thoughts.

⬡ Get Going

Let the class know that each student should construct an explanation on the relationship between land and water differences, and surface temperature. Let them know that they will share their explanation with their group members and then, as a group, they will come up with an explanation for how differences in land and water temperature affect a planet's surface temperature.

Distribute one *Create Your Explanation* page to each student and let students know how much time they have.

△ Guide and Assess

Monitor students. Check to see if students are supporting their claims with evidence from observations they made during the experiment they ran in the previous section and the information provided in this section.

Remind students that if they disagree, this indicates there is something they may still need to investigate and they should list on the class *Project Board*.

When students complete their explanations, have groups meet. Distribute one *Create Your Explanation* page to each group and have them write Group Explanation on the top of their page. Monitor groups for participation and progress. Guide students as needed.

Communicate

15 min.

Groups present their explanations and form a class explanation for how land and water differences affect surface temperature.

Using a *Create Your Explanation* page, you will first write an explanation on your own. Then you will share it with your group. Your group will consider everyone's explanation and create a group explanation.

Communicate

Your class will meet to discuss the group explanations. Your class will select or create the explanation that best explains how land and water affect surface temperatures.

You will have a chance in the future to revise this explanation. At this point, you are making your best attempt based on what you understand.

Update the *Project Board*

At the beginning of this Unit, you began a *Project Board* centered around the idea of surface temperature and habitability. You have completed an investigation. You also read about the Sun's rays. You know more about the factors that affect solar energy striking Earth's surface. You are now ready to fill in the *Project Board* more completely.

You should describe the results from the investigation you just did. You should also provide evidence for those results. Evidence is necessary to answer scientific questions. You will fill in the evidence column based on data and trends you found in your investigations and your understanding of the science readings. You may use the text in this book to help you phrase your new knowledge. As the class fills in the class *Project Board*, make sure to record the same information on your own *Project Board* page.

What's the Point?

In your investigation, you collected data showing that water heated up and cooled down more slowly than sand. Now you have a better understanding as to how heating and cooling of land and water actually affect Earth's temperatures. You also found out that reflection of light affects surface temperatures. These are things you will have to consider as you refine your temperature-prediction map for *Planet X*.

△ Guide

Let students know that each group will be presenting.

"Each group has constructed an explanation for how land and water differences affect a planet's surface temperature. Now each group will present their explanation to the class and we will construct a class explanation. It is important that when you present your explanation to point out the information that supports your claim. It is also important that if something is not clear, you ask questions."

△ Guide and Assess

Have each group present their explanation. Discuss each explanation. Encourage students to ask questions and discuss the supporting evidence. Discuss misconceptions and correct them as needed.

After each group presents, discuss the similarities and differences between groups that have presented. After all groups have presented, have a class discussion on the explanations. Remind students that places where they have disagreement indicate things they need to investigate.

"We have now heard explanations from all the groups. Think about the similarities and differences between these explanations. Things that were similar between all groups are things we want to keep in our class explanation. Things that are different should be discussed and we will need to determine what is best to put in the class explanation. These things may still need to be investigated."

Make a list of all things in the explanations that are similar or common, and a list of the differences. Have a class discussion on these and begin to construct the class explanation. Edit the class explanation as they change and revise it. When it is complete distribute another *Create Your Explanation* page. Have students indicate on this page that it is the class explanation.

◇ Evaluate

At this point, students should understand that Earth's land and water differences are responsible for different temperatures on Earth, especially near shorelines. They should indicate that the different materials that make up land and water absorb different amounts of light energy and require different amounts of energy to raise one gram of the material by one degree. These factors are called the specific heat capacity and the absorption properties of a material.

Update the Project Board

10 min.

Have a class discussion to update the Project Board.

you are making your best attempt based on what you understand.

Update the *Project Board*

At the beginning of this Unit, you began a *Project Board* centered around the idea of surface temperature and habitability. You have completed an investigation. You also read about the Sun's rays. You know more about the factors that affect solar energy striking Earth's surface. You are now ready to fill in the *Project Board* more completely.

You should describe the results from the investigation you just did. You should also provide evidence for those results. Evidence is necessary to answer scientific questions. You will fill in the evidence column based on data and trends you found in your investigations and your understanding of the science readings. You may use the text in this book to help you phrase your new knowledge. As the class fills in the class *Project Board*, make sure to record the same information on your own *Project Board* page.

What's the Point?

△ Guide

Remind the students that the *Project Board* is a means of organizing ideas and questions and seeing how their ideas have changed.

Ask students what they would like to include in Columns 1 and 2.

TEACHER TALK

❝You have new information about how land and water differences affect a planet's surface temperature. This information should be put on the class *Project Board*. The *Project Board* is a tool that helps to organize the information you have and the ideas you want to investigate. We will focus on the third and fourth columns in particular: *What are we learning?* and *What is our evidence?* But, first, we should consider ideas that you and your classmates were not sure of and if these need to be investigated.❞

Ask the class what their ideas are and the evidence that supports those ideas. As a class, edit these before recording them on the *Project Board*.

◇ Evaluate

Make sure the following concepts are included on the *Project Board*.

Column 3 (claim): Land and water change temperatures at different rates which affect the surface temperature.

Column 4 (evidence): Land and water are made of different materials. Materials absorb heat energy differently due to how much light they reflect away from their surface. Water may only absorb 2% to 92% of the light shining on it depending on the angle of the incoming light. Sand absorbs between 40% and 70% of the incoming light. Another factor that affects how a substance changes temperature is how much energy it requires to raise one gram of the substance by one degree Celsius. This quantity is known as the specific heat capacity. Water requires one calorie of heat energy to raise one gram of it by one degree Celsius. Sand only requires 0.19 calories of heat energy to raise one gram of it by one degree Celsius. The higher the specific heat capacity, the slower the rate that heat is transferred to or away from the substance.

Column 3 (claim): The air above water will be warmer during the winter and cooler during the summer than the air above land.

Column 4 (evidence): The higher the specific heat capacity, the slower the rate heat is transferred to or away from the substance. Because water has a higher specific heat capacity than land, it transfers heat energy more slowly than land. The land warms rapidly and cools rapidly, whereas the water slowly warms and cools. The land requires less energy per gram to change its temperature than the water does. As the water cools during the winter, it transfers more energy to the air above it than the land does. As the water warms during the summer, it has to absorb more than five times the energy than the sand to reach the same temperature as the sand.

Assessment Options

Targeted Concepts, Skills, and Nature of Science	How do I know if students got it?
Different substances (such as soil and water) transfer heat energy at different rates and require different amounts of energy to raise their temperatures. The amount of energy needed to raise the temperature of a substance is described by its specific heat capacity.	**ASK:** What factors affect how a substance changes its temperature? **LISTEN:** Students should describe how different materials affect the temperature due to rates of warming and cooling. Students should include how they are affected by how much light energy a substance can absorb and its specific heat capacity.

Teacher Reflection Questions

- What difficulties did students have with the concepts of specific heat capacity and absorption?

- What misconceptions did students have and how did you address them?

- How did you guide students through the reading? Would this work for all your classes?

NOTES

4.4 Investigate

How Do Temperatures Across Bodies of Land and Water Compare at Similar Latitudes?

◀ *1 class period*

A class period is considered to be one 40 to 50 minute class.

Overview

Students explore how land and water differences affect temperatures at similar latitudes. Students use *My World* to gather and compare the differences in surface temperature for locations at various latitudes. Students collect average January temperatures above land and above water and compare them within the same latitude band. From this quantitative data, students predict what temperatures will be like in July (summer) for similar latitudes, applying what they know about the similarity between temperature patterns in the Northern and Southern Hemispheres for different seasons.

Targeted Concepts, Skills, and Nature of Science	Performance Expectations
Scientists often work together and share their findings. Sharing findings makes new information available and helps scientists to refine their ideas and build on others' ideas. When another person's or group's idea is used, credit needs to be given.	Students should work in groups to gather and analyze data, share ideas, and discuss questions.
Scientists must keep clear, accurate, and descriptive records of what they do so they can share their work with others and consider what they did, why they did it, and what they want to do next.	Students should keep clear and accurate records of their results to use in the next sections of the *Learning Set.*
Graphs, maps, and tables are an effective way to analyze and communicate results of scientific investigation.	Students should use charts to analyze and share their data.

Targeted Concepts, Skills, and Nature of Science	Performance Expectations
Scientists make claims (conclusions) based on evidence obtained (trends in data) from reliable investigations	Students should make claims based on their observations about how similar latitudes have similar land and water differences in temperatures for the same seasons.
Temperatures around the Earth's surface vary widely, but can be predicted somewhat by location and season.	Students should be able to describe the temperature differences that occur over land and water based on the data they gather. Students should realize temperatures over water are warmer than over land in the winter and cooler than temperatures over land in the summer.

Materials

1 per group	Computer with *My World* software
1 per classroom	Computer with *My World* software and a projection system
1 per student	*Northern and Southern Hemisphere Temperatures* page

NOTES

Activity Setup and Preparation

Using the information in the student text and the *Section 4.4 Implementation*, go through the procedures using the *My World* software. Determine where your class may have difficulties and what you should emphasize in the demonstration.

Homework Options

Reflection

- **Science Content:** Compare the range of temperatures for land and water in the same latitude band. *(Students' responses should include land areas that generally have a larger range of temperatures than water areas.)*

- **Science Process:** Why is it useful to find the average of a set of data points? *(Students should explain that the average is useful because it is one number that represents many data points, making it easier to make calculations.)*

Preparation for 4.5

- **Science Content:** What information would you use in explaining how land and water differences affect surface temperature? *(Students' responses should include information about specific heat capacity, absorption of light, the experiment they conducted with sand and water, and the data on surface temperatures above land*

NOTES

NOTES

SECTION 4.4 IMPLEMENTATION

4.4 Investigate

How Do Temperatures Across Bodies of Land and Water Compare at Similar Latitudes?

In this investigation, you will refine your predictions about the differences between land and water temperatures. As you conduct your investigation, you will compare the temperatures of land and water at different latitudes.

You will look at four bands of latitude on Earth. For this investigation, you will ignore the Arctic regions because of the effect of other factors on their temperatures. The four bands you will look at are shown in the image below. They are the Northern mid-latitudes (30°N – 60°N), the Northern tropics (0°N – 30°N), the Southern tropics (0°S – 30°S), and the Southern mid-latitudes (30°S – 60°S).

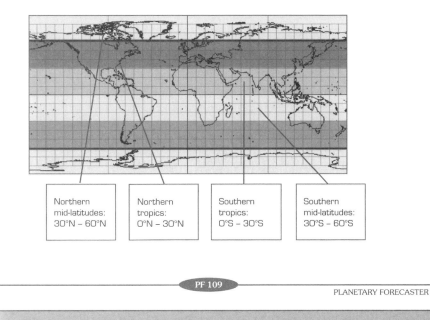

| Northern mid-latitudes: 30°N – 60°N | Northern tropics: 0°N – 30°N | Southern tropics: 0°S – 30°S | Southern mid-latitudes: 30°S – 60°S |

PF 109

PLANETARY FORECASTER

○ **Engage**

Elicit students' ideas about how the temperatures across land and water compare in similar and different latitudes.

4.4 Investigate

How Do Temperatures Across Bodies of Land and Water Compare at Similar Latitudes?
5 min.

Introduce the investigation to students.

---

*A class period is considered to be one 40 to 50 minute class.

❝Consider the image in the student text showing the Northern mid-latitudes, Northern tropics, Southern mid-latitudes, and Southern tropics.

What do you think will be the similarities and differences of temperatures over water within the Northern mid-latitude band? (*Record students' responses*)

What do you think will be the similarities and differences of temperatures over water within the Southern mid-latitude band? (*Record students' responses*)

What do you think will be the similarities and differences of temperatures over water within the Northern mid-latitude band and the Southern mid-latitude band? (*Record students' responses*)❞

△ Guide

Let students know they will be gathering some quantitative data from *My World* to explore the land and water temperature differences. Demonstrate for students how to open the banded January surface-temperature map using *My World* and briefly describe how to collect the data.

❝Each group will be gathering average January temperatures from *My World* for the four different latitude bands. You will be selecting four locations, one from each band. Look at the map in the student text that shows the average temperature for the month of January within that band. This means that all the average temperatures in the month of January for all the locations within the latitude band were averaged together.

When you collect data, you will select locations within these bands and record the overall temperature for the entire band as well as the average temperature for the land and the average temperature for the water within those bands.❞

To get this information you will use the map entitled Banded Jan Land-Water Average from the field drop-down menu. You may want to show students how the other map could be opened, but do not open it. For now, we will be looking at the map shown in the student text.

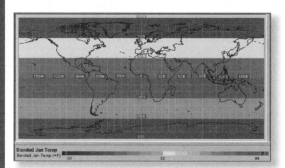

PBIS *Learning Set 4 • How Do Land and Water Affect Surface Temperatures?*

Below is a surface-temperature map for January. Each color band represents the average temperature for the month at that latitude.

- Which latitudes are experiencing the coldest temperatures?
- Which latitudes are experiencing the warmest temperatures?

Predict

In your previous investigation, you saw that water requires a lot of energy to warm up. It takes longer to warm up and cool down than most other substances. You also found that on average, water absorbs more light energy than it reflects. Based on this knowledge, make a set of predictions by completing the following sentences:

- At latitudes experiencing colder temperatures, or winter, you would expect the water to be (*colder than, warmer than, the same as*) the land.

- At latitudes experiencing warmer temperatures, or summer, you would expect the water to be (*colder than, warmer than, the same as*) the land.

- Near the Equator, you would expect the water to be (*colder than, warmer than, or the same as*) the land.

Procedure

You will look at data for January only, but you will fill out data tables on your *Northern and Southern Hemisphere Temperatures* page for summer and winter. In January, it is winter in the Northern Hemisphere and summer in the Southern Hemisphere. Assume that the observations for the Northern and Southern Hemispheres will be reversed in July.

> **META NOTES**
>
> To avoid confusing the effect of land and water differences with elevation, the data sets were averaged, with elevations over 2000 meters excluded. The averages were distributed across the whole selections, so that the higher elevations are concealed.

PF 110

Project-Based Inquiry Science

TEACHER TALK

" Which band of latitudes do you think are experiencing the coldest temperatures? *(The coldest temperatures in the four bands students will explore are in the Northern mid-latitudes.)*

Which band of latitudes do you think are experiencing the warmest temperatures? *(The Southern tropics.)* **"**

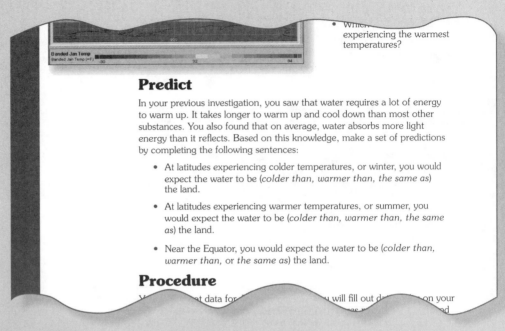

Predict

5 min.

Students have a brief discussion on their predictions.

Predict

In your previous investigation, you saw that water requires a lot of energy to warm up. It takes longer to warm up and cool down than most other substances. You also found that on average, water absorbs more light energy than it reflects. Based on this knowledge, make a set of predictions by completing the following sentences:

- At latitudes experiencing colder temperatures, or winter, you would expect the water to be (*colder than, warmer than, the same as*) the land.

- At latitudes experiencing warmer temperatures, or summer, you would expect the water to be (*colder than, warmer than, the same as*) the land.

- Near the Equator, you would expect the water to be (*colder than, warmer than, or the same as*) the land.

Procedure

△ Guide

Remind students of their investigations into how land and water change temperatures at different rates. Ask students to complete and record the three bulleted prediction statements.

Have a brief class discussion on students' responses.

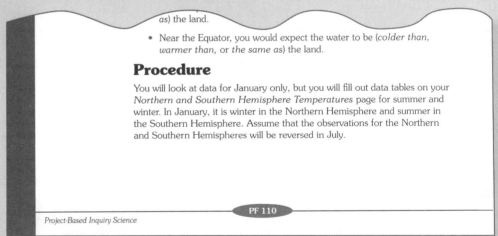

Procedure

10 min.

Students follow the procedure to gather temperature data.

as) the land.

- Near the Equator, you would expect the water to be (*colder than, warmer than,* or *the same as*) the land.

Procedure

You will look at data for January only, but you will fill out data tables on your *Northern and Southern Hemisphere Temperatures* page for summer and winter. In January, it is winter in the Northern Hemisphere and summer in the Southern Hemisphere. Assume that the observations for the Northern and Southern Hemispheres will be reversed in July.

PF 110

Project-Based Inquiry Science

○ Get Going

Let students know how you want groups to use the computers. Emphasize that they will need to record their data in data tables as described in the student text. Let groups know how much time they have.

4.4 Investigate

For each band of the four bands of latitude, you will record three values:

- the overall temperature for the whole band,
- the average temperature for the land in the band, and
- the average temperature for the water in the band.

For each band you will calculate:

- the difference between the land average and the overall average, and
- the difference between the water average and the overall average.

These differences will tell you how much hotter or colder land is than the overall average temperature. It will also tell you how much hotter or colder water is than the overall average temperature. Your current *Planet X* prediction is an overall average that does not show the difference between land and water. You will use these calculations to raise and lower your temperature predictions for land and water.

1. **Open the banded January surface-temperature visualization.**

   a) **Open *My World*.** Select "Planetary Forecaster" from the Data Library drop-down menu.

   b) **Open the "PF Jan Temp Banded" project file.** The default view will show a layer of the overall average January temperatures at different latitudes. The land and water within the same band will appear to have the same temperatures on that map.

2. **Open the January Land-Water Average visualization.**

   a) **Select the "Banded Jan Land-Water Average" field from the "Banded Jan Temp" layer drop-down menu.** You can now view another map that separates the average temperature of land from the average temperature of water within that same band.

      - Where is the water warmer than the land?

      - Where is the water colder than the land?

      - Where is the water temperature the same as the land temperature?

3. **Record your observations.**

⚠ Guide and Assess

Monitor groups as they are working. Check that students have opened the *Banded Jan Land-Water Average* map, as shown in the student text and have recorded where the water is warmer than the land, where it is colder, and where the water and land temperatures are the same (Steps 2 and 3). Students can check the temperature data by clicking on the map.

4. **Prepare the "Banded Jan Temp" field and the "Banded Jan Land-Water Average" field for comparison.**

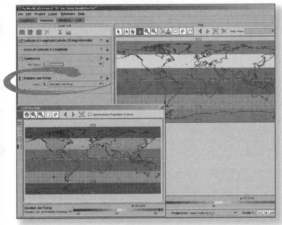

a) **Go to the "Windows" menu. Select "New Child Window."** This selection will open a second small window that contains the "Banded Jan Land-Water Average" map.

b) **Move the child window so that you can see the layer list in the original map.** Select "Banded Jan Temp." You can now view the Land-Water Average map in the child window and the overall Jan Temp map in the main window.

5. **Compare the "Banded Jan Temp" field and the "Banded Jan Land-Water Average" field.**

a) **Collect temperature data from both maps to make comparisons.** Use the "Pointer" tool to collect data. When this button is selected, you can click on any cell on the map. The temperature bar at the bottom of the map will tell you the temperature value for that cell. With a child window open, you can click on either the child window or the main window. The temperature value for the cells in *both* windows will then be shown.

Recording Your Data

On your *Northern and Southern Hemisphere Temperatures* page, write the temperature from "Banded Jan Temp" in the space for "Overall Average." Write the temperature from "Banded Jan Land-Water Average" in the space for "Land." Click on a point of water within the same band, and record the temperature from both maps. The temperature from "Banded Jan Temp"

Check that students record the overall average temperature, the land temperature and the water temperature in the tables as described and shown in Steps 4 and 5. Calculate the differences as described in the student text on their *Northern and Southern Hemisphere Temperatures* pages. Students should have data similar to the following.

While students are collecting their data and working on their lab analysis questions, circulate through the room and ask groups various questions to be sure that they are interpreting their data correctly. Ask students to

Northern and Southern Hemisphere Temperatures　　　4.4.1

Name: _____　　Date: _____

Northern Hemisphere Temperatures on January Map (season: _____*Winter*_____ **)**

	Overall average (°F)	Land (°F)	Water (°F)	Land difference (=land-average) (°F)	Water difference (=water-average) (°F)
mid-latitudes (30°N-60°N)	35.6°F	18.2°F	49.0°F	-17.4°F	13.4°F
tropics (0°-30°N)	74.3°F	65.8°F	77.4°F	-8.5°F	3.1°F

Southern Hemisphere Temperatures on January Map (season: _____*Summer*_____ **)**

	Overall average (°F)	Land (°F)	Water (°F)	Land difference (=land-average) (°F)	Water difference (=water-average) (°F)
mid-latitudes (30°S-60°S)	57.3°F	70.7°F	56.4°F	13.4°F	-0.9°F
tropics (0°-30°S)	79.6°F	78.5°F	79.8°F	-1.1°F	1.3°F

tell you what the seasons are in the Northern and Southern Hemispheres, since they are looking at a map of January. Based on those seasons, which latitudes are receiving lots of solar energy? Which latitudes are not receiving as much solar energy and may be cooling?

As students finish collecting their data, have them begin analyzing their data. Emphasize to groups that they should not work together when they are analyzing their data, and that they will share their analysis with their group members after they have completed it.

Analyze
Your Data

10 min.

---

should be the same. The temperature from "Banded Jan Land-Water Average" should be written in the space for "Water."

Analyze Your Data

For each latitude band, calculate the difference between the land average temperature and the overall average temperature. Subtract the overall average temperature value from the land average temperature value in the same band. If you get a negative number, be sure to record the negative sign in front of the difference. Repeat the process to find the difference between water average temperature and overall average temperature. Record your answers in the data table.

Summarize your findings by completing the following statements with temperature differences in °F, followed by "warmer" or "cooler."

1. In *winter*, the temperature of the land farther from the Equator (with latitudes between 30°S – 60°S) will be _____ _____ °F _____ than the average temperature. The temperature of land closer to the Equator (with latitudes between 0° – 30°S) will be _____ °F _____ than the average temperature.

2. In *winter*, the temperature of the water farther from the Equator (with latitudes between 30°N – 60°N) will be _____ °F _____ than the average temperature. The temperature of water closer to the Equator (with latitudes between 0° – 30°N) will be _____ °F _____ than the average temperature.

3. In *summer*, the temperature of the land farther from the Equator (with latitudes between 30°S – 60°S) will be _____ °F _____ than the average temperature. The temperature of land closer to the Equator (with latitudes between 0° – 30°S) will be _____ °F _____ than the average temperature.

Northern and Southern Hemisphere Temperatures

⬡ Get Going

Have the students use their data to calculate the differences between the land and water averages and fill out these columns on their *Northern and Southern Hemisphere Temperatures* page. Emphasize to groups that they should not work together when they are analyzing their data, and they will share their analysis with their group members after they have completed it.

△ Guide and Assess

Guide and assess students as they complete their analysis using the information below.

1. In *winter*, the temperature of the land farther from the Equator (with latitudes between 30°S–60°S) will be *about -17.4° F cooler* than the average temperature. The temperature of land closer to the Equator (with latitudes between 0°–30°S) will be *-8.5°F cooler* than the average temperature.

   Students may not realize at first that the question is asking for what the land temperatures in the Southern Hemisphere would be in winter, which would be in June. This would be similar to the Northern Hemisphere in winter (January).

2. In *winter*, the temperature of the water farther from the Equator (with latitudes between 30° N–60° N) will be *about 13.4° F warmer* than the average temperature. The temperature of water closer to the Equator (with latitudes between 0°–30° N) will be *3.1° F warmer* than the average temperature.

   These water values can be taken directly from the table since they correspond to winter in the Northern Hemisphere.

3. In *summer*, the temperature of the land farther from the Equator (with latitudes between 30°S–60°S) will be *about 13.4°F warmer* than the average temperature. The temperature of the land closer to the Equator (with latitudes between 0°–30°S will be *1.1°F cooler* than the average temperature.

   These land values can be taken directly from the table since they correspond to summer in the Southern Hemisphere.

4. In *summer*, the temperature of the water farther from the Equator (with latitudes between 30°N–60°N) will be about *0.9°F cooler* than the average temperature. The temperature of water closer to the Equator (with latitudes between 0°–30°N) will be *1.3°F warmer* than the average temperature.

   Students may not realize that this question is asking for what the water temperatures in the Northern Hemisphere would be in the summer, which would be in June. This would be similar to the Southern Hemisphere in summer (January).

5. Students' responses should explain that water generally stays closer to the overall average temperature except in the Northern mid-latitudes. Students should use their data to support this. The data indicates that ¾, or 75%, of the water difference temperatures are under 5°F, but only ¼, or 25%, of the land temperatures are under 5°F. This difference has to do with water turning into ice as detailed in the *Understanding for Teachers* segment at the beginning of this *Learning Set*.

6. Students should support their responses with reasoning.

NOTES

4. In *summer*, the temperature of the water farther from the Equator (with latitudes between 30°N – 60°N) will be _____ °F _____ than the average temperature. The temperature of water closer to the Equator (with latitudes between 0° – 30°N) will be _____._____ °F _____ than the average temperature.

5. Which material stays closer to the overall average temperature at a particular latitude, land or water? Use evidence from your previous investigation, your readings, and this investigation to support your answer.

6. How will this information affect your prediction for *Planet X*?

Conference

Share your ideas with the rest of your group. Discuss your findings. Listen to each group member's ideas. Also bring up any questions you have. Someone else may help you to find the answers. Teams of scientists often hold group discussions to solve problems. You are doing the same thing.

What's the Point?

In this section, you revisited your prediction about the effect of land and water on surface temperatures. Previously, you determined that water absorbs more heat energy than land and that water has a higher specific heat. You used *My World* to find the temperature differences between land and water at different latitude bands.

Even at the same latitude, land and water are different temperatures.

Project-Based Inquiry Science

Conference
10 min.

Students share their results with their group members.

△ Guide
Let groups know how much time they have to share their responses.

△ Guide and Assess
Monitor groups and check that all group members are participating. Groups should determine land is warmer than water in the summer and cooler than water in the winter.

Assessment Options

Targeted Concepts, Skills, and Nature of Science	How do I know if students got it?
Temperatures around the Earth's surface vary widely, but can be predicted somewhat by location and season.	**ASK:** What are the differences in summer and winter average temperatures on land and water for different locations on Earth? **LISTEN:** Students should be able to describe that the surface temperatures in winter above water are generally warmer than those above land, and the surface temperatures in summer above water are cooler than those above land.

Teacher Reflection Questions

- What difficulties did your students have with answering the questions in the *Analyze Your Data* segment and how did you guide them?
- How did the *Conference* assist students understanding?
- What difficulties arose with assessing students and how did you handle it?

NOTES

4.5 Revise Your Explanation

Land and Water Differences as a Factor Affecting Surface Temperatures

◀ *1 class period*

A class period is considered to be one 40 to 50 minute class.

Overview

Students revise their explanations of how land and water differences affect surface temperatures. They begin by reviewing their previous explanation and answering questions designed to guide their revisions by using their observations, analysis, and information presented during this *Learning Set.* Students use an iterative process, like scientists do, to come up with an explanation the class agrees on. They share their revised explanations with their group members and formulate an explanation their group agrees on. Groups share their explanations with the class and the class constructs an explanation. The class updates their *Project Board* to include what they are learning and the evidence that supports it.

Targeted Concepts, Skills, and Nature of Science	Performance Expectations
Scientists often work together and share their findings. Sharing findings makes new information available and helps scientists to refine their ideas and build on others' ideas. When another person's or group's idea is used, credit needs to be given.	Students should work individually, in groups, and with the class to explain how land and water differences affect surface temperatures. The class updates their *Project Board* to include information on what this means for their temperature predictions of *Planet X.*
Scientists must keep clear, accurate, and descriptive records of what they do so they can share their work with others and consider what they did, why they did it, and what they want to do next.	Students should refer to their records to construct their revised explanations. They will use these records to share their ideas with others and to create their prediction maps in the next section.

Targeted Concepts, Skills, and Nature of Science	Performance Expectations
Graphs, maps, and tables are an effective way to analyze and communicate results of scientific investigation.	Students should construct tables of information to assist them in constructing their explanation of how land and water differences affect surface temperature.
Scientists make claims (conclusions) based on evidence obtained (trends in data) from reliable investigations	Students should make claims about how land and water differences affect surface temperatures based on the information they obtained in this *Learning Set*.
Explanations are claims supported by evidence, accepted ideas and facts.	Students should work alone, in groups, and with the class to explain how land and water differences affect surface temperatures based on the experimental evidence they have and science knowledge presented in the student text.

Materials	
3 per student	*Create Your Explanation* page
1 per student	*Project Board* page
1 per class	Class *Project Board*

Homework Options

Reflection

- **Science Content:** Summarize how shape, tilt, and land and water differences affect surface temperature. *(Students should describe how the shape of a planet and its tilt affect the directness of sunlight striking the surface and how much energy is absorbed. Students should also describe how different materials, such as land and water, absorb energy differently based on how much light they absorb and their specific heat capacity–the amount of energy needed to change one gram of the substance by one degree Celsius.)*

4.5 Revise Your Explanation

Land and Water Differences as a Factor Affecting Surface Temperatures

Previously, you developed a class explanation for how land and water bodies affect a planet's surface temperatures. You have accumulated new information since you created your first explanation. It is now time to review your explanation and make any necessary changes. You will need to supply evidence from your investigations and your readings to support the claim you are making. The revised explanation you write will show what you now know about how land and water differences affect the surface temperatures of a planet. It will also be vital in creating your predictions for *Planet X*.

Reflect

Before you revise your explanation, answer these questions:

1. Describe how land and water differences affect temperature.

2. Describe your current understanding of how land and water differences affect temperature the way they do. Use evidence from your investigations to support your answer.

3. Complete a chart, similar to the one shown. Show how much land and water differences affect temperature. Show the differences between overall average temperature and land temperature in different locations on the planet during both winter and summer. Use your results from the previous section to help you. Also, show the differences between overall average temperature and water temperature.

PF 115

PLANETARY FORECASTER

4.5 Revise Your Explanation

Land and Water Differences as a Factor Affecting Surface Temperatures

< 5 min.

Students use their new knowledge and experiences to revise their explanations.

△ Guide

Let students know they will each revise the class explanation they constructed previously to include the new information they have about how land and water differences affect surface temperatures.

*A class period is considered to be one 40 to 50 minute class.

Reflect

10 min.

Students answer questions to engage thinking about their explanations.

Factor Affecting Surface Temperatures

Previously, you developed a class explanation for how land and water bodies affect a planet's surface temperatures. You have accumulated new information since you created your first explanation. It is now time to review your explanation and make any necessary changes. You will need to supply evidence from your investigations and your readings to support the claim you are making. The revised explanation you write will show what you now know about how land and water differences affect the surface temperatures of a planet. It will also be vital in creating your predictions for *Planet X*.

Reflect

Before you revise your explanation, answer these questions:

1. Describe how land and water differences affect temperature.

2. Describe your current understanding of how land and water differences affect temperature the way they do. Use evidence from your investigations to support your answer.

3. Complete a chart, similar to the one shown. Show how much land and water differences affect temperature. Show the differences between overall average temperature and land temperature in different locations on the planet during both winter and summer. Use your results from the previous section to help you. Also, show the differences between overall average temperature and water temperature.

Land & Water Temperature Difference			4.5.1

Name: _____ Date: _____

January		
Latitude band	Land difference (= land - average)	Water difference (= water - average)
30°N — 60°N (winter)		
0° — 30°N (winter)		
0° — 30°S (summer)		
30°S — 60°S (summer)		

July		
Latitude band	Land difference (= land - average)	Water difference (= water - average)
30°N — 60°N (summer)		
0° — 30°N (summer)		
0° — 30°S (winter)		
30°S — 60°S (winter)		

△ Guide

Let students know the questions are designed to help refine their explanations. Once they have finished with the *Reflect* segment, they should continue to refine the last class explanation.

△ Guide and Assess

Monitor students as they are working.

1. Students' descriptions should include how land and water require different amounts of energy to raise one gram of each substance by one degree Celsius and that this is called the specific heat of the substance. They should include that water requires more energy than sand. Students should also describe how absorption affects the temperature. Water absorbs between 2% of the light energy when the light is very indirect and 92% of the light energy when it is direct, sand absorbs between 40% and 70% of the

light energy striking it. The light absorbed is the heat energy transferred by radiation to the substance. When the air becomes cooler, surface temperatures are affected by the amount of heat energy that is transferred from these objects back to the air above. In general, land will be cooler in the winter and warmer in the summer than water because it requires less energy to heat and cool and transfers heat to and away from at a greater rate. Water will generally be warmer than the air in the winter and cooler in the summer, causing the surface temperatures above the water to be warmer than those above land in the winter and cooler in the summer.

2. Students should use the experiment they conducted with sand and water to describe how the specific heat capacity of sand and water affect the rate at which it transfers heat to and away from the substance. Students should also refer to the quantitative data from *My World* showing how surface temperatures above water are warmer in the winter and cooler in the summer than those of land.

3. Students should complete the charts with results similar to those shown.

NOTES

Land and Water Temperature Differences
4.5.1

Name: _____ Date: _____

January

Latitude band	Land difference (land – average)(°F)	Water difference (water – average)(°F)
30°N — 60°N (winter)	-17.4	13.4
0° — 30°N (winter)	-8.5	3.1
0° — 30°S (summer)	-1.1	1.3
30°S — 60°S (summer)	13.4	-0.9

July

Latitude band	Land difference (land – average)(°F)	Water difference (water – average)(°F)
30°N — 60°N (summer)	13.4	-0.9
0° — 30°N (summer)	-1.1	-1.3
0° — 30°S (winter)	-8.5	3.1
30°S — 60°S (winter)	-17.4	13.4

Explain

Based on your answers to the questions, revise your explanation of how land and water differences affect surface temperatures. Use a *Create Your Explanation* page to rewrite your claim and the explanation on your own.

Share your explanation with your group. Your group will then consider everyone's explanations and create a group explanation.

Communicate

Your class will meet to discuss the answers to the *Reflect* questions and the group explanations. Your class will select or create a new class explanation.

Update the *Project Board*

Now that you have run these investigations and completed your explanations, you need to update your *Project Board*. Once again, you will focus on the two columns *What are we learning?* and *What is our evidence?* When you record your new knowledge in the third column, you will be answering some question or set of questions from the *What do we need to investigate?* column. You should describe what you gained from the investigations you completed and the evidence they provided. Remember, evidence is always necessary to answer scientific questions. You will fill in the evidence column based on data and trends you found in your investigations and your understandings of the science readings. You may use the text in this book to help you phrase your new understanding. As the class fills in the *Project Board*, make sure to record the same information on your own *Project Board* page.

What's the Point?

Your challenge is to determine how the differences between land and water bodies might affect the planet's temperature. You developed and revised an explanation for this factor. This explanation will be important as you develop your prediction for *Planet X*.

Explain

10 min.

Students record their explanations and discuss with their groups to construct a group explanation.

⬡ Get Going

Distribute a *Create Your Explanation* page to each student and ask students to record their explanations on it. Let students know how much time they have.

△ Guide

Let groups know they will be meeting to share their explanations and to create a group explanation. They should begin by having each group member present their responses to the questions and their explanation to the group. After everyone has presented, they should discuss the similarities and differences between their explanations. Where they have differences they should look at the data supporting the parts of the explanations to help them determine what their best explanation will be.

⬡ Get Going

Distribute a *Create Your Explanation* page to each student and ask students to write Group Explanation on it. Let students know how much time they have.

△ Guide and Assess

Monitor groups and assist them as needed. Model appropriate language as needed.

TEACHER TALK

❝ I don't understand how the science knowledge backs up your explanation. Could you walk me through it?

I don't see how ... is supported by your data. Could you show me?

This statement doesn't make sense to me. Could you state it another way?

I'm not sure if I understand this. Do you mean: ... ❞

everyone's explanations and create a group explanation.

Communicate

Your class will meet to discuss the answers to the *Reflect* questions and the group explanations. Your class will select or create a new class explanation.

Update the Project Board

Communicate

15 min.

Students participate in a class discussion on groups' explanations and create a class explanation.

△ Guide

Let students know each group will be presenting their explanation. Emphasize that after each presentation, if anything was not clear, students should ask questions to the presenting group to make sure they understand the explanation and how the evidence and science knowledge supports the claim. When needed, model appropriate language.

Consider having the class point out the claim, the evidence, and the science knowledge if the presenting group is not getting many questions. Encourage the presenting group to answer the person asking the question.

After all groups have presented, guide the class to discussing the similarities and differences between all the explanations. Record the points the class agrees on. Discuss why the differences arise and what the class thinks would be best to include in the explanation.

Have the class construct an explanation. Once the class explanation is completed, distribute another *Create Your Explanation* page and have the class record their class explanation indicating at the top of the page that it is the class explanation.

◇ Evaluate

The final class explanation should contain a claim about how the surface temperature above water and along a coastline is warmer in the winter and cooler in the summer than above land. They should support this claim with information about how land and water differences affect the amount of heat energy transferred to and away from land and water and how this affects the air temperature above the land and water. A description of specific heat capacity and absorption of light should be included. Students should refer to their data in their explanation and list the results of their analysis. Graphs and/or tables should be included as appropriate.

An example explanation is given below.

> *Land and water differences effect the range of temperatures a planet experiences. The surface temperatures above water or near a coastline are warmer in the winter and cooler in the summer because water requires more than five times the energy than land does to raise its temperature. It also requires more energy than land to lower its temperature. As a result, land warms and cools more quickly than water does.*
>
> *Different materials absorb heat energy differently due to how much light they reflect away from their surface. Water may only absorb 2% to 92% of the light energy shining on it depending on the angle of the incoming light. Sand absorbs between 40% and 70% of the incoming light energy. Another factor that affects how a substance changes temperature is how much energy it requires to raise one gram of the substance by one degree Celsius. This quantity is known as the specific heat capacity. Water requires one calorie of heat energy to raise one gram of it by one degree Celsius. Sand only requires 0.19 calories of heat energy to raise one gram of it by one degree Celsius. The higher the specific heat capacity, the slower the rate that heat is transferred to or away from the substance. We observed that water did not change its temperature as much or as rapidly as sand when heated or cooled over a duration of 12 minutes of heating and 12 minutes of cooling. Using My World, we also observed data showing that land and water differences vary with latitude. Within the tropics the data showed land*

is slightly warmer than water in the summer and slightly colder than water in the winter. However, at the mid-latitudes, land tends to be about 15°F warmer than water in the summer and approximately 30°F colder than water in the winter.

Update the Project Board
15 min.

The class updates their Project Board with any new science knowledge and any questions that students now have.

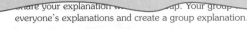

...share your explanation with...up. Your group...everyone's explanations and create a group explanation.

Communicate

Your class will meet to discuss the answers to the *Reflect* questions and the group explanations. Your class will select or create a new class explanation.

Update the *Project Board*

Now that you have run these investigations and completed your explanations, you need to update your *Project Board*. Once again, you will focus on the two columns *What are we learning?* and *What is our evidence?* When you record your new knowledge in the third column, you will be answering some question or set of questions from the *What do we need to investigate?* column. You should describe what you gained from the investigations you completed and the evidence they provided. Remember, evidence is always necessary to answer scientific questions. You will fill in the evidence column based on data and trends you found in your investigations and your understandings of the science readings. You may use the text in this book to help you phrase your new understanding. As the class fills in the *Project Board*, make sure to record the same information on your own *Project Board* page.

What's the Point?

Your challenge is to determine how the differences between land and water bodies might affect the planet's temperature. You developed and revised an explanation for this factor. This explanation will be important as you...

△ Guide

Students have already updated their *Project Board* at the end of the last section and may have difficulty finding new things to add. They should review their *Project Board* and determine if they would like to add or revise anything on it.

Record students' responses.

Ask students what they would like to enter in Column 5 (*What does it mean for the challenge or question?*) Remind them that the challenge is to determine which regions of *Planet X* have appropriate temperatures for a human colony.

Students should include information about how land and water differences must be taken into account since it affects the range of temperatures a planet experiences and how it affects the temperature. Students should note that the surface temperatures above water or near a coastline are warmer in the winter and cooler in the summer because water requires more energy than land in order to raise its temperature, it also loses more energy than land to lower its temperature. As a result, land warms and cools more quickly than water does.

Students should understand that within the tropics, land is slightly warmer than water in the summer and slightly colder than water in the winter. However, at the mid-latitudes, land tends to be about 15°F warmer than water in the summer and approximately 30°F colder than water in the winter.

Teacher Reflection Questions

- How did the questions help guide students?

- How effective was the iterative process of revising their explanation?

- How did you keep students focused on task and in participating in the discussions?

NOTES

NOTES

Back to the Big Challenge

Which Regions of a Newly Discovered Planet have Surface Temperatures Appropriate for a Human Colony?

◀ *2 class periods*

A class period is considered to be one 40 to 50 minute class.

Overview

Students copy and revise their previous prediction maps for January and July. They share their predictions during a *Solution Briefing* to communicate their ideas to the rest of the class so students can better understand how other people approached the problem.

Targeted Concepts, Skills, and Nature of Science	Performance Expectations
Scientists often work together and share their findings. Sharing findings makes new information available and helps scientists to refine their ideas and build on others' ideas. When another person's or group's idea is used, credit needs to be given.	Students should work in groups and present their solutions to the class.
Scientists must keep clear, accurate, and descriptive records of what they do so they can share their work with others and consider what they did, why they did it, and what they want to do next.	Students should use records created during this *Learning Set* to construct their maps. During the *Solution Briefing*, students should take notes of other presentations on what they did and ideas on how they want to change their own prediction maps.
Graphs, maps, and tables are an effective way to analyze and communicate results of scientific investigation.	Students should update their prediction maps of the average monthly temperatures for July and January for *Planet X* to include land and water differences. Students should update their habitability map based on these. These maps are used to convey students' ideas during the *Solution Briefing*.

Targeted Concepts, Skills, and Nature of Science	Performance Expectations
Explanations are claims supported by evidence, accepted ideas and facts.	Students should use their explanations to construct their maps and to support the prediction maps to be presented in the *Solution Briefing*.
Different substances (such as soil and water) transfer heat energy at different rates and require different amounts of energy to raise their temperatures. The amount of energy needed to raise the temperature of a substance is described by its specific heat capacity.	Students should apply what they have learned about water and land temperature differences and how they affect surface temperatures when constructing their temperature prediction maps.

Materials

1 per classroom	Computer with *My World* software and projection system
1 per group	Computer with *My World* software
1 per student	*Solution Briefing Notes* page *Project Board* page *Land and Water Differences* page (filled in from *Section 4.5*)
1 per class	Class *Project Board*

NOTES

....

....

....

....

....

....

Activity Setup and Preparation

Modify the temperature prediction map for January and July and a prediction map showing regions of habitability from the *Back to the Big Challenge* in *Learning Set 3*. Decide what to emphasize when you demonstrate for students how to revise their maps. Use the instructions in the student text and the *Back to the Big Challenge Implementation*.

If you do not have computers available, the students can complete this project by coloring printed copies of maps.

Decide how students will present their ideas during the *Solution Briefing*. You could have students present their ideas using a computer projection system, or using print outs that are projected.

Homework Options

Reflection

- **Science Content:** How did you change your prediction map for January? *(Students' responses should describe how they changed the temperatures of the land and water following the data they collected for the average temperature differences for land and water in latitude bands of Earth.)*

Preparation for Learning Set 5

- **Science Content:** How do you think elevation affects surface temperatures? *(The purpose of this question is to elicit students' initial ideas and get them thinking about how land and water might affect a planet's surface temperature.)*

NOTES

NOTES

Learning Set 4

Back to the Big Challenge

Which regions of a newly discovered planet have surface temperatures appropriate for a human colony?

You will modify your *Planet X* temperature map based on what you now know about land and water temperature differences. You now know where land masses and oceans are on *Planet X*. Therefore, you need to revise your predictions to show how the temperatures are different for land and water. Use your data from the previous investigations and your final class explanation to update your prediction for the temperatures on *Planet X*. Once you have updated your prediction, modify your prediction of habitable areas on *Planet X*.

Make Your January Temperature Prediction

In *Learning Set 3*, you created a January field and a July field to better represent the seasonal temperature changes that happen as a result of tilt. In this section, you will update these prediction maps to reflect what you know about differences in land and water temperatures.

Procedure: Prepare the January Fields.

1. **Open your *Planet X* project file in *My World*.** Select "Open Project" in the File drop-down menu.

2. **Show habitable and non-habitable areas.** In the "Visualize" tab, turn off the "Tilt Habitabilty" selection by selecting the "All (highlighting off)" radio button in the *Planet X* layer. This will show your prediction for the whole planet, including both habitable and non-habitable areas.

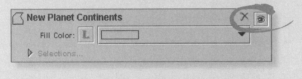

Learning Set 4

Back to the Big Challenge

< 5 min.

Students review and revise their Planet X *temperature maps based on their new science knowledge from the* Learning Set.

○ **Engage**

Engage students by having them consider how they would revise their average January temperature prediction map for *Planet X*. Record students' responses.

❝How would you revise your January temperature prediction map for *Planet X* and what information would you use to help you?❞

*A class period is considered to be one 40 to 50 minute class.

△ Guide

Briefly review what students have written in Columns 3 (*What have we learned?*), 4 (*What is our evidence?*), and 5 (*What does it mean for the challenge or question?*) of their class *Project Board*.

Let students know that now they will be revising the temperature prediction maps they created at the end of *Learning Set 3*.

TEACHER TALK

❝Based on what is on your *Project Board* about land and water temperature differences, you should update your previous surface temperature maps of *Planet X* which were based on the shape and the tilt of the planet and the habitability map you constructed.❞

Make Your January Temperature Prediction

< 5 min.

Students prepare for the procedures.

Use your d_____ the previous investigation_____ your final class exp_____ to update your prediction for the temperatures on *Planet X*. Once you have updated your prediction, modify your prediction of habitable areas on *Planet X*.

Make Your January Temperature Prediction

In *Learning Set 3*, you created a January field and a July field to better represent the seasonal temperature changes that happen as a result of tilt. In this section, you will update these prediction maps to reflect what you know about differences in land and water temperatures.

Procedure: Prepare the January Fields.

1. **Open your *Planet X* project file in *My World*.** Select "Open Project" in the File drop-down menu.

2. **Show habitable and non-habitable areas.** In the "Visualize" tab, turn off the "Tilt H_____ ____election b_____ing the "All ____ ____ off)"

⬡ Get Going

Ask students to read through the procedures and let them know you will be demonstrating to the class how they will be using the *My World* software to revise part of the January maps by going through the examples in the student text. Let students know once they begin revising their maps, they will complete the procedures for the maps for January, July, and habitability.

NOTES

....

....

....

3. **Show *Planet X* continent outlines on your temperature visualization.** In the Layer List, find the layer titled "New Planet Continents." This layer is currently inactive. Select the empty box on the right to reveal an eye.

4. **Duplicate the *Planet X* Tilt January Field.**

   a) **Go to the "Edit" tab. Select the *Planet X* layer to edit that layer.** Be sure *"Tilt January"* is selected from the Edit Field drop-down menu.

   b) **Click "Add Field..." in the bottom right corner of the screen.** Select "Duplicate an Existing Field."

   c) **Create a duplicate of "Tilt January."** Name the new field *"LandWater January."* Click OK. You now have a new field to edit called "LandWater January."

5. **Change the "LandWater January" visualization to represent predicted land and water differences.** In Section 4.5, you calculated the differences between the average temperature and the land and water temperatures at different latitudes. *For example, you found that in January at the northern mid-latitudes (30°N to 60°N) the land is about 17.6° cooler than the average temperature, and the water is about 13.4° warmer than the average temperature.* Use the following steps to either add or subtract from the average temperatures on land and water to best represent the land/water differences on *Planet X*.

   a) **Focus on the land or water in a latitude range. Select the land or water and latitude range using the radio buttons in the *Planet X* layer.**

   Example 1: Land at 30° to 60° North. Select the "Land: 30-60 North" radio button in the Planet X layer.

   Example 2: Water at 30° to 60° North. Select the "Water: 30-60 North" radio button in the Planet X layer.

   Your average predicted January temperatures at that latitude will be displayed and all other temperatures hidden.

   b) **Determine if the land or water at that latitude is warmer or colder than the average temperature in January.** Use the land and water differences calculations from Section 4.5.

Procedure: Prepare the January Fields
20 min.

Demonstrate the procedures to the class, then groups complete the procedures.

△ Guide

Using the procedures described in the student text, demonstrate Steps 1 and 2 showing students how to open their project file and turn off the tilt habitability section by selecting All (highlighting off.)

Show students how to turn on the visualization of the continents if it is not already turned on. In the image above the continents are turned on. The student text explains how to turn this on. Simply click on the button of the eye for the New Planet Continents selection.

Show students how to duplicate their map following Step 4, which should look like the image shown below.

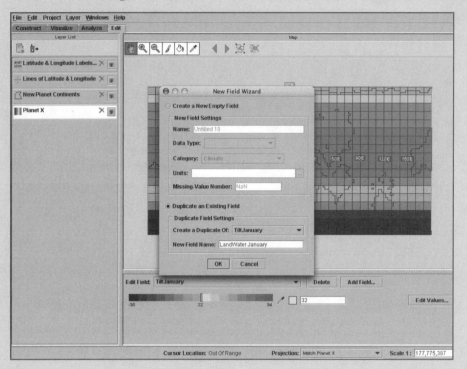

Show students how to complete Step 5 for both examples described in the student text. Below is an image showing how to complete Step 5a in which a latitude band is selected.

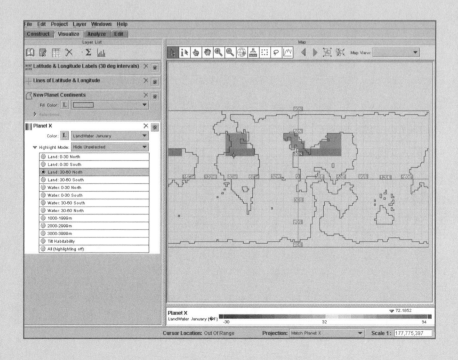

Example 1: At 30° to 60° North, the land is 17.6° colder or lower than the average temperature.

Example 2: At 30° to 60° North, the water is 13.4° warmer or higher than the average temperature.

c) **Subtract or Add a constant value to all the land or water temperatures at that latitude.**

- Go to the "Analyze" tab. Go to "Add Fields to Layer," and select "By Math Operation."

- Add a Field to the Table of Layer *"Planet X"* by computing a "Difference (subtraction)" or a "Sum."

Example 1: On the land, the temperature decreases, so "Difference (subtraction)" would be selected.

Example 2: On the water, the temperature increases, so "Sum" would be selected.

- You are going to add or subtract a constant value from the Land-Water January field. In the next section of the screen, select "LandWater January" from the first drop-down menu. Select "Constant Value" from the second drop-down menu.

- The "Constant Value" is the land difference you calculated in Section 4.5. Enter this value in the space to the right of "Constant Value."

Example 1: "17.6°" would be entered in that box.

Example 2: "13.4°" would be entered in that box.

- Select the focus latitudes from the "Compute for:" drop-down menu. The constant value will only be added to or subtracted from either the land or water temperature at those latitudes.

Example 1: Land 30-60 North

Example 2: Water 30-60 North

- Check the box marked "Copy Results Into Existing Field" and select "LandWater January" from the drop-down menu.

- "Results Name" should follow model in the example. Click "OK."

PF 119

PLANETARY FORECASTER

Walk students through how to complete steps 5b and 5c emphasizing that they should use their *Land and Water Differences* pages from *Section 4.5* and the student text to navigate through *My World*.

Show students how to save their work and emphasize to them that they should save their work after revising all the land and water temperatures for all the latitude bands.

PBIS — *Learning Set 4 • How Do Land and Water Affect Surface Temperatures?*

Example 1: Land30-60NJan

Example 2: Water30-60NJan

The cells that you changed should now be a different color or at least represent different values. You may want to look at the entire *Planet X* temperature visualization. Select the "All (highlighting off)" radio button in the *Planet X* layer.

Example 1: Analyze field for Land 30-60 North.

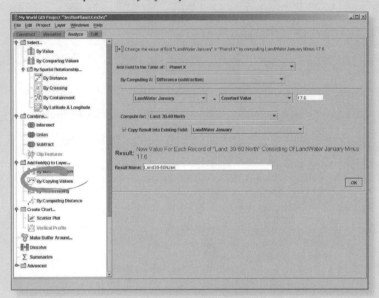

6. **Save your changes.** "Save Project" in the File menu.

7. **Return to the "Analyze" tab.** Repeat Step 5 for the remaining latitude bands on the "LandWater January" map. Below is a list to help you keep track of those you have completed.

NOTES

○ Get Going

Let groups know that once they have completed their January map they should continue on to complete their July and habitability maps. Let the class know how much time they have.

△ Guide and Assess

Monitor students' progress as they are revising their maps. Check that they are referring to their data from *Section 4.5* and that all group members are participating. Assist students as needed.

As students are completing their January fields have them print a map if they will need it for the *Solution Briefing* and then work on their July maps. The January maps should look similar to the following:

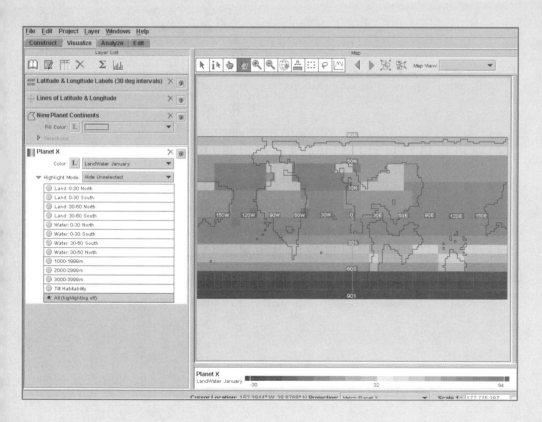

NOTES

....

....

Procedure: Prepare the July Fields

10 min.

Groups complete the procedure to update their temperature maps.

Land: 30-60 North; Result Name "Land30-60NJan"

Water: 30-60 North; Result Name "Water30-60NJan"

Land: 0-30 North; Result Name "Land0-30NJan"

Water: 0-30 North; Result Name "Water0-30NJan"

Land: 0-30 South; Result Name "Land0-30SJan"

Water: 0-30 South; Result Name "Water0-30SJan"

Land: 30-60 South; Result Name "Land30-60SJan"

Water: 30-60 South; Result Name "Water30-60SJan"

Procedure: Prepare the July Fields.

1. **Open your *Planet X* project file in *My World*.** Select "Open Project" in the File drop-down menu. If this is already open, skip to Step 3.

2. **Show habitable and non-habitable areas.** In the "Visualize" tab, turn off the "Tilt Habitabilty" selection by selecting "All (highlighting off)" radio button in the *Planet X* layer. This will show you your prediction for the whole planet, including both habitable and non-habitable areas.

3. **Show *Planet X* continent outlines on your temperature visualization.** In the Layer List, find the layer titled "New Planet Continents." This layer is currently inactive. Select the empty box on the right to reveal an eye.

4. **Duplicate the *Planet X* Tilt July Field.** Go to the "Edit" tab. Select the *Planet X* layer to edit that layer. Be sure *"Tilt July"* is selected from the Edit Field drop-down menu. Click "Add Field…" in the bottom right corner of the screen. Select "Duplicate an Existing Field." Create a duplicate of "Tilt January." Name the new field *"LandWater July."* Click OK! You now have a new field to edit called "LandWater July."

PF 121

PLANETARY FORECASTER

△ Guide and Assess

Monitor students' progress and guide them as needed. Students' July maps should look similar to the map shown. Remind students to print out the map, if needed, and to continue on to complete their habitability map.

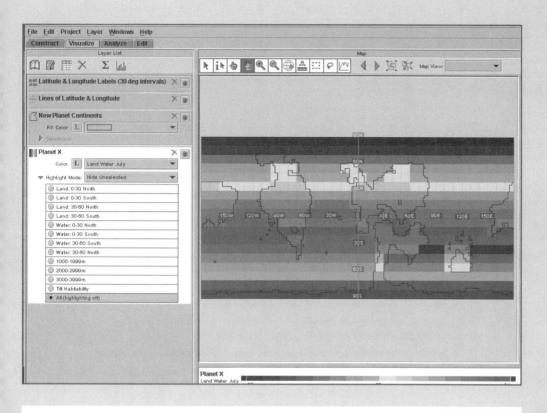

NOTES

5. **Change the "Land Water July" visualization to represent predicted land and water differences.** In Section 4.5, you calculated the differences between the average temperature and the land and water temperatures at different latitudes. *For example, you found that in July at the northern mid-latitudes (30°N to 60°N) the land is about 13 degrees warmer than the average temperature and the water is 1 degree colder than the average temperature.*

Use the following steps to either add or subtract from the average temperatures on land and water to best represent the land/water differences on *Planet X*.

a) **Focus on the land or water in a latitude range. Select the land or water and latitude range using the radio buttons in the *Planet X* layer.**

Example 1: Land at 30° to 60° North. Select the "Land: 30-60North" radio button in the Planet X layer.

Example 2: Water at 30° to 60° North. Select the "Water: 30-60North" radio button in the Planet X layer.

Your average predicted July temperatures at that latitude will be displayed and all other temperatures hidden.

b) **Determine if the land or water at that latitude is warmer or colder than the average temperature in July.** Use the land and water differences calculations from Section 4.5.

Example 1: At 30° to 60° North the land is 13° warmer or higher than the average temperature.

Example 2: At 30° to 60° North the water is 1° colder or lower than the average temperature.

c) **Subtract or Add a constant value to all the land or water temperatures at that latitude.**

• Go to the "Analyze" tab. Go to "Add Fields to Layer," and select "By Math Operation."

• Add a Field to the Table of Layer "*Planet X*" by computing a "Difference (subtraction)" or a "Sum."

Example 1: On the land, the temperature increases, so "Sum" would be selected.

PF 122

Project-Based Inquiry Science

NOTES

....

....

Example 2: On the water, the temperature decreases, so "Difference (subtraction)" would be selected.

- You are going to add or subtract a constant value from the LandWater July field. In the next section of the screen, select "LandWater July" from the first drop-down menu. Select "Constant Value" from the second drop-down menu.

- The "Constant Value" is the land difference you calculated in Section 4.5. Enter this value in the space to the right of "Constant Value."

Example 1: "13" would be entered in that box.

Example 2: "1" would be entered in that box.

- Select the focus latitudes from the "Compute for:" drop-down menu. The constant value will only be added to or subtracted from either the land or water temperatures at those latitudes.

Example 1: Land 30-60 North

Example 2: Water 30-60 North

- Check the box marked "Copy Results Into Existing Field" and select "Land-Water July" to show.

- "Results Name" should follow model in the example. Click "OK."

PF 123

PLANETARY FORECASTER

NOTES

Example 1: Land30-60NJuly

Example 2: Water30-60NJuly

The cells that you changed should now be a different color or at least represent different values. You may want to look at the entire *Planet X* temperature visualization. Select the "All (highlighting off)" radio button in the *Planet X* layer.

Example 1: Analyze field for Land 30-60 North.

6. **Save your changes.** "Save Project" in the File menu.

7. **Return to the "Analyze" tab. Repeat Step 5** for the remaining latitude bands on the "LandWater July" map. Below is a list to help you keep track of those you have completed.

Land: 30-60 North;
Result Name "Land30-60NJuly"

Water: 30-60 North;
Result Name "Water30-60NJuly"

Land: 0-30 North;
Result Name "Land0-30NJuly"

Water: 0-30 North;
Result Name "Water0-30NJuly"

Land: 0-30 South;
Result Name "Land0-30SJuly"

Water: 0-30 South;
Result Name "Water0-30SJuly"

Land: 30-60 South;
Result Name "Land30-60SJuly"

Water: 30-60 South;
Result Name "Water30-60SJuly"

When the Sun hits the water indirectly, little of the sunlight is absorbed.

NOTES

....

....

Procedure: Identify Habitable Areas

You have created (and saved) a January and a July prediction map for *Planet X*. Your prediction map now represents the shape, tilt, and land/water differences factors. CSA wants to know where on *Planet X* is habitable all year. Use the January and July temperature maps to create a new habitability map.

1. **Open your *Planet X* project file in *My World*.** Select "Open Project" in the File drop-down menu. This project file may still be open after creating the LandWater January and July fields.

2. **Identify ranges for areas that are habitable in both January and July.**

   a) **Go to the Analyze tab.** Go to the Select folder and select by Value.

   b) **Under the "Select Records From:" drop-down menu, choose "Planet X."** Under the "Whose" drop-down menu, choose "LandWater July." Check "Less Than" and enter 85. Select "Greater Than or Equal to" and enter 25.

   c) **Click the button marked with a small plus sign to the right of the screen.** This will allow you to add a second set of requirements for your selection.

   d) **Under the second "Whose" drop-down menu, choose "LandWater January."** Check "Less Than" and enter 85. Select "Greater Than or Equal to" and enter 25.

   e) **Under "Results Name," type in the title "LandWater Habitability."** Do **not** check the box called "Make Selection a New Layer."

   f) **After you have filled out the page to select by value, click "OK."**

Procedure: Identify Habitable Areas

5 min.

Groups complete the procedures updating their habitability maps.

△ Guide and Assess

Monitor students' progress and assist them as needed. Remind students to save their work. Have students print out maps if needed. Habitability maps should look similar to the map shown.

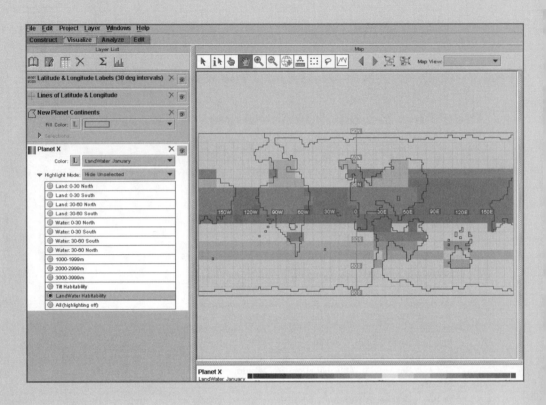

NOTES

....

....

....

....

....

....

....

....

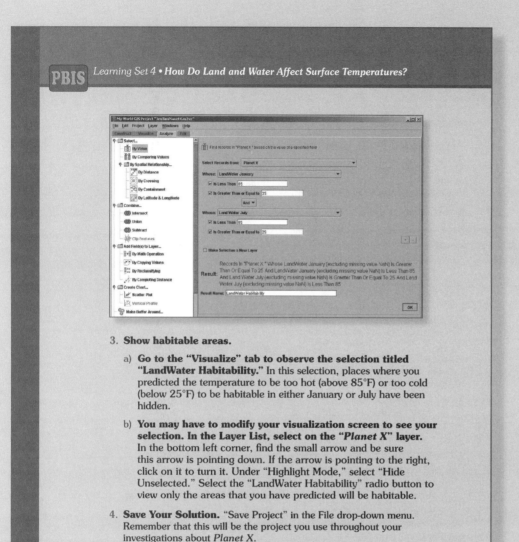

3. **Show habitable areas.**

a) **Go to the "Visualize" tab to observe the selection titled "LandWater Habitability."** In this selection, places where you predicted the temperature to be too hot (above 85°F) or too cold (below 25°F) to be habitable in either January or July have been hidden.

b) **You may have to modify your visualization screen to see your selection. In the Layer List, select on the *"Planet X"* layer.** In the bottom left corner, find the small arrow and be sure this arrow is pointing down. If the arrow is pointing to the right, click on it to turn it. Under "Highlight Mode," select "Hide Unselected." Select the "LandWater Habitability" radio button to view only the areas that you have predicted will be habitable.

4. **Save Your Solution.** "Save Project" in the File drop-down menu. Remember that this will be the project you use throughout your investigations about *Planet X*.

NOTES

....

....

Communicate Your Solution
Solution Briefing

20 min.

Students participate in a class discussion on groups' ideas about temperature predictions and habitability for Planet X.

Communicate Your Solution

Solution Briefing

Remember, a *Solution Briefing* is a presentation that allows presenters and audiences to communicate effectively about an idea or solution. The *Solution Briefing* provides an opportunity to see what people have tried and what they have gained from their attempts at solving a challenge.

Your *Solution Briefing* should focus on the following points:

- Present the general look of your solution. Explain where temperature differences appear on your map.
- Tell others how the data you collected and science you gained in this *Learning Set* support your decisions about the temperature on *Planet X*.
- Discuss how the class explanation of land and water differences supports the solution you have developed so far. If your map purposely does not match the explanation, tell your audience why this is so. Provide them with an explanation that better fits your idea.

As you listen to *Solution Briefings* of other groups, it will be important to carefully look at each solution. You should ask questions about how the solution matches up with the ideas and knowledge you have gained during this *Learning Set*. Be prepared to ask (and answer) questions, such as these:

- As the map was being developed, what changes did you make that cannot be seen in the final map?
- How well does the map match up with the class's explanation of how shape affects temperature?
- Are there areas that do not seem to match the explanation?
- Which areas seemed difficult to map? Which areas were easy to map?
- Are there any changes this person might want to make on their map at this time? If so, why?

Be sure to fill out a *Solution Briefing Notes* page as you listen to everyone's presentation.

PF 127

PLANETARY FORECASTER

△ Guide

Remind students that the goal of a *Solution Briefing* is for everyone to hear how other students approached the challenge and to see a variety of solutions that might work.

Emphasize to the class that they will need to address each of the three bullets listed in the student text. As they listen to other groups present, they will need to answer the following set of the bulleted questions.

They need to look at each map and consider if the maps fit what they understand about how land and water differences affect a planet's surface temperature. Remind students they will be taking notes using the *Solution Briefing Notes* page as they listen to presentations.

⬡ Get Going

Distribute the *Solution Briefing Notes* page and let groups know how much time they have to prepare their presentations and how much time they have for their presentations.

△ Guide and Assess

Have groups present. As each group is presenting check that they have addressed the three bulleted points listed in the student text.

After each presentation, encourage students to ask questions, especially if anything was not clear or if one of the bulleted items was not addressed. Students should ask the suggested questions listed in the student text and/or other questions they may have.

Remind students to take notes as they are listening to the presentation and the responses to questions.

After each group has presented, discuss the similarities and differences between groups' ideas.

META NOTES

Students will need a way to project their maps (either a projection of an electronic version or a printed copy.)

NOTES

Reflect

10 min.

Students participate in a class discussion on their responses.

Reflect

Answer the following questions. Be prepared to share your answers with your group and the class.

1. How did you use your land and water differences explanation to determine the temperature of *Planet X*?

2. How is the location/size of the habitable areas different than it was for shape and tilt? Why?

3. Think back to the initial list of factors. Identify the ones that have something to do with land and water differences. Describe how each of those factors would affect surface temperatures.

4. So far you have studied the effects of three major factors on surface temperature. You still need to study elevation. What do you think will happen to your possible habitable locations on *Planet X* before you make your final proposal to the CSA? Do you think they will get bigger, smaller, or stay the same?

This Hawaiian coastline lies at approximately 16°N. How different from one another will the temperatures of the land and water be?

⬡ Get Going

Let students know they will be sharing their answers to the four questions with their group and with the class. Let students know how much time they have.

△ Guide and Assess

Have a class discussion on students' responses.

1. Students should describe how they used their land and water differences explanation to determine their predictions for the temperatures of *Planet X*.

2. Students should compare and contrast the habitable area maps they created. Students should note some of the locations in the Northern Hemisphere that were in the habitable temperature range that are no longer habitable (these were all over water) and some locations in the Southern Hemisphere that were not considered habitable that now are.

3. Students should describe how they think the initial list of factors affecting a planet's surface temperature might affect the land and water differences. The factors are shape, tilt, land and water temperature differences, and elevation. Students should realize that the more direct the sunlight and the more hours of sunlight there are, the more the sun's energy is absorbed. Both shape and tilt affect the directness of the sunlight and tilt affects the number of hours sunlight reaches the surface during a day. Land and water differences occur because different materials absorb light differently and require different amounts of energy to raise their temperatures.

4. Students should support their predictions based on their experiences using *My World*, new science knowledge, class discussions, and any other experiences from the *Learning Set*.

NOTES

Update the Project Board

< 5 min.

Students update the Project Board *with new ideas and questions.*

Update the *Project Board*

Now that you have completed this *Learning Set*, you know more about how land and water differences affect surface temperatures. You are now ready to fill in the *Project Board* more completely.

You will focus on the two columns *What are we learning?* and *What is our evidence?* When you record what you are learning in the third column, you will be answering a question or set of questions from the *What do we need to investigate?* column. You should describe what you gained from the investigation you just did. Make sure to provide evidence to support this information.

As the class fills in the *Project Board*, record the same information on your own *Project Board* page.

What's the Point?

You have just used what you discovered about land and water differences to improve your proposal to the Cooperative Space Agency. You still have one more factor to investigate. As you learn about this factor, elevation, you will continue to update your habitability predictions. Your predictions for the habitable areas of *Planet X* may change again as you investigate elevation in the next *Learning Set*.

PF 129

PLANETARY FORECASTER

△ Guide

Have a class discussion after the *Solution Briefing* and update the *Project Board* if needed. Students should be able to add information to Column 5 (*What does it mean for the challenge or question?*)

Teacher Reflection Questions

- What difficulties did students have applying the information they learned to create the computer models at the end? How did you guide them?

- How did the *Solution Briefing* help students' understanding of the challenge?

- What went well during the *Solution Briefing?* What would you like to do differently next time?

NOTES

NOTES

LEARNING SET 5 INTRODUCTION

Learning Set 5

How Does Elevation Affect Surface Temperatures?

Students investigate how elevation affects surface temperature by comparing temperature data from My World *for different elevations and exploring density, air pressure, and convection.*

Overview

Students investigate how elevation affects surface temperatures. Students begin by viewing an elevation map of *Planet X* and predicting how elevation affects surface temperatures. Students analyze temperature data for different elevations and similar latitudes on Earth using data from *My World* to come to the conclusion that air at higher elevations is cooler. Students read about density and air pressure and that air pressure is lower at higher elevations. Students investigate how temperature, pressure, and elevation are related using data in *My World*. From their analysis they observe that both temperature and pressure decrease with increasing elevation and support this by measuring how temperature changes when pressure changes for the same elevation. Students read about convection. Students revise their original prediction maps of how and why elevation changes affect surface temperature and use them to show the impact of elevation changes in their predictions for *Planet X*. Using the data and explanations students have, students write a recommendation to the *CSA* of the most habitable locations on *Planet X*.

◀ $8\frac{1}{2}$ *class periods*

A class period is considered to be one 40 to 50 minute class.

LOOKING AHEAD

You will need 2-L bottles for *Section 5.5*. Consider collecting these now.

Targeted Concepts, Skills, and Nature of Science	Section
Scientists often work together and share their findings. Sharing findings makes new information available and helps scientists to refine their ideas and build on others' ideas. When another person's or group's idea is used, credit needs to be given.	5.1, 5.2, 5.6, BBC
Scientists must keep clear, accurate, and descriptive records of what they do so they can share their work with others and consider what they did, why they did it, and what they want to do next.	5.1, 5.2, 5.4, 5.5, 5.6, BBC, ABC I

Targeted Concepts, Skills, and Nature of Science	Section
Graphs, maps, and tables are an effective way to analyze and communicate results of scientific investigation.	5.2, 5.4, 5.5, BBC, ABC I
Identifying factors that lead to variation is an important part of scientific investigation.	5.1
Scientists make claims (conclusions) based on evidence obtained (trends in data) from reliable investigations	5.2, 5.4, 5.5
Explanations are claims supported by evidence, accepted ideas and facts.	5.6, BBC, ABC I
Heat energy may be transferred through conduction, radiation, or convection.	5.6
Temperatures around the Earth's surface vary widely, but can be predicted somewhat by location and season.	5.2
The atmosphere is made up of molecules. The density and pressure of air decreases with increasing elevation.	5.3
Surface temperature changes with changes in elevation and air pressure. As elevation increases, the air pressure and temperature decrease. As the pressure increases the temperature increases.	5.4, 5.5, 5.6, BBC

Students' Initial Conceptions and Capabilities

In studies of students' learning about Earth Science topics, students have several recurring misconceptions about the surface temperature factor of elevation.

- Students may believe that higher elevations are warmer because these locations are closer to the Sun.

- Students may think high elevations are warmer because warm air rises.

- Students might believe higher elevations are colder because these locations are closer to outer space which is cold.

- Students may think higher elevations are colder because there is more wind at high levels of the atmosphere.

- Students may have difficulty understanding that air is matter with mass and density.

Students' Initial Conceptions and Capabilities	• Students may have problems understanding how energy transfers between molecules of air through motion.

Understanding for Teachers

At the end of the *Learning Set,* students should be able to explain the relationship between temperature, elevation, and surface air pressure. They should understand that energy is exchanged between Earth's surface and the air near the surface by contact between the ground and the air via conduction and radiation. They should also understand that this energy transfer is most efficient in areas where the air is denser, i.e. at lower elevations and that the gravitational pull by Earth on the atmosphere causes the air to be densest. Students should understand that as the heated air rises via convection into less dense altitudes, it expands and loses much of its energy and drops in temperature. In addition to expansion, molecules of air can lose heat by conduction to other molecules they bump into and by radiation.

Most of the Sun's radiation passes through the atmosphere to Earth's land and water. Some solar energy that reaches Earth's atmosphere is reflected back, some is absorbed by Earth's atmosphere, and some is absorbed by Earth's surface. Earth's surface is primarily heated by energy that is reradiated by Earth's surface in the form of infrared radiation. Most molecules in the atmosphere cannot absorb the energy reradiated by Earth. Only certain molecules such as those of carbon dioxide, water vapor, methane, nitrous oxide, ozone, and CFCs are able to absorb infrared energy emitted by Earth's surface. These gases, known as greenhouse gases, radiate some of this absorbed energy back to Earth's surface and results in the warming of Earth's surface. This is known as the greenhouse effect. The gases involved in this process are present throughout the atmosphere and contribute to the heating of Earth everywhere. Without the greenhouse effect, the Earth's surface would be much cooler.

The lower atmosphere is primarily heated by energy radiated and conducted from the surface of Earth. Some factors that cause the air at lower elevations to be warmer than those at higher elevations are the density of air and convection. Heated air rises to higher altitudes due to convection and loses much of its energy as it expands to lower pressures, causing it to cool. Because the air is denser at lower elevations due to the gravitational pull there are more greenhouse gases present and more radiation is absorbed, affecting the temperatures at lower elevations to be greater.

An understanding of these phenomena will allow students to account for the differences between temperatures on mountains, in mid-elevation areas, in valleys, and on coasts, making their final recommendations for habitable locations on *Planet X* more realistic.

When the pressure decreases (such as when air expands), the temperature decreases. When gases expand, they do work on their surroundings. When there is no external source of energy (heat), i.e. the gas is in thermal equilibrium with its surroundings, the gas must expend internal energy to do this work (adiabatic expansion). The temperature of an ideal gas depends entirely on its internal energy. Therefore, the temperature decreases as the energy decreases.

The law of adiabatic expansion or compression states that any gas will cool that is allowed to expand freely from a higher pressure to a lower pressure without the transfer of external energy to the gas. Similarly, a gas will heat if compressed from a lower to a higher pressure in the absence of a transfer of energy from the gas.

The amount the temperature decreases per fixed unit of height or elevation (for example, 1000 meters) is called the environmental lapse rate. The average is 6.5°C (11.7°F), but the lapse rate in any specific area depends on the humidity. The latent heat of water makes temperatures fall off more gradually in more humid areas. Over dry areas, such as deserts, the temperature falls off more quickly (~9.8°C/km or 17.64°F/km). This is why the nights are so cold in the desert.

NOTES

....

....

....

....

....

....

....

LEARNING SET 5 IMPLEMENTATION

◀ $8\frac{1}{2}$ *class periods* *

Learning Set 5

How Does Elevation Affect Surface Temperatures?

TO: Scientific Research Team
FROM: The Cooperative Space Agency
SUBJECT: Surface Elevation of *Planet X*

Your work to date has been outstanding. The final factor you need to investigate is the effect of elevation on surface temperature. The Cooperative Space Agency has received data confirming the surface elevations of the landmasses on *Planet X*. A map has been provided with this information.

The agency has also been able to confirm that the structure of the lower atmosphere on *Planet X* is similar to that on Earth. The CSA would like you to investigate the importance of that information. You should be able to present your final recommendation for *Planet X* shortly. The success of this project now rests with you.

You have discovered how three different factors affect the surface temperature of a planet. You now know that land and water heat up and cool down at different rates, affecting the surrounding air temperature. The shape and tilt of a planet are also factors responsible for temperature differences.

There is one last factor to investigate and that is elevation. The picture above provides you with a clue about the effects of elevation. It is your job now to take it further and provide some solid evidence. You can begin by reading the bulletin (at left) from the Cooperative Space Agency.

The peak of Grand Teton, in Wyoming, is 4197 m (13,770 ft) above sea level.

PF 130

Project-Based Inquiry Science

Learning Set 5

How Does Elevation Affect Surface Temperatures?

5 min.

Introduce the Learning Set *and elicit students' initial ideas.*

META NOTES

Keep a record of students' initial ideas to make sure they are addressed at appropriate times during the *Learning Set.*

○ Engage

Introduce the CSA bulletin and elicit students' initial ideas about how elevation might affect temperature. Record students' ideas.

*A class period is considered to be one 40 to 50 minute class.

TEACHER TALK

"This *Learning Set* focuses on how elevation affects surface temperature. *CSA* has sent another bulletin informing us that they have received data confirming the surface elevations of the landmasses on *Planet X*. They have also confirmed that the structure of the lower atmosphere on *Planet X* is similar to Earth's atmosphere.

How do you think elevation affects surface temperature and why?"

After recording students' ideas about elevation, ask them to look in the student text at the image of Grand Teton in Wyoming and ask which month of the year they think the picture was taken. *(Students should infer based on the flowers and grass in the lower elevations it is likely that the picture was taken between May and August.)*

Let students know they will be exploring how elevation affects surface temperatures of a planet.

NOTES

SECTION 5.1 INTRODUCTION

5.1 Understand the Challenge

Predict the Effect of Elevation on Surface Temperatures

◄ $\frac{1}{2}$ *class period*

A class period is considered to be one 40 to 50 minute class.

Overview

Students investigate how elevation affects surface temperatures. Students begin by viewing an elevation map of *Planet X* and predicting how elevation will affect surface temperatures. The class considers three other ideas of how elevation may affect surface temperature and discusses what they agree with, what they disagree with, and what they need more information on. Students then update their *Project Board* including what they think they know about how elevation affects surface temperatures and questions they need to investigate.

Targeted Concepts, Skills, and Nature of Science	Performance Expectations
Scientists often work together and share their findings. Sharing findings makes new information available and helps scientists to refine their ideas and build on others' ideas. When another person's or group's idea is used, credit needs to be given.	Students should share their predictions and ideas with the class and, as a class, identify what they think they know about elevation and what they think they should investigate.
Scientists must keep clear, accurate, and descriptive records of what they do so they can share their work with others and consider what they did, why they did it, and what they want to do next.	Students should record their ideas and keep records of the class *Project Board* that organizes their ideas, questions, and what they are learning.
Identifying factors that lead to variation is an important part of scientific investigation.	Students should identify what they need to investigate about elevation to determine how it affects surface temperature.

Materials	
1 per class	Class *Project Board*
1 per student	*Project Board* page

Homework Options

Reflection

- **Science Process and Content:** Select one of the items from the class *Project Board* that the class needs to investigate and describe how you could investigate it? *(Students should be able to describe some observations of temperature change between the top and bottom of the mountain in the picture.)*

Preparation for 5.2

- **Science Process:** How could you obtain temperature data on the mountain in order to make a comparison? *(Students should describe some way to collect data, such as taking temperature readings at the top and the bottom of the mountain at the same time.)*

NOTES

SECTION 5.1 IMPLEMENTATION

◄ $\frac{1}{2}$ *class period**

5.1 Understand the Challenge

Predict the Effect of Elevation on Surface Temperatures

You have been asked to answer the question *How does elevation affect surface temperatures?* Look at the picture on the previous page. The snow-covered mountains are obviously higher than the surrounding land. Think about what this tells you about the *effect of elevation on temperature.* If you have ever traveled up a mountain, you may have noticed a drop in temperature. Look at the map below, provided by the Cooperative Space Agency. It shows the elevations of land on *Planet X.*

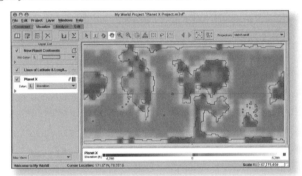

Get Started

Find a place on the map where there are several different colors close together. These color changes represent where the elevation is changing and there may be steep slopes. Now find a place on the map where the color is all the same across a large area. The same color indicates that the elevation is not changing. This land is relatively flat.

- What color represents the highest elevations?
- What color represents elevations closest to sea level?

5.1 Understand the Challenge

Predict the Effect of Elevation on Surface Temperatures

< 5 min.

Students are introduced to the elevation map and then make observations to better understand surface temperatures.

Get Started

5 min.

Students become familiar with the elevation map.

△ Guide

Let students know that the first thing they will do is study the elevation map that the *CSA* has provided. They should consider what they think they know about elevation so far.

△ Guide

Let students know at the bottom of the map there is a legend or key that shows how the colors in the map are related to the elevations. Have a class discussion on students' answers to the two bulleted questions.

*A class period is considered to be one 40 to 50 minute class.

Ask students what the maximum difference in elevation is that could be shown on the map. *(A total difference of 11,580 feet (5790 x 2).)*

◇ **Evaluate**

Make sure that students are able to comprehend the color scheme that makes up the elevation scale on the map. They should be aware that the units are feet. Students should realize that the highest elevations are represented by the color yellow-white, while green represents elevations close to sea-level.

△ **Guide and Assess**

Ask students where they think the land is relatively flat and where they think it is mountainous.

Students should select areas with little color variation as being relatively flat and areas with a lot of variation as mountainous.

NOTES

....

....

....

....

....

....

....

....

....

....

Predict

1. Describe your initial prediction about how elevation influences surface temperatures. Justify your reasoning.

2. Based on what you know, how confident are you about this prediction?

3. Below are some students' ideas about how elevation might affect surface temperatures. As you are reading, think about your own prediction and what you know. Which statements do you agree with? Which ones do you disagree with? What do you need to learn more about to know for sure?

Christopher: "Mountains are very cold because of the snow, so the surface temperatures are cold because of the snow, too."

Keara: "There are places of high elevation all over the world that are not cold. Many high-elevation places are hot. So, I do not see how elevation would matter."

Giovanni: "I think elevation only matters at very high elevations, like at the top of mountain ranges. Surface temperatures are affected only by elevation at extreme heights."

Update the *Project Board*

As you and your classmates share your ideas, you will discover connections between elevation and temperature. You probably feel confident in saying that elevation does affect temperature. However, you may have lots of questions about where, how, and why. Add your current understanding to the *What do we think we know?* column of the *Project Board*. Any new questions or ideas that you are not quite sure about should be written in the *What do we need to investigate?* column.

What's the Point?

You have collected data confirming the effects of three factors on surface temperatures—shape, tilt, and land/water differences. Elevation is the last factor left to investigate before you can begin to pull it all together and make a final recommendation about which places on *Planet X* are habitable. As you move forward, keep the other factors in mind and consider how they might work together.

Predict

10 min.

Students make predictions about how they believe elevation affects surface temperatures.

◯ Get Going

Ask students to write down their responses to the questions and let them know how much time they have.

△ Guide

Have a class discussion on students' responses. Use the information below to guide and assess the class.

1. Record students' initial ideas about how elevation affects surface temperatures. Make sure students provide reasoning for their ideas.

2. Students should describe why they are confident and base it on their reasoning.

3. Students should read the ideas out loud and discuss what they agree with and disagree with. Encourage students to discuss what they are unsure of and remind them these are areas they should investigate further. Ask the class what questions they need to answer.

Update the Project Board
10 min.

The class updates their Project Board *with new information and questions about surface temperature and elevation.*

top of mountain ranges. Surface temperatures are affected only by elevation at extreme heights."

Update the *Project Board*

As you and your classmates share your ideas, you will discover connections between elevation and temperature. You probably feel confident in saying that elevation does affect temperature. However, you may have lots of questions about where, how, and why. Add your current understanding to the *What do we think we know?* column of the *Project Board*. Any new questions or ideas that you are not quite sure about should be written in the *What do we need to investigate?* column.

What's the Point?

△ Guide

Ask students what they think they know about elevation and how it might affect the temperature of a planet. Record students' responses in the first column of the *Project Board*.

Review with students their predictions and what they would like to investigate further. Ask the class what they would like you to record in Column 2 (*What do we need to investigate?*) of the class *Project Board*. Record students' investigative questions and remind them that these are the questions they will need to answer to help them make their prediction map for *Planet X*.

Assessment Options

Targeted Concepts, Skills, and Nature of Science	How do I know if students got it?
Identifying factors that lead to variation is an important part of scientific investigation.	**ASK:** What variables do you think you will need to investigate to understand how elevation affects surface temperature? **LISTEN:** Students should identify what they need to investigate about elevation to determine how it affects surface temperature.

Teacher Reflection Questions

- What misconceptions did your students have?
- How did the class discussion help students construct questions to investigate?
- How did you guide the discussions?

NOTES

....

....

....

....

NOTES

SECTION 5.2 INTRODUCTION

5.2 Investigate

Comparing Temperatures at Different Elevations

◀ $1\frac{1}{2}$ *class periods*

A class period is considered to be one 40 to 50 minute class.

Overview

Students investigate how elevation affects surface temperatures. Students begin by viewing an elevation map of *Planet X* and predicting how elevation will affect surface temperatures. The class considers three other ideas of how elevation may affect surface temperature and discusses what they agree with, what they disagree with, and what they need more information on. Students update their *Project Board* to include what they think they know about how elevation affects surface temperatures, and questions they need to investigate.

Targeted Concepts, Skills, and Nature of Science	Performance Expectations
Scientists often work together and share their findings. Sharing findings makes new information available and helps scientists to refine their ideas and build on others' ideas. When another person's or group's idea is used, credit needs to be given.	Students should work in groups collecting and analyzing data. Then share their results with the class during an *Investigation Expo*.
Scientists must keep clear, accurate, and descriptive records of what they do so they can share their work with others and consider what they did, why they did it, and what they want to do next.	Students should keep clear, accurate, and descriptive records so they can share with the class their observations and ideas.
Graphs, maps, and tables are an effective way to analyze and communicate results of scientific investigation.	Students should construct graphs and tables based on results obtained from maps in *My World*. The tables and graphs should help students analyze how temperature varies with elevation and they should use these to communicate their results and ideas to the class.

Targeted Concepts, Skills, and Nature of Science	Performance Expectations
Scientists make claims (conclusions) based on evidence obtained (trends in data) from reliable investigations	Students should make claims about how temperature decreases as the elevation increases based on the data analysis.
Temperatures around Earth's surface vary widely, but can be predicted somewhat by location and season.	Students should describe how temperatures are affected by changes in elevation for similar latitudes.

Materials

1 per student	*Elevation and Temperature Data 1* page *Elevation and Temperature Data 2* page Optional: *Project Board* page
1 per group	Computer with *My World* software Poster paper and markers
1 per classroom	Computer with *My World* software and a projection system Optional: class *Project Board*

NOTES

....

....

....

....

....

....

....

Activity Setup and Preparation

Using the information in the student text and the *Section 5.2 Implementation*, go through the procedures using the *My World* software. Determine where your class may have difficulties and what you should emphasize in the demonstration.

If there are not enough computers, students could obtain data from your demonstration, or from printed copies showing the data.

Consider updating the class *Project Board* at the end of the *Investigation Expo*.

Homework Options

Reflection

- Science Content: What do you know about how elevation affects temperature and what do you think causes it? *(Students should describe how temperature decreases with increases elevation and support this with the data from* My World.*)*

Preparation for Section 5.3

- **Science Content:** Do you think that the air is any different at sea level than it is at higher elevations? Why? *(The purpose of this question is to elicit students' initial ideas about air.)*

NOTES

....

....

....

....

....

....

....

NOTES

SECTION 5.2 IMPLEMENTATION

5.2 Investigate

Comparing Temperatures at Different Elevations

Elevation is height above **sea level**. Sea level is determined by taking the average height of all the oceans. Today, satellites such as TOPEX/Poseidon can measure ocean height within 5 cm. The highest point above sea level in the United States is Mt. McKinley Denali in Alaska. It is 6194 m (20,320 ft) above sea level. Mitre Peak, in New Zealand, rises directly from the ocean floor to a height of 1692 m (5560 ft) above sea level.

elevation: height above sea level.

sea level: average height of all oceans.

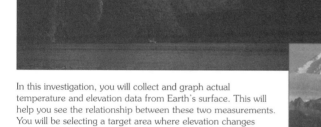

At a height of 1692 m (5560 ft), Mitre Peak in New Zealand is one of the highest mountains in the world that rises directly from the ocean floor.

Alaska's Mount McKinley Denali, at 6194 m (20,320 ft), has the highest elevation of any point in the U.S.

In this investigation, you will collect and graph actual temperature and elevation data from Earth's surface. This will help you see the relationship between these two measurements. You will be selecting a target area where elevation changes rapidly over a very short distance. By taking temperature readings at different heights above sea level, you will be able to see the effects of this factor.

PF 133

PLANETARY FORECASTER

5.2 Investigate

Comparing Temperatures at Different Elevations

< 5 min.

Students use My World *to observe the differences in temperatures as elevation changes.*

○ Engage

Ask students what type of experiences they have had at higher elevations. Students may comment on temperature changes, weather changes, changes in wind patterns, rain patterns, or air pressure. Record these ideas to refer to later in this Unit.

*A class period is considered to be one 40 to 50 minute class.

△ Guide

Let students know the definition of elevation and how it is measured using the information in the student text.

❝Elevation is defined as the height above sea level. Sea level is determined by the average height of all the oceans today.

How do you think they measure the height of the oceans?❞

Discuss the satellites TOPEX/Poseidon that can measure ocean heights within 5 cm. Consider showing them 5 cm on a meter stick or drawing it.

Describe the images in the student text of Mount McKinley and Mitre Peak. Let students know they will be collecting and analyzing actual elevation and temperature data using *My World* to get a better idea of how elevation affects temperature.

NOTES

....

....

....

....

....

....

....

....

....

Predict

Write a prediction about the effect of elevation on surface temperatures. Record your prediction. Complete the following statement:

- As elevation increases, the surface temperature (*increases, decreases,* or *is not affected*).

Procedure: Effects of Elevation on Surface Temperature

1. **Prepare the January temperature and elevation maps.**

   a) **Open *My World*.** Select "Planetary Forecaster" from the Data Library drop-down menu. Open the project file "PF Jan Temp Elevation.m3v." The default will open a January Temperature Map. Notice the "Temperature and Elevation" data layer. This layer has January temperature, elevation, and surface pressure data.

   b) **Open a Child Window to view both the "Elevation" field and "Jan Temp" at the same time.** Go to the "Windows" menu and select "New Child Window." This will open a second small window that contains January temperatures. Move the Child Window so that you can see the layer list in the original map. Click on the arrow on the right side of the drop box to open the "Elevation" map.

2. **Focus on the "Study Area."**

   a) **Show the Study Area layer.** To show a data layer, click the box on the right side of the layer box to reveal an open eye. You will need to do this in the Child Window as well.

   b) **Look more closely at the Study Area.** Use the "Zoom In" tool to magnify the area with the red rectangle. Both the elevation map and January temperature map in the Child Window will zoom in.

   The Study Area will be highlighted with a small rectangle outline in Asia.

PF 134

Project-Based Inquiry Science

Predict

< 5 min.

Students record their predictions to be tested with My World.

Procedure: Effects of Elevation on Surface Temperature

20 min.

Students collect data using My World.

⃝ Get Going

Have students complete the statement. Consider having the class share their predictions.

△ Guide

Demonstrate the procedures using *My World* to the class. Show students which file to open (Step 1).

Show students how to open the New Child Window following the procedures described in Step 1b.

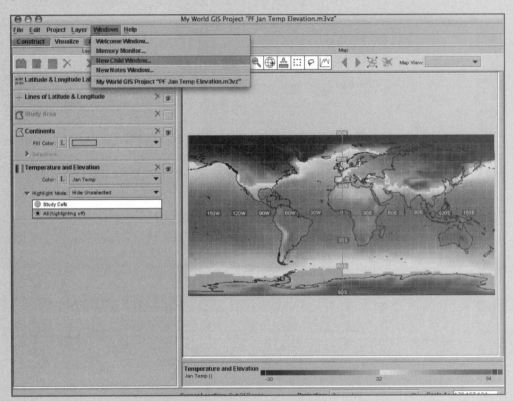

Show students how to select the elevation map described in Step 1.

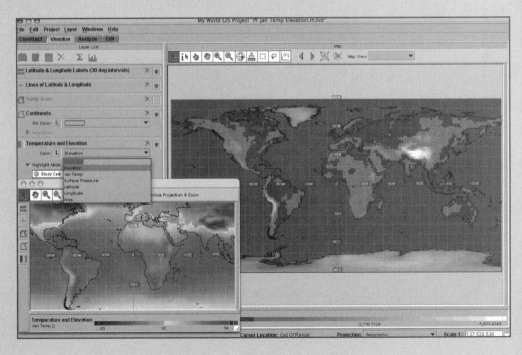

This is an area where the elevation changes rapidly over a very short distance, while other factors that affect temperature, such as latitude and land/water differences, are constant. This means you can assume that any big changes in temperature are due to elevation.

3. **Compare the January temperature and elevation data maps.**

   a) **Collect the locations, temperatures, and elevations of the cells in the Study Area.** Use the "Pointer" tool to click on each cell, one at a time. The "Cursor Location" at the bottom of the screen will tell you the latitude and longitude of the cell you clicked. An arrow on the color scheme bar at the bottom of the temperature map will point to the temperature of that cell. An arrow on the color scheme bar of the elevation map will point to the elevation.

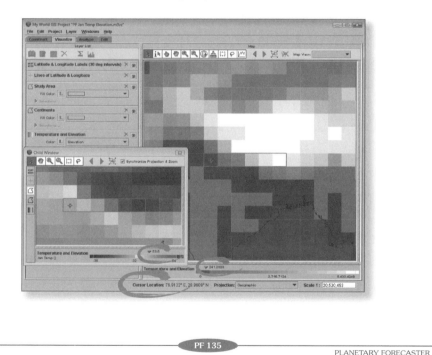

META NOTES

Students should record atmospheric pressure data in the last column of the table in *Elevation and Temperature Data 1* in *Section 5.4*.

Demonstrate for students how to turn on the Study Area by clicking the button with the eye. Zoom into the area with the rectangle around it. This area is located in Asia around 80°E, 28°N (in the Himalayan Region around Nepal which is between India and China.)

Show students how to zoom in on the area and describe how they will be collecting data from locations within the rectangle. Emphasize that this location was selected because it contains many different elevations.

⬡ Get Going

Distribute the *Elevation and Temperature Data 1* and *Elevation and Temperature Data 2* pages. Emphasize to students that they will need to record their data on these pages and the last column in the first data table should be left blank. Let students know that after they collect their data they should complete the *Analyze Your Data* Segment. Then let students know how much time they have.

△ Guide and Assess

Monitor students' progress and check that students are following the procedure for *My World* as written in the text. Make sure that they record the data they collect on their *Elevation and Temperature Data* pages.

Each row of the data table should contain information from within the same cell on the map. Check to see if students are collecting and entering their data correctly.

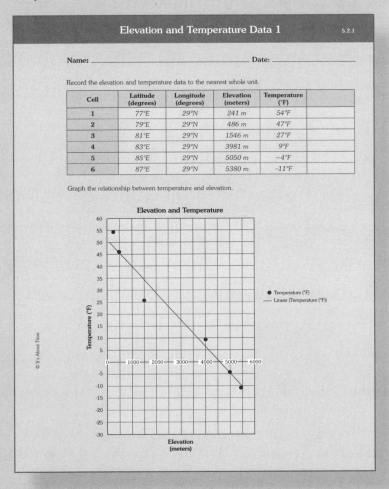

As students complete their data tables, have them continue to the *Analyze Your Data* segment.

Recording Your Data

Record the elevation and temperature data on Page 1 of the *Temperature and Elevation Data* pages. Record data to the nearest whole unit.

Analyze Your Data

1. Use Page 1 of the *Temperature and Elevation Data* page to graph the relationship between elevation and temperature. Use a ruler to mark a straight line through the middle of all of your data points. It does not have to touch *every* data point. The overall distance between the points above and below the line should be about the same.

   a) In which direction does the line slope? What does that mean?

   b) What could the direction of the slope tell you about the surface temperatures of a planet like *Planet X* with properties similar to those on Earth?

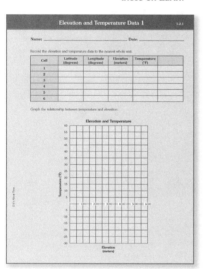

2. Find the average temperature for every 1000 m elevation change. Use the line you made between the data points on your graph to estimate the temperature at every 1000 m. Record these average temperatures on Page 1 of the *Temperature and Elevation Data* pages.

   a) How much did the temperature change from an elevation of 1000 m to an elevation of 2000 m?

   b) How much did the temperature change from 0 m to 1000 m?

   c) Find the difference in temperature for each 1000 m change in elevation. Record this temperature difference in your data table. Remember that if the temperature decreases, the difference will be negative. Be sure to put a negative sign (-) in front of this number if that is the case.

Project-Based Inquiry Science

Analyze Your Data

20 min.

Students complete questions using their observations from this experiment.

⚠ Guide

You may need to give the students some additional help completing the graph if you see them struggling with scale, or starting and ending points, etc.

1. Students should use their data to construct a temperature and elevation graph on their *Elevation and Temperature Data 1* pages. The graph should contain six data points and a best-fit line that students estimate.

a. Students should note that the line slopes downward. This indicates that as elevation increases, the temperature drops.

b. Students should respond that since *Planet X* is similar to Earth, the temperature on *Planet X* should also decrease with elevation.

2. Students should complete their data pages with the calculations they made. Data tables should look similar to the sample *Elevation and Temperature Data 2* page.

a. Students should have a value around -12°F.

b. Students should have a value around -11°F.

c. Students should have values similar to those in the chart above, ranging between -10°F and -15°F.

d. Students should calculate a value between -11°F and -12°F for the average temperature change per increase of 1000 m.

3. Students should use the average temperature change per 1000 m that they calculated in Question 2 to complete the second data table on their *Elevation and Temperature Data 2* page. Example data is shown in the sample page.

> **META NOTES**
>
> The first entry is one and a half times the average temperature change per 1000 m. For the remaining entries, add the average temperature change per 1000 m.

NOTES

_____

_____

_____

_____

_____

_____

_____

Elevation and Temperature Data 2

5.2.2

Name: _____ Date: _____

Find the average temperature for every 1000 m change in elevation.

Elevation (m)	Average temperature (°F)	Temperature change (°F)
0	52°F	0°F
1000	41°F	−11°F
2000	29°F	−12°F
3000	18°F	−11°F
4000	6°F	−12°F
5000	−5°F	−11°F
6000	−17°F	−12°F
	Average temperature change per 1000 m	−11.5°F

Calculate the average change in temperature per 1000 m change in elevation.

If you travel _____ above sea level	The temperature changes by:
1500 m	−17.25°F
2500 m	−28.75°F
3500 m	−40.25°F
4500 m	−51.75°F
5500 m	−63.25°F

NOTES

....

....

....

d) Calculate the average change in temperature per 1000 m change in elevation. To get this number, average the numbers in your "Temperature Change" column.

3. Using the average temperature change, determine how much the temperature would change with each elevation shown in the table on page 2 of the *Temperature and Elevation Data* pages.

Stop and Think

1. By how much does the temperature change for every 1000 m increase in elevation?

2. Using your calculation, by how much does the temperature change

   a) for every 500 m increase in elevation?

   b) for every 2000 m increase in elevation?

3. Jimmy is hiking in the mountains. He is going to hike up 2000 m over the next few days.

   a) How will the temperature change as he hikes up the mountain?

   b) If the surface temperature is 50°F where he starts, what can he expect the surface temperature to be at his check point, 2000 m higher in elevation?

4. How will your temperature predictions for *Planet X* change now that you understand temperature changes at different elevations?

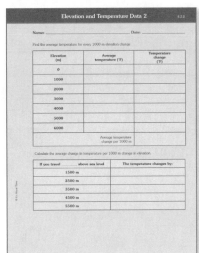

Stop and Think
10 min.

Groups discuss answer to the questions.

⬡ Get Going

Let the class know they will be using the information they have gathered to answer the questions and they will be presenting their data, analysis, and answers to these questions during the *Investigation Expo*. Let groups know how much time they have.

△ Guide and Assess

Monitor students' progress. Check that all group members are participating.
Use the information below to guide students and assess students as needed.

1. Students should list the value they obtained for the average
   temperature change per 1000 m calculated in Question 2 of the
   Analyze Your Data segment. Answers should be near -11.5 °F
   (e.g. between -10.5 °F and -12.5 °F).

2. **a.** Students' responses should be half the value of the average
   temperature change per 1000 m that they calculated. For the
   example data provided this value is -5.25°F.

   b. Students' responses should be twice the value of the average
   temperature change per 1000 m that they calculated. For the
   example data provided this value is -23°F or a drop of 23°F.

3. **a.** Students should describe that the temperature will drop.

   b. Students' responses should be (50°F – twice the average
   temperature change per 1000 m that they calculated). For the
   example data provided this value is 27°F.

4. Students' responses should include a description of decreasing
   temperatures as elevation increases based on their data analysis.

NOTES

Communicate Your Data: *Investigation Expo*

25 mins.

The class discusses the results of their investigations in an Investigation Expo.

Communicate Your Data

Investigation Expo

In your *Investigation Expo,* you are going to explain the temperature changes you observed as elevation changed. Your graph should make this very easy to show.

Develop a poster that includes your data and graph. You may also want to include a diagram of a mountain, showing sea level. Include as many details as possible, such as any areas that showed significant changes in temperature. These visuals will help you communicate your ideas to the audience.

Make sure you answer all the following questions in your presentation:

1. What trends did you observe in your data? What did these trends tell you?

2. How do you think the data would change if the mountain had a gentler slope, that is, if the elevation did not increase so rapidly?

3. What general statement can you make about the relationship between elevation and surface temperatures?

△ Guide

Let students know each group should make a poster that includes answers to the questions listed in the student text, their data and analysis, and their graph. Suggest to students to include a diagram showing how elevation changes temperature, such as the one described in the student text. Emphasize that the class will review and discuss the answers to the *Analyze Your Data* questions and the *Stop and Think* questions.

◯ Get Going

Distribute materials and let students know how much time they have to complete their poster. Let students know where they should display their posters when they are done.

△ Guide and Assess

Monitor students' progress and determine results you might want to highlight in class.

Once all posters are complete, have groups visit each poster for a minute or so. Then have a class discussion on the results.

Students' data may differ due to how precisely they drew their graphs and lines of best fit. It might also vary depending on where inside the grid cell the students clicked. You may want to mention what they have done is an approximation based on one set of observations at one location. This location was chosen because it is known to represent the global average temperature-elevation relationship. This approximation for Earth will help them approximate temperatures on *Planet X*.

Have groups present to the class. After each presentation, have a discussion about students' responses to the analysis questions and the *Stop and Think* questions. Conclude each discussion by describing how students will apply the information to their temperature prediction maps of *Planet X* (Question 4 of the *Stop and Think* segment).

After all the presentations, have a class discussion on the similarities and differences of the results. Emphasize the similarities and differences in data and trends and ask the class what claims they can make about how elevation affects surface temperature.

Consider updating the class *Project Board*. If you do, have students record their claims in Column 3 (*What are we learning?*) and their supporting evidence in Column 4 (*What is our evidence?*). Students should also update Column 2 (*What do we need to investigate?*).

NOTES

....

....

Once every group has completed their poster, each poster will be displayed in the classroom. As a class, review and discuss the answers to the *Analyze Your Data* questions. If there are differences in sets of data, are the trends still the same? Can each group claim to have evidence that elevation affects surface temperatures?

What's the Point?

In this section, you investigated elevation and the effect of elevation on surface temperatures. You made predictions about how you thought surface temperatures might change as elevation increased.

You have investigated the effects of changes in elevation on surface temperatures at one location. The data showed that as the elevation increased, the temperature decreased. At higher elevations, the temperatures are colder than at lower elevations. In developing a graph to show this relationship, you noticed that the change in temperature was constant as elevation decreased. This occurs even when you consider temperature at the same latitude. To apply this information to other locations, including *Planet X*, you need to understand how and why this occurs.

The hiking trail at Mt. Katahdin, in the state of Maine, starts at an elevation of 183 m and rises to 1605 m. If the temperature at the start of the trail is 75°, what might the temperature be at the top of the trail?

◇ Evaluate

Students should be able to claim from their data that temperature decreases as elevation increases in approximately a constant (linear) way for locations at the same latitude.

Assessment Options

Targeted Concepts, Skills, and Nature of Science	How do I know if students got it?
Graphs, maps, and tables are an effective way to analyze and communicate results of scientific investigation.	**ASK:** How did you use maps, tables, and graphs? **LISTEN:** Students should describe how they constructed graphs and tables based on results obtained from maps in *My World.* They should also describe how the tables and graphs helped them analyze how temperature varies with elevation by organizing the data and making it easier to see trends. Students should also describe how they used tables and graphs to communicate their results and ideas to the class and how these make it easier to point out trends in the data.
Scientists make claims (conclusions) based on evidence obtained (trends in data) from reliable investigations	**ASK:** What claims can you make? **LISTEN:** Students should be able to claim from their data that temperature decreases as elevation increases in an approximately constant (linear) way for locations at the same latitude.

Teacher Reflection Questions

- What difficulties did students have with the calculations needed and graphing? How could you guide them next time?
- How did the *Stop and Think* questions help students?
- What classroom management issues arose during this section?

NOTES

5.3 Read

What is Different Between Lower Elevations and Higher Elevations?

◀ $\frac{1}{2}$ *class period*

A class period is considered to be one 40 to 50 minute class.

Overview

The class discusses how air pressure changes with elevation. Students read about how air is a gas although it behaves like a fluid. Students read about compression and how the air at lower elevations is more compressed than the air at higher elevations. During this discussion, density is introduced and air pressure is further studied. Students prepare to investigate patterns in elevation, temperature, and surface air pressure data.

Targeted Concepts, Skills, and Nature of Science	Performance Expectations
The atmosphere is made up of molecules. The density and pressure of air decreases with increasing elevation.	Students should be able to describe air as a gas made up of particles with density and air pressure that increase with decreasing elevation due to the amount of air above it.

Materials	
1 per classroom (Optional)	Balloon
1 per class (Optional)	Class *Project Board*
1 per student (Optional)	*Project Board* page

Activity Setup and Preparation

Decide on the method the class will use for reading.

Homework Options

Reflection

- **Science Content:** How is a gas similar to and different from a liquid and a solid? *(Students' answers should include the following: all are made of particles (atoms/molecules), gases can expand and compress much more than liquids and solids, gases are like liquids and take on the shape of their container, solids can keep their own shape.)*

- **Science Content:** Which force acts on air molecules to change the density of air at different elevations? *(Students should identify gravity.)*

Preparation for Section 5.4

- **Science Content:** How do you think air pressure is related to temperature and elevation? *(The purpose of this is to get students thinking about why temperatures decrease with increased elevation. Students should suggest that as the elevation increases, the air pressure decreases and the temperature decreases.)*

NOTES

SECTION 5.3 IMPLEMENTATION

5.3 Read

What Is Different Between Lower Elevations and Higher Elevations?

In the previous investigation, you noticed that the temperature decreased as elevation increased. Mountain climbers also notice this difference in temperature. It gets very cold as they reach the top of a high mountain. What is different about lower elevations and higher elevations that causes the temperature to be lower at high elevations?

The Atmosphere Is an Ocean of Air

analogy: the similarity between things that are different.

fluid: a substance that is able to flow (takes the shape of its container).

To help answer that question, scientists often use an **analogy**. They describe the atmosphere as an ocean of air. This is helpful because you are able to see what happens in liquids like oceans. You are not able to see what is happening in gases like the atmosphere.

Scientists can make an analogy between the atmosphere and an ocean because gases and liquids have an important thing in common. The individual molecules in liquids and gases are able to move around. This is what makes liquids and gases different from solids. The molecules in a solid are stuck together. Because the molecules in a solid are stuck together, the solid has a definite shape. It keeps that shape on its own. Gases and liquids do not stay in any shape on their own unless they are surrounded by a solid. When they are surrounded by a solid, they take on the shape of the solid. For example, water in a bowl takes on the shape of the bowl.

While liquids and gases are similar, the molecules in a liquid are much closer together. In fact, a molecule in a liquid is almost always touching its neighbors. In a gas, the molecules are separated by empty space. They touch only when they bump into each other.

Scientists use the term **fluid** to describe substances like liquids and gases. A fluid is a large quantity of individual things (called *particles*) that can move independently from one another. Air and water are fluids. Collections of solid particles can also behave like fluids. For example, sand has the properties of a fluid. As you read about the differences in the air at high elevations and at low elevations, keep in mind the idea that air is a fluid.

PF 140

Project-Based Inquiry Science

5.3 Read

What Is Different Between Lower Elevations and Higher Elevations?

< 5 min.

Students are introduced to the topic of the section.

◯ Engage

Elicit students' initial ideas and record their responses.

TEACHER TALK

❝In the last section you gathered evidence showing that as the elevation increases the temperature decreases. What do you think causes this?❞

*A class period is considered to be one 40 to 50 minute class.

Let students know that they will be exploring what causes temperature to decrease with elevation during this *Learning Set.*

The Atmosphere is an Ocean of Air

15 min.

Students participate in a discussion about the properties of solids, liquids, and gases while focusing on air.

META NOTES

Because some students may not believe air has mass, they may have trouble understanding air pressure. Eliciting students initial ideas about air and discussing the expansion of the balloon should help students understand air pressure.

---

analogy: the similarity between things that are different.

fluid: a substance that is able to flow (takes the shape of its container).

as elevation increased. Mountain climbers also notice this difference in temperature. It gets very cold as they reach the top of a high mountain. What is different about lower elevations and higher elevations that causes the temperature to be lower at high elevations?

The Atmosphere Is an Ocean of Air

To help answer that question, scientists often use an **analogy**. They describe the atmosphere as an ocean of air. This is helpful because you are able to see what happens in liquids like oceans. You are not able to see what is happening in gases like the atmosphere.

Scientists can make an analogy between the atmosphere and an ocean because gases and liquids have an important thing in common. The individual molecules in liquids and gases are able to move around. This is what makes liquids and gases different from solids. The molecules in a solid are stuck together. Because the molecules in a solid are stuck together, the solid has a definite shape. It keeps that shape on its own. Gases and liquids do not stay in any shape on their own unless they are surrounded by a solid. When they are surrounded by a solid, they take on the shape of the solid. For example, water in a bowl takes on the shape of the bowl.

While liquids and gases are similar, the molecules in a liquid are much closer together. In fact, a molecule in a liquid is almost always touching its neighbors. In a gas, the molecules are separated by empty space. They touch only when they bump into each other.

Scientists use the term **fluid** to describe substances like liquids and gases. A fluid is a large quantity of individual things (called *particles*) that can move independently from one another. Air and water are fluids. Collections of solid particles can also behave like fluids. For example, sand has the properties of a fluid. As you read about the differences in the air at high elevations and at low elevations, keep in mind the idea that air is a fluid.

PF 140

Project-Based Inquiry Science

○ Engage

Ask the students to describe what air is and if it has mass. Consider blowing up a balloon and asking students what causes the balloon to expand and keep its shape.

△ Guide

Consider having students read the text on their own or in groups.

Have a class discussion on the atmosphere, air and the properties of gases, liquids, and solids. Consider having students summarize what they read. Emphasize the atmosphere surrounds Earth and is made up of different gases. Discuss the differences between gases, liquids, and solids as described in the student text.

How Much Air Is Above You at High and Low Elevations?

Imagine you could start walking into the ocean at the coast. You continue to walk on the sea floor as the water gets deeper and deeper. One thing you would notice is that you would start to feel squeezed by the water around you. The weight of the water above you would be weighing down on you and the water around you. In fact, a human body at the bottom of the deepest ocean would be crushed by the weight of the water in just the same way a body would be crushed by having a load of bricks on it.

What is the effect of having a tall stack of molecules above them on the molecules at the bottom of the ocean? They get squeezed closer together. Scientists use the term **compression** to describe the squeezing of substances together. The amount of compression force that is acting on a substance is called **pressure**. The pressure on the molecules at the bottom of the ocean is much greater than the pressure on the molecules at the top. The water at the bottom of the ocean is compressed by the weight of the water above it. What is causing this compression? Gravity causes the particles at the top of a fluid to push down on the molecules below them. The molecules in a liquid like ocean water are already close together. Therefore, there is a limit to how much closer the individual molecules can get. However, they do get a little bit closer. As a result, the same number of water molecules at the bottom of the ocean takes up less space than they would at the top of the ocean.

Pressure in the atmosphere works the same way. It is just harder to imagine. That is because you are not used to thinking of air as having weight. But it does. You live at the bottom of an ocean of air. However, you are not aware of the weight of the air above you. Your body is sensitive only to very large changes in pressure. You experience such large changes only if you travel deep in the ocean or high in the atmosphere.

So, even though we don't feel it, gravity is pulling all of the air molecules in the atmosphere down toward Earth's surface the same way it pulls the water molecules in the ocean down toward the ocean floor. At lower elevations, there are more molecules of air above Earth's surface than there are at higher elevations. That means the air at sea level is more compressed than it is at the top of a mountain range.

compression: squeezing.

pressure: amount of compression force acting on a substance.

How Much Air is Above You at High and Low Elevations?

15 min.

Students participate in a class discussion on density and air pressure.

△ Guide

Discuss the analogy in the student text of walking in water with increasing depth and how it might feel. Provide another analogy such as covering themselves with sand. Have them imagine how it would feel if they buried their arm under one foot of sand or under five feet of sand. Ask students how it would feel different.

Using these analogies, discuss the idea of compression and air pressure.

> **TEACHER TALK**
>
> **"**You would feel more weight or pressure (force per area) on your hand if it was buried under more sand because there is more sand being pulled down above your hand. The air at sea level feels more weight or pressure (force per area) than the air at 1000 m above sea level because there is more air pushing down on it.**"**

Discuss how weight is another term used for the gravitational force acting on an object and its effects.

> **TEACHER TALK**
>
> **"**All the air particles are being pulled down toward Earth because of gravity, the same way all the particles of water and sand are pulled down toward Earth. Since air is a gas, it can compress, meaning that the air particles can get closer together. The air near sea level is compressed because of all the other air above it being pulled down.**"**

Check students' understanding by asking them to imagine containing air inside a box. Ask them, Which would have more air particles in it, a box of air at sea level, or the same box filled with air on top of a mountain? Discuss density as the mass per volume of a substance and describe how air is denser at lower elevations.

Introduce the idea of air pressure. Explain that it is the amount of force per area from the air particles colliding with a surface. Air pressure increases when there are more air particles (a denser gas) and when the air particles are moving faster. Remind students that the air is denser at sea level. Ask if the pressure is higher at sea level or on a mountain top. Let students know that air pressure is important when they fill their bicycle tires or basketball, and atmospheric pressure is a special term to define the pressure due to the amount of air above a surface.

NOTES

For gases and solids, changes in pressure can result in differences in **density**. Scientists define density as the mass of a substance in a given volume. When you compress a gas by putting more gas molecules in a container, you increase the density of the gas. After adding more molecules to a container of the same volume, the mass in the volume increases while the volume stays constant. So, the water at the bottom of the ocean is denser than the water at the top. The air at the bottom of the atmosphere is denser than the air at higher elevations.

People sometimes notice changes in atmospheric pressure as their ears start "popping." This happens because your ears contain chambers (spaces) of air. Suppose you are in an elevator or an airplane that goes down quickly. Your ears experience a feeling of pressure. The high-density air is applying a force on the outside of your ear chamber. That force is trying to compress the chamber inside your ear. To relieve the pressure, your ears must allow additional air into their air chambers. When the air enters these chambers, you feel a "popping." The extra air in your ear chambers causes the density of air inside your ear to be the same as the density outside your ear. That means you no longer feel an imbalance in forces outside and inside your ear. The compression force outside your ear and the expansion force inside your ear are equal. You feel better.

density: the mass of matter per unit volume.

Mountain climbers also notice an effect of the density change with elevation. As climbers get close to the peak of Mount Everest, they not only notice the cold, they also get short of breath. Climbers often say the air is "thinner" at higher elevations. This is because there are fewer molecules of air to breathe. If the air is less dense, then there are fewer oxygen molecules available to be inhaled. In fact, most climbers must use oxygen tanks (containers of compressed oxygen) to be able to breathe on the peak of a high mountain, such as Mount Everest.

The diagram on the next page shows the difference in density between air at high and low elevations. The circles represent air molecules. As you can see, there are fewer air molecules at higher elevations, and they are more spread out. There are very few air molecules to push down on the surface.

Define atmospheric pressure. Let students know that atmospheric pressure is equal to the amount of force (in this case weight) per area of all the air above for an area on the planet's surface.

Ask students who have flown on an airplane or driven high into the mountains to describe the sensation that occurs when their ears pop. Ask them what they think is happening when this occurs. Students should realize that when they travel to higher elevations, the air pressure decreases. The popping experience is caused by the air inside their ears rushing outward to occupy the low-pressure area.

1000 m

0 m

What's the Point?

The air pressure is different at different elevations. At lower elevations, the weight of more air molecules presses down on Earth's surface. This higher pressure also squeezes the air molecules closer together. At higher elevations, there are fewer air molecules above Earth's surface to press down on it, so there is less pressure. The lower pressure allows the molecules to spread out. In the next investigation, you will explore patterns in elevation, temperature, and surface air pressure data.

Mountain climbers often bring canisters of oxygen with them since there are fewer molecules of air at higher elevations.

PF 143

PLANETARY FORECASTER

☐ Assess

Ask students to look at the picture of the mountain surrounded by air molecules. Ask the students to describe the air in terms of density and air pressure at the various locations. You may wish to point to two areas (one higher and one lower) and have them compare the density and air pressure at those two locations. Students should understand that air near the top of the mountain is less dense and under lower pressure than the air near the base of the mountain.

△ Guide

Consider having the class update their *Project Board*. If you choose to do this, students should add claims to the Column 3 (*What are we learning?*) and evidence to Column 4 (*What is our evidence?*) on how elevation, surface air pressure, and air density are related, and what air is made of.

Assessment Options

Targeted Concepts, Skills, and Nature of Science	How do I know if students got it?
The atmosphere is made up of molecules. The density and pressure of air decreases with increasing elevation.	**ASK:** What is the atmosphere made of? Describe atmospheric pressure and density. How do the atmospheric pressure and density of air change for increasing elevation? **LISTEN:** Students should describe the atmosphere as a gas made up of air particles. Students should define density as the mass per volume and atmospheric pressure as the amount of force acting on an area due to the weight of the air above it. Students should state that the density and air pressure decrease with increasing elevation due to the amount of air above it.

Teacher Reflection Questions

- Which concepts did students have difficulty understanding and how did you guide them?
- How did the image of the mountain help students?
- What difficulties did you have getting students to participate in class discussions?

NOTES

5.4 Investigate

How Are Temperature, Elevation, and Surface Air Pressure Related?

◀ *1 class period*

A class period is considered to be one 40 to 50 minute class.

Overview

Students investigate how temperature, elevation, and surface air pressure are related. Students use *My World* to collect surface air pressure data for the same locations they collected temperature and elevation data for previously. The quantitative data should support the conclusion that as elevation increases, air pressure and temperature decrease.

Targeted Concepts, Skills, and Nature of Science	Performance Expectations
Scientists often work together and share their findings. Sharing findings makes new information available and helps scientists to refine their ideas and build on others' ideas. When another person's or group's idea is used, credit needs to be given.	Students should work in groups to gather and analyze pressure, temperature, and elevation data using *My World.* Groups should then share their results.
Scientists must keep clear, accurate, and descriptive records of what they do so they can share their work with others and consider what they did, why they did it, and what they want to do next.	Students should keep clear and accurate records to refer to later.
Graphs, maps, and tables are an effective way to analyze and communicate results of scientific investigation.	Students should use maps in *My World* to collect data and construct tables and graphs.
Scientists make claims (conclusions) based on evidence obtained (trends in data) from reliable investigations	Students should make claims of how temperature, elevation, and surface air pressure are related.

Targeted Concepts, Skills, and Nature of Science	Performance Expectations
Surface temperature changes with changes in elevation and air pressure. As elevation increases, the air pressure and temperature decrease. As the pressure increases the temperature increases.	Students should observe as the elevation increases the pressure and temperature decrease.

Materials

1 per student	*Elevation and Temperature Data 1* page from *Section 5.2* (Optional) *Project Board* page
1 per group	Computer with *My World* software
1 per classroom	Computer with *My World* software and a projection system (Optional) class *Project Board*

NOTES

Activity Setup and Preparation

Using the information in the student text and the *Section 5.4 Implementation*, go through the procedures using the *My World* software. Determine where your class may have difficulties and what you should emphasize in the demonstration.

If there are not enough computers, students could obtain data as you demonstrate, or from printed copies.

Students are asked to describe what a graph of the data might look like. Consider asking students to graph the data.

Consider updating the class *Project Board* at the end of the section.

Homework Options

Reflection

- **Science Content:** How do you think the temperature and air pressure would compare between locations at the top of a high mountain and at the bottom of a valley located at the same latitude? *(Students' responses should state that at the top of the mountain, temperatures and air pressure are lower than those in the valley.)*

- **Science Content:** Why is it important to make comparisons of locations at or near the same latitudes? *(Students should recall latitude has an effect on surface temperature. By comparing locations at the same latitude, these differences are excluded.)*

Preparation for Section 5.5

- **Science Content:** How do you think the temperature and air pressure would compare between locations at the top of a high mountain and at the bottom of a valley located at the same latitude? *(Students' responses should state at the top of the mountain, temperatures and air pressure are lower than those in the valley.)*

NOTES

◀ *1 class period* *

5.4 Investigate

How Are Temperature, Elevation, and Surface Air Pressure Related?

In this investigation, you will add surface-pressure data to the elevation and temperature data you have already collected. You will look at how air pressure varies at the study area, as well as at other regions of varying elevations.

You have already determined that at higher elevations the temperatures are cooler. You found that temperature changes between 10°F and 15°F for every 1000 m of elevation change.

Predict

Complete the following statements. Choose the terms that best fit your predictions.

New Orleans sits at sea level and has little change in elevation.

- Mount Everest is the tallest mountain in the world. At the top of the mountain you would expect to find (*lower, higher*) temperatures than at the bottom and (*low, high*) surface pressure.

- The city of New Orleans, Louisiana actually has an elevation that is just below sea level. You would expect to find (*lower, higher*) temperatures than at the top of Mount Everest and (*low, high*) surface pressure.

- Places with high elevations will have (*low, high*) surface pressure.

- Places with low elevations will have (*low, high*) surface pressure.

- Places with higher elevations will have (*lower, higher*) surface temperatures.

- Places with lower elevations will have (*lower, higher*) surface temperatures.

PF 144

Project-Based Inquiry Science

5.4 Investigate

How Are Temperature, Elevation, and Surface Air Pressure Related?

< 5 min.

Students investigate surface temperature using My World.

△ Guide

Let students know that they will be using *My World* to collect the surface-pressure data for the same locations around the Himalayas that they already collected temperature and elevation data for. Remind students they found that the temperature decreases between 10°F and 15°F every 1000 meters and each of them already calculated an average temperature drop.

*A class period is considered to be one 40 to 50 minute class.

Predict

5 min.

Students predict how surface air pressure, temperature, and elevation are related.

---

cooler. You found that temperature changes between 10°F and 15°F for every 1000 m of elevation change.

Predict

Complete the following statements. Choose the terms that best fit your predictions.

New Orleans sits at sea level and has little change in elevation.

- Mount Everest is the tallest mountain in the world. At the top of the mountain you would expect to find (*lower, higher*) temperatures than at the bottom and (*low, high*) surface pressure.

- The city of New Orleans, Louisiana actually has an elevation that is just below sea level. You would expect to find (*lower, higher*) temperatures than at the top of Mount Everest and (*low, high*) surface pressure.

- Places with high elevations will have (*low, high*) surface pressure.

- Places with low elevations will have (*low, high*) surface pressure.

- Places with higher elevations will have (*lower, higher*) surface temperatures.

- Places with lower elevations will have (*lower, higher*) surface temperatures.

PF 144

Project-Based Inquiry Science

⬡ Get Going

Ask the students to choose one of the terms within the parentheses to complete the statement in order to make a prediction about how surface-air pressure, temperature, and elevation are related. For each statement, students should choose between either low and high, or lower and higher.

Consider having students share their predictions.

NOTES

....

....

....

5.4 Investigate

Procedure

1. **Prepare January temperature, elevation, and surface-pressure maps.**

   a) **Open My World.** Select "Planetary Forecaster" from the Data Library drop-down menu. Open the project file "PF Jan Temp Elevation.m3vz." This layer has January temperature, elevation, and surface-pressure data.

   b) **Open two Child Windows to View the "Elevation," "Jan Temp" and "Surface Pressure" maps at the same time.**

   - **Click on the arrow on the right side of the drop box** to open the "Elevation" map.

   - **Go to the "Windows" menu and select "New Child Window."** This will open a second small window that contains the elevation map. Move the Child Window so you can see the Layer List in the original map.

   - **Click on the arrow on the right side of the drop box** to open "Surface Pressure" map.

PF 145

PLANETARY FORECASTER

Procedure

15 min.

Students observe a demonstration of the My World *software and then collect their own data.*

⚠ Guide

Let students know they will be using *My World* to collect the surface-pressure data for January from the same map they already used to collect the elevation and temperature data.

- **Go to the "Windows" menu and select "New Child Window."** Move the Child Window so you can see the Layer List in the original map.

- **Click on the arrow on the right side of the drop box** to open "Jan Temp."

2. **Focus on the "Study Area."**

   a) **Show "Study Area" layer.** To show a data layer, click the box on the right side of the layer box to reveal an open eye. The study area will be highlighted with a small rectangle outline in Asia. Show this layer in the Child Windows by selecting the third button down on the left. This is the same area you looked at when you compared elevation and temperature.

   b) **Look more closely at the Study Area.** Use the "Zoom In" tool to magnify the area with the red rectangle. All three maps should be synchronized so all three maps will zoom in.

   The Study Area is an area where the elevation changes rapidly over a very short distance, while other factors that affect temperature, such as latitude and land/water differences, are constant. This means you can assume that any big changes in temperature are due to elevation.

3. **Compare January temperature, elevation, and surface-pressure data maps.**

   a) **Collect the locations, temperatures, and elevations of the cells in the Study Area.** Use the pointer tool to click on each cell, one at a time, and record the cell location, temperature, and elevation. Latitude and longitude are recorded at the bottom of the window. Once a cell is selected, the data can be read on the color scheme bar at the bottom of each data map.

   b) **Collect surface-pressure data for each cell in the Study Area.** This data should be added to the data you already collected about surface temperature and elevation. Be sure to select the cells in the same order.

Demonstrate for students how to obtain the data using the procedures in the student text. Let them know these procedures are similar to the procedures they followed in *Section 5.2*, but they will now have three maps open during their investigation. The following images show the procedures of Step 1b.

After opening the file *PF Jan Temp Elevation.m3vz*, select the elevation map from the drop box as shown.

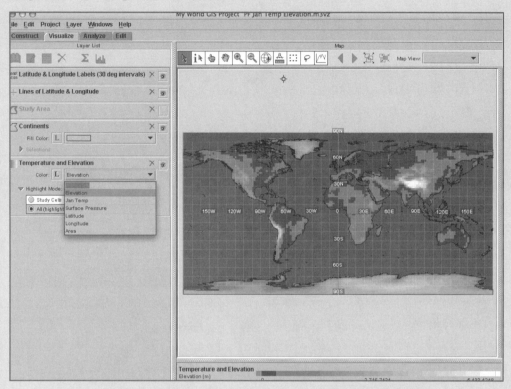

Remind students how to open a new map window by selecting New Child Window from the Windows menu.

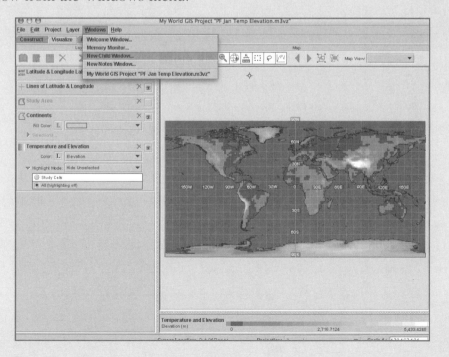

Show students how to select the Surface Pressure map.

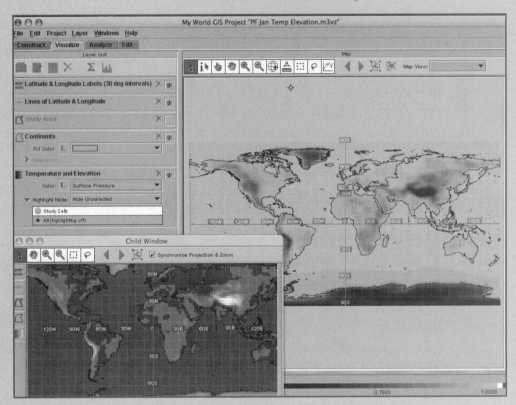

NOTES

....

....

....

....

....

....

Demonstrate how students should open another new map window by selecting New Child Window again. Make sure students know they may need to move the windows around so that they can open the surface temperature map.

Remind students how to open the study area as described in the student text and shown below.

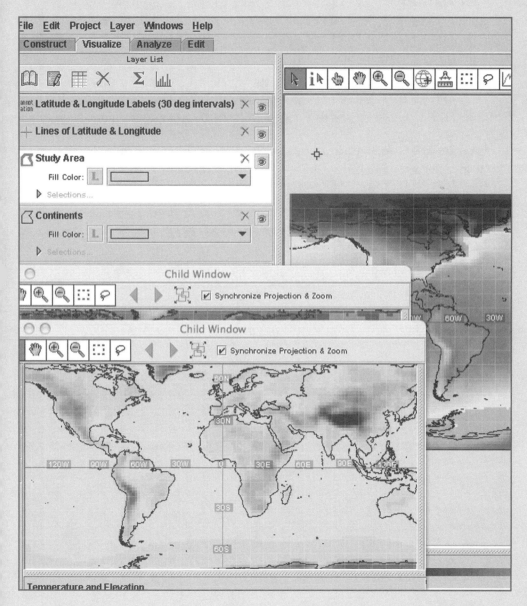

Show students how to zoom into the study area and how to collect data as described in the student text.

Emphasize to students they should record their data on the *Temperature and Elevation Data 1* page in the last column, and they should call this column *Surface Pressure*. Make sure they include the units, *atm*, which stands for standard atmospheres. Consider letting students know that the one standard atmosphere is about 14.7 pounds per square inch.

⬡ Get Going

Let students know they should take out their *Elevation and Temperature Data 1* pages from earlier. They will need to be careful when they record the atmospheric data to place it in the correct row of the data table.

Have groups follow the procedure in the student text and let them know how much time they have. Let students know that when they finish gathering their data they should complete the *Analyze Your Data* segment.

△ Guide and Assess

Monitor students. Check that students are matching the elevation and temperature data so they can record the atmospheric data in the correct row.

Students' data should look similar to the following.

Elevation and Temperature Data 1   5.2.1

Name: _____ Date: _____

Record the elevation and temperature data to the nearest whole unit.
The last column will be used in a later investigation.

Cell	Latitude (degrees)	Longitude (degrees)	Elevation (meters)	Temperature (°F)	Surface pressure (atm)
1	77°E	29°N	241 m	54°F	0.94
2	79°E	29°N	486 m	47°F	0.94
3	81°E	29°N	1546 m	27°F	0.89
4	83°E	29°N	3981 m	9°F	0.82
5	85°E	29°N	5050 m	−4°F	0.69
6	87°E	29°N	5380 m	−11°F	

5.4 Investigate

Recording Your Data

Add the surface-pressure data to the data table on Page 1 of the *Elevation and Temperature Data* pages you used earlier when comparing surface temperature to elevation.

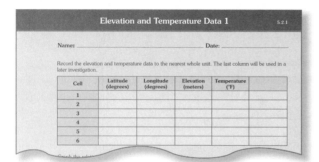

Elevation and Temperature Data 1   5.2.1

Name: _____   Date: _____

Record the elevation and temperature data to the nearest whole unit. The last column will be used in a later investigation.

Cell	Latitude (degrees)	Longitude (degrees)	Elevation (meters)	Temperature (°F)	
1					
2					
3					
4					
5					
6					

Analyze Your Data

1. Recall the question you answered after you investigated elevation and temperature: "Jimmy is hiking in the mountains. He is going to hike up to 2000 m over the next few days. How will the temperature change as he hikes up the mountain?" How will the air pressure change as he hikes up the mountain?

2. What is the relationship between surface pressure and air temperature?

3. If you made a graph comparing elevation to surface pressure, what would that graph look like?

What's the Point?

In this section, you observed and described the relationship among elevation, temperature, and surface pressure for one location on Earth. The data showed that as the elevation increased, the pressure and temperature decreased.

Analyze Your Data

20 min.

Students participate in a discussion of their responses.

META NOTES

Consider asking students to graph the data for Question 3.

⬡ Get Going

Let students work in their groups to complete the questions when they finish completing collecting the data. Let students know how much time they have.

△ Guide and Assess

Have a class discussion on groups' responses. Guide and assess students using the information below.

1. Students' responses should describe how the temperature changes on the average about -11.5°F per 1000 m and should change by twice the average temperature value they calculated on the *Elevation and Temperature Data 2* page (about -25°F). Students may try to calculate the average pressure drop following a similar procedure as they did for the average temperature. The pressure does not drop linearly like the temperature, as shown in the graph in Question 3. Consider projecting this graph for students after completing Question 3. Students should note that the air pressure decreases but they do not have enough information to say by how much.

2. Students' responses should describe a direct relationship between the surface pressure and the temperature. As the temperature increases, the surface pressure increases.

3. Students should describe how a graph indicating a decrease in air pressure as the elevation increases would look. Consider projecting the graph below and discussing it with the class.

Consider having the class update their *Project Board.* If you choose to do this, students should add claims to the Column 3 (*What are we learning?*) and evidence to Column 4 (*What is our evidence?*) on how surface pressure, temperature, and elevation are related.

NOTES

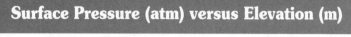

Surface Pressure (atm) versus Elevation (m)

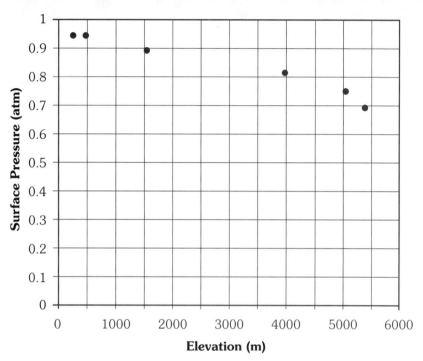

NOTES

Assessment Options

Targeted Concepts, Skills, and Nature of Science	How do I know if students got it?
Surface temperature changes with changes in elevation and air pressure. As elevation increases, the air pressure and temperature decrease. As the pressure increases the temperature increases.	**ASK:** What happens with the surface temperature and air pressure as the elevation increases? **LISTEN:** Students should describe how the temperature decreases with increasing elevation and how the pressure decreases with increasing elevation. They should support their responses with the data they collected and analyzed using *My World*.

Teacher Reflection Questions

- What difficulties did students have relating temperature, surface pressure, and elevation?

- How did the analysis segment help students? Did students try to graph the data or find an average value as they did in *Section 5.2?*

- What management issues arose with the small groups, using the computers, or the class discussions?

NOTES

....
....
....
....
....

SECTION 5.5 INTRODUCTION

5.5 Investigate

How Does Temperature Change as Pressure Changes?

◀ 1 class period

A class period is considered to be one 40 to 50 minute class.

Overview

Students consider what happens to a gas under high pressure as it expands and investigate the relationship between temperature and pressure. Student groups fill a bottle with air so that the air pressure inside the bottle is higher than the air pressure of the room. A thermometer is inside the bottle to monitor temperature. After the bottle has reached room temperature, students measure the mass of the bottle and the air, determine how much they can compress the bottle (to get an idea of the air pressure), and measure its temperature. Students release the excess air, allowing the air in the bottle to reach room air pressure and again measure how much they can compress (or squeeze) the bottle, the mass (weight), and temperature. Students draw conclusions that air has mass since the mass decreases after the high-pressure air is released, and temperature decreases with decreasing air pressure. At the end of this section, students have evidence to support the information presented in *Section 5.6*.

Targeted Concepts, Skills, and Nature of Science	Performance Expectations
Scientists often work together and share their findings. Sharing findings makes new information available and helps scientists to refine their ideas and build on others' ideas. When another person's or group's idea is used, credit needs to be given.	Students should work in groups to investigate how changes in air pressure affect air's temperature.
Scientists must keep clear, accurate, and descriptive records of what they do so they can share their work with others and consider what they did, why they did it, and what they want to do next.	Students should keep clear and accurate notes to refer to later when constructing their explanation on how temperature and pressure are related.

Targeted Concepts, Skills, and Nature of Science	Performance Expectations
Graphs, maps, and tables are an effective way to analyze and communicate results of scientific investigation.	Students should use tables to help analyze their data.
Scientists make claims (conclusions) based on evidence obtained (trends in data) from reliable investigations	Students should claim that air has mass supported by their measurements of reduced mass when air was released from the bottle. Students should also claim that as the air pressure decreases, the air's temperature decreases.
Surface temperature changes with changes in elevation and air pressure. As elevation increases, the air pressure and temperature decrease. As the pressure increases the temperature increases.	Students' observations should support the claim that as the pressure increases the temperature increases.

Materials	
1 per student	Safety glasses or goggles
1 per group	2-L bottle
	Temperature strip
	Pressure pump
	Balance or scale

NOTES

....

....

....

....

....

Activity Setup and Preparation

Clean and dry one 2-L plastic soda bottle for each group. Place a temperature strip inside the bottle. Make sure the strip is arranged so that it can be read. The strip should be tilted and touching the bottle only at the top and bottom of the strip. If it is flat against the side of the bottle, it will be measuring the temperature of the side instead of the temperature of the air inside the bottle.

Complete the experiment prior to class to familiarize yourself with the experiment and to determine where your students may have difficulties.

Consider how you want students to conduct this experiment. Once the bottles are pumped, they should rest for 30 minutes to come to room temperature before students begin to make their measurements. Students could begin reading *Section 5.6* while they wait, or the bottles could be pumped prior to class. If you choose to pump the bottles prior to class, you could pump the bottles prior to your first class, have your first class pump the bottles for your second class, have the second class pump the bottles for the third class, and so on.

Students should release the pressure themselves at the end of the experiment because hearing the gas escape can help solidify the idea that the gas is a substance with mass that had been forced into the bottle and is now coming out.

Homework Options

Reflection

- **Science Content:** How could you apply your observations to surface temperature? *(Students should describe how atmospheric pressure decreases with increasing elevation. They should state temperatures should be higher at lower elevations where the atmospheric pressure is higher. Students may still have difficulties with the idea that hot air rises and as it rises, it expands and cools.)*

Preparation for 5.6

- **Science Content:** What is temperature a measure of? Why do you think the temperature drops as the air pressure decreases? *(Students should describe temperature as the average kinetic energy of the atoms and molecules that make up an object. The purpose of the second question is to get students thinking about why the average kinetic energy decreases and to elicit their initial ideas.)*

455

NOTES

SECTION 5.5 IMPLEMENTATION

5.5 Investigate

How Does Temperature Change as Pressure Changes?

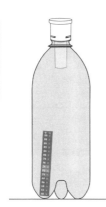

⚠
The bottle can explode, so be sure to wear your goggles.

Materials
• safety glasses or goggles
• 2-L bottle
• temperature strips
• pressure pump
• balance or scale

You have noticed that higher elevations have lower temperatures. You have also seen that higher elevations have lower pressure. In this investigation, you will see if there is a relationship between air pressure and temperature.

Predict

Complete these "if. . .then. . ." statements to make a prediction.

If high-pressure air is released and allowed to expand, its pressure will (*increase, stay the same, decrease*).

If high-pressure air is released and allowed to expand, its temperature will (*increase, stay the same, decrease*).

Procedure

1. Start with an empty clean, dry 2-L plastic bottle.

2. Drop a temperature strip inside the bottle.

3. Put on your goggles. You will need to keep your goggles on as long as the bottle is pressurized.

4. Screw a pressure pump onto the neck of the bottle.

5. Pump 200 times into the bottle. Do not pump more than 200 times or the bottle might burst. The sides of the bottle should be firm and somewhat difficult to squeeze.

6. Allow the bottle to sit about 30 minutes so the air in it comes to room temperature. Do not handle it during this time.

PF 148

Project-Based Inquiry Science

5.5 Investigate

How Does Temperature Change as Pressure Changes?

5 min.

Students are introduced to the experiment.

◯ Engage

Remind students of the information they obtained about atmospheric pressure, elevation, and temperature.

*A class period is considered to be one 40 to 50 minute class.

❝From the previous investigations, you know hot air rises and you know temperature is lower at lower elevations. Why do you think the air pressure and temperature decrease with increasing elevation?❞

Record students' responses.

Ask students if changing the air pressure for air at the same elevation would change the temperature. Record students' responses.

Predict

< 5 min.

Students record their predictions.

Procedure

15 min.

Students run the procedures.

The bottle can explode, so be sure to wear your goggles.

...seen that higher e... ...ower pressure... ...on, you will see if there is a relationship between air pressure and temperature.

Materials
- safety glasses or goggles
- 2-L bottle
- temperature strips
- pressure pump
- balance or scale

Predict

Complete these "if. . .then. . . " statements to make a prediction.

If high-pressure air is released and allowed to expand, its pressure will (*increase, stay the same, decrease*).

If high-pressure air is released and allowed to expand, its temperature will (*increase, stay the same, decrease*).

Procedure

1. Start with an empty clean, dry 2-L plastic bottle.

2. Drop a temperature strip inside the bottle.

3. Put on your goggles. You will need to keep your goggles on as long as the bottle is pressurized.

4. Screw a pressure pump onto the neck of the bottle.

5. Pump 200 times into the bottle. Do not pump more than 200 times or the bottle might burst. The sides of the bottle should be firm and somewhat difficult to squeeze.

6. Allow the bottle to sit about 30 minutes so the air in it comes to room temperature. Do not handle it during this time.

PF 148

Project-Based Inquiry Science

⬡ Get Going

Have the students complete the prediction statements by choosing one of the words to complete each sentence. Consider having a brief discussion of students' predictions.

△ Guide

Discuss the procedure with students.

Let students know that while they pump air into a 2-L bottle and while they release the air from the bottle, they need to wear goggles. Emphasize that they should not pump more than 200 times otherwise the bottle could burst.

Explain to students that they will need to let the bottle rest for 30 minutes to observe what happens when a gas under high pressure expands. Let students know they will be measuring three things: how squeezable or compressible the bottle is (this is an indication of the air pressure), the mass of the bottle, and the temperature inside the bottle.

NOTES

7. Use your *Air Pressure and Temperature* page to record data during this investigation.

8. After a half hour, compare the temperature in the bottle to the temperature in the classroom. You may need to shake the bottle gently to move the thermometer to a place where you can read it. When these temperatures are the same, move on to the next step.

9. Determine the bottle's squeezability (hard, medium, or easy to squeeze) and measure its weight. When you pumped air into the bottle, you increased the number of molecules in the space. That increased the pressure of the air in the bottle. The air in the bottle is at a higher pressure than the air in the room around you. Record the bottle's squeezability, temperature, and weight in the "High Pressure" row.

10. Pointing the top of the bottle away from you and others, carefully open the bottle, holding tightly onto both the bottle and the pump. Allow the air to leave the bottle slowly.

⚠ Point the bottle away from you and others. Open slowly.

11. Determine the bottle's "squeezability," and measure the temperature and weight again. Record your measurements in the "Low Pressure" row. Put the pump back on the bottle before weighing it, but don't pump any air into the bottle.

12. Record and calculate the change in squeezability, weight, and temperature.

Air Pressure and Temperature 5.5.1

Name: _____ Date: _____

	Squeezability	Mass	Temperature
High Pressure			
Low Pressure			
Change in Pressure			

PF 149

PLANETARY FORECASTER

Students should record their results on their *Air Pressure and Temperature* pages and consider their predictions as they make their measurements.

Demonstrate how the temperature strip should sit in the bottl: with only its top and bottom touching the sides of the bottle. Explain that this is to assure that the thermometer is reading the temperature of the air inside and not the side of the bottle. The side of the bottle may change its temperature differently.

Let students know that after they make their initial observations, they should carefully release the high-pressure air inside the bottle by loosening the pump. Demonstrate how to loosen the pump while keeping it covered with the palm of your hand. Then let them know that after they release the air, they should again measure the temperature, weight, and squeezability of the bottle.

○ Get Going

Have students begin and let them know how much time they have. Let them know if they will be using bottles that were pumped earlier and then pumping a bottle for another class, or if they will be reading *Section 5.6* while they wait 30 minutes for their pumped bottle to reach room temperature. Remind them to record their observations on their *Air Pressure and Temperature* pages.

△ Guide and Assess

Monitor groups as they work, making sure the students screw the pressure pump onto the neck of the bottle correctly and do not pump more than 200 times. If the bottle is pumped more than 200 times, it may burst. Test the bottle by squeezing it gently. The sides should be firm and somewhat difficult to squeeze. Allow the bottles to sit for 30 minutes to come to room temperature.

Check that students are recording their data in their data tables during the investigation.

At the end of the experiment, let students release the pressure. Hearing the gas escape can help solidify the idea that the gas is a substance with mass forced into the bottle and is now coming out. Be sure students open the pressurized bottles carefully with their palms covering the top of the pump and have a good grip on both the bottle and the pump. Make sure students do not point the bottles toward any other students while opening the pressurized bottles.

When students loosen the pump, they should clearly see a temperature decrease as the air expands.

When groups have collected their data, have them complete the *Analyze Your Data* segment. Let students know that they should first answer the questions on their own and then discuss them with their group.

It is very important that students wear goggles during this procedure to avoid any injuries.

Analyze Your Data

20 min.

Students participate in a class discussion on groups' responses.

Analyze Your Data

1. What happened to the weight of the bottle after you released the pressure? Why do think it changed the way it did?

2. What happened to the temperature after you released the pressure? Why do you think it changed the way it did?

3. What happened to the squeezability after you released the pressure? Why do you think it changed the way it did?

4. What relationship between air pressure and air temperature do you see?

5. Suppose the bottle of air under high pressure represents atmospheric pressure at sea level. What does the low-pressure bottle of air represent?

6. Mount Everest has the highest elevation on Earth. Use your results from this experiment to explain why the top of Mount Everest is so cold.

What's the Point?

Your investigation should have revealed the relationship between pressure and temperature. As you released the pressure from the bottle, the temperature in the bottle decreased. In the next section, you will read more about this and how this relates to lower temperatures at higher elevations.

The air pressure at the top of Mount Everest is very low compared to the air pressure at its base.

PF 150

⬡ Get Going

Ask groups to complete the questions to analyze the data they collected. They should first answer the questions on their own and then share their responses with their group.

△ Guide and Assess

Have a class discussion on students' responses. Use the following information to guide and assess students.

1. Students should state that the weight decreased and infer that this indicates air has mass and the mass decreased because there were fewer molecules of air in the bottle of air. Consider asking about the density of air in the bottle before and after releasing the excess air. Students should state that the density (mass per volume) of air in the bottle was greater before releasing the air. Ask if air has mass. Students should state yes, if they do not, discuss further what happened when they released the excess air and how it felt.

2. Students should state that the temperature decreased as the pressure was decreased (as air was released from the bottle). Assist students as needed to relate this to what happens to the temperature of a gas that is expanding. Gases decrease in temperature as they expand. Consider having another discussion of what temperature is and how as pressure is released the air expands and cools.

3. Students should state that the bottle was more easily squeezed after air was released. The squeezability is an indicator of the pressure inside the bottle. Students should realize that the more squeezable the bottle, the less air pressure there is inside the bottle. Guide students to understand that if everything is the same temperature, the bottle is less squeezable and there are fewer particles of air in the bottle.

4. Students should state that as pressure decreases the temperature decreases.

5. This question is meant to get students to relate the information they obtained in the last section with their observations. Students should recall that air pressure is higher at lower elevations. If the bottle of air under high pressure represents the air at sea level, then the bottle of air at low pressure represents the air at high elevations such as the air around peaks of mountains.

6. Students should state that the air pressure is very low at the top of Mount Everest and the molecules of air are spread out and have less energy than high-pressure molecules of air at sea level. The air pressure is low because there is less air above it that compresses this air. At lower elevations there is more air above that pushes down and compresses the air below. Because the air is not as dense, it does not transfer heat energy as well. Students should mention in their data that the temperature is lower as well. Students should have enough evidence to recognize that as a gas expands, it cools. They may not be able to recognize

how expanding and rising warm air from lower elevations moves toward higher elevations and cools. Convection is discussed in the next section.

◇ Evaluate

Check that students can conclude based on their observations that the temperature of the air inside the bottle drops dramatically because the air is expanding.

Assessment Options

Targeted Concepts, Skills, and Nature of Science	How do I know if students got it?
Surface temperature changes with changes in elevation and air pressure. As elevation increases, the air pressure and temperature decrease. As the pressure increases the temperature increases.	**ASK:** What claims can you make based on your observations? Support these claims with your data. **LISTEN:** Students should claim that air has mass based on their investigation. They should use examples such as: air has mass because the weight of the bottle with more air in it was measured to be _____grams more than the bottle after air was released. Students should claim that as a gas expands (after they released air out of the bottle) it decreases in temperature, or they may state that as the pressure decreases the temperature decreases. Students should list their measurements to support this.

Teacher Reflection Questions

- What difficulties did students have connecting their observations from this experiment with surface temperature for different elevations? How could you address these in the next section?

- How did the analysis questions help students connect their observations with the surface temperature measurements for different elevations?

- How did you decide to manage the 30-minute wait after the bottle was pumped? What would you do differently?

5.6 Read

Why Is the Air at Higher Elevations Cooler?

◀ *1 class period*

A class period is considered to be one 40 to 50 minute class.

Overview

Students are introduced to convection and how the land at high elevations affects the air temperature. Students begin by reviewing the evidence they have and read how an expanding gas does work on the environment and cools down. From this, they have two parts of what they need to explain why temperature is lower at higher elevations: temperature decreases with decreasing pressure/volume, and air pressure decreases with elevation because of gravity. Students review the process of heat transfer by conduction and radiation. Students are introduced to convection and gain understanding of how warm air rises, expands, and cools off. Students then compare how the land at high altitudes warms the air to that at low altitudes by considering a specific example.

Targeted Concepts, Skills, and Nature of Science	Performance Expectations
Scientists often work together and share their findings. Sharing findings makes new information available and helps scientists to refine their ideas and build on others' ideas. When another person's or group's idea is used, credit needs to be given.	Students should construct an explanation of how and why elevation affects surface temperature individually and then revise it with their groups. They should share their group explanation with the class and the class should construct an explanation based on all the group explanations.
Scientists must keep clear, accurate, and descriptive records of what they do so they can share their work with others and consider what they did, why they did it, and what they want to do next.	Students should keep records of their explanation and refer to their previous records when constructing their explanation.

Targeted Concepts, Skills, and Nature of Science	Performance Expectations
Heat energy may be transferred through conduction, radiation, or convection.	Students should describe warm air rising, air molecules spreading out and cooling as they reach higher, less-dense elevations resulting in heat being transferred through the atmosphere by the convection process. Students should describe convection as a process in which currents carry heat energy from one location to another, such as warm air rising and being replaced with cooler surrounding air.
Surface temperatures change with changes in elevation and air pressure. As elevation increases, the air pressure and temperature decrease. As the pressure increases the temperature increases.	Students should describe the relationships between pressure, temperature, and air pressure and understand how these are related.
Explanations are claims supported by evidence, accepted ideas and facts.	Students should work alone, in groups, and with the class to explain how elevation affects surface temperatures based on the experimental evidence they have and the science knowledge presented in the student text.

Materials	
1 per classroom (Optional)	Maps, satellite images, and/or photos of Denver, CO and St. Joseph, MO Class *Project Board*
3 per student	*Construct Your Explanation* page
1 per student (Optional)	*Project Board* page

Activity Setup and Preparation

Decide how students will read this section, either on their own, together in groups, or as a class.

Homework Options

Reflection

- **Science Content:** Describe why warm air rises. *(Students should explain that warm air rises because the molecules of warm air move around more and the air expands. It expands upward because the air is less dense as you move away from Earth. Because there is less push back from the air above it than the air below it, the air rises.)*

- **Science Content:** Describe heat transfer by radiation, conduction, and convection and provide an example. *(Students should describe how conduction requires contact between two interacting objects. In this interaction, the warmer object transfers heat through collisions between the atoms/molecules of the two objects. Students should explain that radiation is the transfer of energy by waves moving through space. They may choose to use an example of standing close to a fireplace. When a person stands near the fireplace, they will absorb the radiation, which increases their thermal energy. Convection occurs in fluids (liquids and gases). In this interaction, the warmer, more energetic fluid rises because it is expanding and is easier to push out of the way than the less dense fluid above it. As it pushes the fluid above it out of the way (through collisions) it transfers heat energy, reducing its own average energy (temperature) – cooler fluid replaces the rising warmer fluid. Students may or may not describe flow patterns.)*

Preparation for **Back to the Big Challenge**

- Science Content: What changes should you make to your temperature prediction maps for *Planet X* and why? *(The purpose of this is to get students thinking about how they will apply what they now know about surface temperatures to their predictions of Planet X's surface temperatures.)*

NOTES

SECTION 5.6 IMPLEMENTATION

5.6 Read

Why Is the Air at Higher Elevations Cooler?

Air Molecules Cool as They Spread Out

In the previous investigation, you lowered the pressure in a bottle, and the temperature dropped. Why did this happen? You can use the model of air as a fluid to help explain this. The change in temperature with pressure helps to explain why the air is cooler at higher elevations.

At the start, the air molecules in the bottle were under high pressure. They were compressed, or very close together. When you released the pump, many air molecules escaped from the bottle. With fewer molecules in the bottle, the density of the air decreased. In other words, there were fewer molecules in the same amount of space.

As the air molecules in the bottle moved around to spread out, they used some of their energy. Scientists call this process of using energy to move *work*. The more a gas molecule moves, the more work it does. Therefore, it has less energy to keep it moving, so it slows down. Recall that the temperature of a gas is a measure of the average speed of the molecules in that gas. The more slowly the molecules move, the lower the temperature reading.

So, this investigation demonstrates that when you decrease the pressure on a group of air molecules, the temperature goes down. That is because of the work the air molecules do in moving around to fill up the extra space. This decrease in temperature is different from the decrease in temperature you read about earlier when you explored radiation and conduction. From the data in *My World*, you know that the air pressure at higher elevations is lower than it is at lower elevations. You already discovered that the air pressure is lower at higher elevations because there is less air above it, weighing down on it. Now you have two parts of the explanation for why temperatures are lower at higher elevations.

- Temperature decreases when the pressure in a volume of air molecules decreases.

- Air pressure at a higher elevation in the atmosphere is lower than air pressure at a lower elevation in the atmosphere.

PF 151

PLANETARY FORECASTER

5.6 Read

Why Is the Air at Higher Elevations Cooler?

Students discuss how gases behave when warmed and cooled.

Air Molecules Cool as they Spread Out
10 min.

Students learn more about the effects of pressure changes on air and are introduced to the concept of work.

○ Engage

Elicit students' ideas about why the expanding gas in their last investigation decreased in temperature. Record students' ideas

TEACHER TALK

"You have observed that changing pressure causes changes in temperature. Why do you think that occurs?**"**

*A class period is considered to be one 40 to 50 minute class.

△ Guide

Let students know how you want them to read this section.

Discuss how molecules of air spread out as they cool using the information in the student text. Begin by describing the last investigation they did.

TEACHER TALK

"In the previous investigation you released air under high pressure from a bottle. The atoms and molecules of gas left in the bottle were able to expand and travel further before colliding with another atom or molecule.

The gas leaving the bottle had to push the air outside the bottle out of the way. When something pushes or pulls on another object and makes it move, it does work. The atoms and molecules of air leaving the bottle did work on the atoms and molecules of air outside the bottle and transferred some of their energy to these particles. The atoms and molecules of air in the bottle, behind the escaping air atoms, pushed on the escaping atoms and molecules, doing work on these atoms and molecules and transferring energy as they pushed them out of the bottle. When atoms and molecules do work on their surroundings and transfer energy, they decrease in their motion and their kinetic energy. Remember that the average kinetic energy of the atoms and molecules that make up an object, like a bottle of air, is the temperature of the object. The gas remaining in the bottle has a lower temperature and a lower pressure because there is less air now in the bottle."

Emphasize the two points in the student text that explain why temperatures are lower at higher elevations. Let students know they need to know more about how air in the atmosphere decreases in pressure with elevation changes and transition the class into the following segment.

NOTES

....

....

....

....

There is only one thing missing to explain why the temperature at higher elevations is lower than the temperature at lower elevations. Our explanation for lower pressure causing lower temperatures requires air molecules to a decrease in pressure. To fill in the missing element of the explanation, you need to know when air at higher elevations a decrease in pressures. It happens when warm air rises.

Warm Air Rises

convection: movement of heat energy from one location to another as a result of the movement of particles that are storing that energy.

air mass: a large body of air with similar characteristics of temperature, air pressure, and water vapor throughout.

You have probably heard before that warm air rises. In fact, you may even have wondered how the air at higher elevations could be cooler if warm air rises. As odd as it seems, the reason air high in the atmosphere is cooler than air down below is because warm air rises.

Warm air does rise. To be exact, air that is warmer than the air around it rises. The atmosphere is full of currents of warmer air rising and cooler air descending. These currents of air in the atmosphere are just like currents of water in the oceans. When a portion of a fluid heats up more than the areas around it, that portion of the fluid will rise. The cooler surrounding fluid will move in to fill in for the fluid that is rising. This process of currents carrying heat energy from one location to another happens in both water and air. It is called **convection**.

So, why does the warmer air rise? Warmer air rises for the same reason that you float in water. It is less dense than the air around it. To understand why warm air rises, imagine a large quantity of air, enough to fill a football stadium. Scientists call a large volume of air an **air mass**. Air masses in the atmosphere are not held by containers. However, imagine that an air mass is inside an enormous balloon. Imagining the air mass being contained by a balloon makes it easy to imagine the entire air mass moving together. (In reality, all the molecules around the edges of an air mass do behave a little bit like the skin of a balloon.)

Now, imagine that this air mass is resting above a small island in the middle of a very large lake at sunrise. In *Learning Set 4*, you discovered that sunlight causes land to heat up more quickly than water. As the day goes on, the Sun heats both the land and the water. The land will heat up more. As a result, the land will conduct more heat to this air mass than the water will to the air above it. That means the molecules in the air mass will be moving around more than the surrounding air molecules. What effect will that have on the imaginary balloon around the air mass? It will expand. In other words, the air mass will begin to expand. Remember that the air mass

PF 152

Project-Based Inquiry Science

Warm Air Rises
10 min.

Students are introduced to convection.

△ Guide

Let students know how you want them to read this section. Consider having students create an illustration describing what they have read.

Have a class discussion on convection. Consider illustrating the sequence of events described in the student text on the board, or have students create and share their own illustrations. Make sure students label the air masses and include descriptions of their relative temperatures. Have them illustrate sequences that show the movement of the air masses. Illustrations should look similar to what is shown below. Students may not at this time include that the air mass eventually falls downward and the cycle continues.

META NOTES

The convection cycle resulting in local winds is discussed in *Section 6.5*.

The air mass reaches air of the same pressure and stops rising. The air mass has expanded and cooled by transferring its energy to the air it pushed out of the way.

The cooled air mass eventually gets pushed out of the way by another air mass. It falls over the water as Earth pulls it towards its surface and compresses it.

The air mass expands and moves upward, pushing away air above it and transferring energy to that air.

The air mass warmed by land rises.

A cool air mass from over the water moves in, replacing the rising warm air mass.

Describe to students how air being warmed increases its kinetic energy and the molecules in air move farther apart because they have more kinetic energy. As these molecules try to move farther apart, they push on their surroundings. It is easier to move upward and push away the molecules of air above because the air above does not push back as much and is less dense than the air below. The air above is also a lower temperature and has less kinetic energy.

will still have the same number of molecules when it expands as it had when it was smaller. This means that the air within the air mass becomes less dense than the air around it. When an object in a fluid is less dense than the fluid around it, it starts to rise. You are very familiar with this. It is the reason why people float in water. It is also why helium balloons float in ordinary air. Helium is less dense than air. Even an air mass made up of the same kinds of molecules as the air around it will float upwards if it is less dense than the surrounding air.

Why will the air mass rise? One way to understand the answer is to think of the imaginary balloon around the air mass as pushing outward on the air around it. It might be easier to imagine this by returning to the analogy of the atmosphere as an ocean. Think of the air inside and outside the imaginary balloon as fluids. As the imaginary balloon begins to expand, it will try to push the fluid on its outside out of the way to make room for itself. Since that fluid is under pressure from above, it will not get out of the way. It will push back. However, the fluid above the imaginary balloon is under less pressure than the air inside the imaginary balloon. It will not push back as hard as the other air around the balloon, so the balloon will be able to push it out of the way. The balloon will then move upward into the space it makes as it pushes the air above out of the way. As it moves up, air from either side will flow in to fill the space that the balloon is leaving. As the balloon expands, it rises. At the next level up, if the fluid around the balloon is still under more pressure than the fluid inside the balloon, the process will continue. For every bit of expansion, it rises a little bit. Eventually, it reaches a level where the pressure inside the balloon is the same as the pressure outside. It stops rising and stops expanding.

So, as a result of being heated more than the air around it, a warm air mass expands and rises like a balloon. It will continue to expand and rise until the density of the air mass matches the density of the air around it. At this point, the air pressure in the air mass will be the same as the air pressure in the atmosphere around it.

The rising and expanding of an air mass provides the part of the explanation that was missing of why temperatures are lower at higher elevations. Just like the air inside the bottle in your investigation, the temperature of an air mass decreases as it expands. The molecules are not only using energy to move within the air mass, they are also using energy to push themselves up against the surrounding molecules. The energy they use to do this work causes the molecules to move more slowly. This results in a lower temperature. The air starts moving up because it is warmer than the

Go through the analogy in the student text of a large air mass contained in a balloon above an island. Emphasize that the land warms up faster than the water, so the air above the land is warmer than above the water. The air above the land will move around more and try to expand, causing it to move upward. The air above the water is cooler because water does not warm up as quickly, so this cooler air will move over the land. As the balloon rises, it has to push the air above it out of the way. When this happens, it transfers some of its energy to the air above it.

Eventually, the balloon reaches air that is the same pressure and temperature and it stops rising and expanding.

Students may wonder why the density of air above increases as warm air keeps rising. Let them know how the cool air sinks as it is pulled down by gravity. This sets up a loop of rising and falling air. Emphasize that the transfer of heat energy because of the expansion of a fluid (gas or liquid) is called convection.

Ask students to describe how this effects the temperature of air at higher elevations.

TEACHER TALK

"Warm air rises. Using what you know, why is the air at higher elevations not warmer?"

Emphasize that this is an important part of understanding why the air is cooler at higher elevations. Make sure students understand the warm air rising and expanding transferred energy to the surrounding air, resulting in a decrease of temperature.

NOTES

surrounding air. By the time it is finished rising, it has cooled off. This comes as a result of using its energy to perform the work of expansion.

Now you can understand why the air at higher elevations is cooler. The air molecules have not always been there. They rose to the top of the atmosphere as a result of being heated from below. However, the work the air molecules did in rising to that level caused them to slow down. In the end, this results in air above being cooler than the air it left below.

What Is the Effect of High-Elevation Land on High-Elevation Air Temperature?

There is one difference between the air in your imaginary air mass and the air you are concerned about in your prediction for *Planet X*. The air mass you have been thinking about was high above the land. The high-elevation air, whose temperature you want to predict on *Planet X,* is right at the surface of the land. However, that land is at a high elevation. How can you predict its temperature?

Consider a specific example. Think about the temperature in Denver, Colorado. Denver is called "The Mile High City." Its elevation is about one mile (1600 m) above sea level. If you were trying to predict the surface temperature in Denver, you would have to consider two factors. First, it is high above sea level. That means the air pressure is low. Second, surface temperature is measured close to the ground, where the air is heated by the planet's surface through conduction.

To understand how the effect of being at high elevation combines with the effect of being just above the ground in a place like Denver, consider two other locations nearby. The first location is St. Joseph, Missouri. It is about 540 mi (850 km) east of Denver. You can see the locations of Denver and St. Joseph on the map on the next page. They are at nearly the same latitude. They are both very far away from any large body of water. You would expect them to have the same temperature if they were at the same elevation. However, they have very different elevations. St. Joseph is about 1350 m lower than Denver. It is at 250 m above sea level. The second location to consider is in the atmosphere above St. Joseph. It is at the same elevation as Denver, 1600 m above sea level.

Consider the following questions:

- How do you think the surface temperature in Denver compares with the surface temperature in St. Joseph?

What is the Effect of High Elevation Land on High Elevation Air Temperature?
20 min.

Students have a class discussion on the differences of pressure between two locations.

△ Guide

Go through the example with the class. You may want to find additional photographs, maps, or satellite images of the two locations to help students visualize the differences between the climate and elevation of the locations.

Have students read the text up to the three bulleted questions. Then discuss what they read and their responses.

Describe how St. Joseph is about 250 m above sea level and Denver is about 1350 m above sea level, both are far from water and nearly the same latitude.

• How do you think the surface temperature in Denver compares to the temperature in the atmosphere 1350 m above St. Joseph?

• Is Denver's temperature closer to the temperature in St. Joseph or to the air temperature 1350 m above St. Joseph?

You have now read about two factors that influence Denver's surface temperature:

• heating by Earth's surface, and

• cooling as air rises to high elevations.

Based on what you know, you can answer the first two questions. The air in Denver is warmer than the air 1350 m above St. Joseph because it has been heated by the land. Denver tends to be cooler than St. Joseph because Denver is at a higher elevation.

To answer the third question, you need to know which factor makes more of a difference in determining actual temperature—heating by Earth's surface or cooling as air rises to high elevations? The answer is that for elevations as high as Denver's, the high elevation makes more of a difference than being close to the surface. This means that the surface temperature in Denver tends to be closer to the air temperature 1350 m above St. Joseph than it is to the surface temperature in St. Joseph. The land in both places heats up about the same amount from the Sun. However, land at higher elevations is less effective in heating the air than land at lower elevations. There are several reasons for this. The most important reason is simply that air at higher elevations starts at a lower temperature than air at lower elevations. The surface air temperature in Denver will generally be warmer than the air 1350 m over St. Joseph. That is because it is being heated by the surface. However, because of the effect of elevation, the surface air temperature in Denver will still tend to be closer to the temperature at 1350 m above St. Joseph than the surface air temperature in St. Joseph.

△ Guide and Assess

Elicit students' responses to the bulleted questions. Record students' ideas so they can be referred to later. Students' responses should be similar to the following:

- Students should predict that Denver should be cooler than St. Joseph based on the data they collected using *My World*.

- Students should give reasoning for why higher elevations above the ground are cooler and less dense, and the air near land is warmer. The air above Denver at 1350 m should be warmer than the air 1350 m above St. Joseph because the land warms the air above Denver. The air high above St. Joseph is not warmed by the land.

- Students' responses may be supported by and should not contradict that temperature decreases with decreasing pressure for a given volume of air, air pressure decreases as you move higher in the atmosphere, and that air pressure decreases with increasing land elevation.

△ Guide

After the class has discussed students' ideas to the bulleted questions, have students continue reading while referring back to their ideas.

To answer the last question, it is important for students to know which factor causes a greater change in temperature—warming by Earth's surface or cooling as air masses rise. Let students know for high land elevations, the process of air masses cooling as they rise makes a greater difference than the warming of the land, so Denver's temperature is closer to the temperatures of air at 1350 m above sea level than to St. Joseph's surface temperature. This happens partly because the air at high elevations starts at a lower temperature and needs to absorb more radiant energy to reach temperatures similar to St. Joseph's. Another factor that contributes to this is that the air at lower pressures (higher elevations) does not transfer heat energy at as great a rate between molecules of air because there are fewer collisions between the atoms and molecules due to the reduced number of atoms and molecules in the air.

☐ Assess

Have students close their books and discuss why the air just above Denver is closer to the temperature of air 1350 m above ground at sea level.

△ Guide

Ask students to construct their explanation for how elevation affects surface temperature.

TEACHER TALK

❝You have all the parts you need to construct an explanation for how elevation affects surface temperatures. You know that the temperature decreases when the pressure of an air mass decreases. You know that atmospheric pressure decreases as you go up in altitude. You know that air is heated by Earth's surface and hot air rises and cools as it rises. Now it is time to construct an explanation. You will first construct your own explanation, and then meet with your groups to construct an explanation. Finally we will construct an explanation, together as a class.❞

⬡ Get Going

Distribute the *Create Your Explanation* pages to students and let them know how much time they have.

△ Guide and Assess

As soon as students have completed their explanations, have them meet with their groups for a few minutes.

After all groups have presented, guide the class to discussing the similarities and differences between all the explanations. Record the points the class agrees on. Discuss why differences arose and decide what is best to include in the explanation.

Have a discussion with the class to construct an explanation. Once the class explanation is completed, distribute another *Create Your Explanation* page and have the class record their class explanation, indicating at the top of the page that it is the Class Explanation.

NOTES

....

....

....

....

◇ Evaluate

The final class explanation should contain a claim about how the surface temperature decreases with increasing elevation and why. The claims should be supported by the data they collected from *My World*. They should describe how temperature drops with elevation and supply the numerical value they calculated for this and they should describe how pressure drops with increasing elevation. They should support their claim with the science knowledge presented about how temperature decreases with decreasing pressure for a given air mass and include a description of this supported by their experiment. To further support their claim, they should include a description of air being warmed by the land and the process of convection.

An example of an explanation is provided below:

It is colder at higher elevations (the tops of mountains) because there is less air pressure and the air is more spread out. This claim is supported by data we analyzed using My World*. The data showed that the temperature decreased an average of 11.5°F with each 1000 m increase in elevation, and the pressure decreased as the elevation increased. The factors that affect this are how heat energy is transferred to air and how air transfers heat energy in the atmosphere. When there is less air pressure, heat energy is not as easily transferred to the molecules in the air from the land by conduction. Higher in the atmosphere, there is less air pressure because there is less air pushing down from above (being pulled down by gravity). Air that is warmed rises and expands because its particles have more average kinetic energy. As it rises and expands, it transfers energy to other molecules when it pushes them out of the way. This was supported by our experiment of releasing compressed air from a bottle in which we measured a decrease in temperature of the gas remaining in the bottle after it was allowed to expand. The air remaining in the bottle was at a lower temperature because it transferred energy to the surrounding air as it pushed it out of the way.*

△ Guide

Consider having students update the class *Project Board*.

NOTES

Assessment Options

Targeted Concepts, Skills, and Nature of Science	How do I know if students got it?
Heat energy may be transferred through conduction, radiation, or convection.	**ASK:** Describe how heat energy is transferred by conduction, radiation, and convection. **LISTEN:** Students should describe how conduction requires contact between two interacting objects, and that the warmer object transfers heat through collisions between the atoms/molecules of the objects. Heat transfer by radiation occurs as an interaction between two objects with different temperatures. The warmer object radiates electromagnetic waves absorbed by the cooler object and transforms it into kinetic energy. Convection occurs in fluids (liquids and gases). The warmer fluid rises because it expands as it increases its average kinetic energy and becomes less dense. The rising fluid transfers heat energy to cooler fluid as it pushes it out of the way (this transfer is due to collisions)—cooler fluid replaces the rising warmer fluid and currents (circular patterns of motion) are set up.

Teacher Reflection Questions

- What difficulties did your students have with the concept of convection?

- How did the example help students understand the factors that affect a locations surface temperature?

- How would you address various reading levels in the classroom?

Back to the Big Challenge

Which Regions of a Newly Discovered Planet have Surface Temperatures Appropriate for a Human Colony?

◀ *2 class periods*

A class period is considered to be one 40 to 50 minute class.

Overview

Student groups apply what they now know about how elevation affects surface temperature to their January and July temperature prediction maps for *Planet X*. Students use their calculations of how temperature decreases with elevation on Earth and apply these to *Planet X* using the elevation information provided by the *CSA*. From their new prediction maps, students construct a habitability map. Students then share their predictions during a *Solution Briefing* to communicate their solutions to the rest of the class so that students can better understand how other people approached the problem. Students reflect on what they have learned about shape, tilt, land and water differences, and elevation and then update their class *Project Board*.

> **LOOKING AHEAD**
>
> Students will need printed copies of the maps they construct in this section for the next section.

Targeted Concepts, Skills, and Nature of Science	Performance Expectations
Scientists often work together and share their findings. Sharing findings makes new information available and helps scientists to refine their ideas and build on others' ideas. When another person's or group's idea is used, credit needs to be given.	Students should work in groups to construct their temperature prediction maps and share their ideas with the class and update their *Project Boards*.
Scientists must keep clear, accurate, and descriptive records of what they do so they can share their work with others and consider what they did, why they did it, and what they want to do next.	Students should use their records from this *Learning Set* and their previous maps to assist them in revising their temperature prediction maps.

Targeted Concepts, Skills, and Nature of Science	Performance Expectations
Graphs, maps, and tables are an effective way to analyze and communicate results of scientific investigation.	Students should revise their maps to include what they now know about how elevation effects surface temperature, and use these to communicate their results to the class.
Explanations are claims supported by evidence, accepted ideas and facts.	Students should describe how their class's explanation supports their temperature prediction maps.
Surface temperature changes with changes in elevation and air pressure. As elevation increases, the air pressure and temperature decrease. As the pressure increases the temperature increases.	Students should change their surface temperature prediction maps to show decreases in temperature based on elevation changes using the average temperature change per 1000 m they calculate earlier.

Materials

1 per group	Computer with *My World* software Poster paper and markers
1 per classroom	Computer with *My World* software and a projection system Class *Project Board*
1 per student	*Solution-Briefing Notes* page *Project Board* page

NOTES

....

....

....

....

Activity Setup and Preparation

Prior to class create a temperature prediction map for January and July and a prediction map showing regions of habitability and decide what to emphasize when you demonstrate how to prepare maps. Use the instructions in the student text and the *Back to the Big Challenge Implementation* to guide you.

If you do not have computers available, the students can complete this project by coloring printed copies of maps.

Decide how students will present their ideas during the *Solution Briefing*. You could have students present their ideas using a computer projection system or using printouts that are projected.

Homework Options

Reflection & Preparation for ABC I

- **Science Content:** : Summarize how shape, tilt, land and water differences, and elevation affect surface temperature. *(Students should describe how surface temperature is effected primarily by how much sunlight strikes the planet and how much of it is absorbed and later emitted. They should include that shape and tilt effect the amount of incoming sunlight, how land and water differences effect how much incoming sunlight is absorbed, and how elevation effects surface temperature because the air is less dense at higher elevations due to gravity and affects how much heat energy can be transferred to it by conduction from the land.)*

Preparation for ABC I

- **Science Content:** What would you include in a recommendation to the *CSA* about habitable regions of *Planet X? (The purpose of this is to prepare students for writing a recommendation to the CSA about habitable regions of Planet X.)*

NOTES

◀ *2 class periods* *

Learning Set 5

Back to the Big Challenge

Which regions of a newly discovered planet have surface temperatures appropriate for a human colony?

It is time to use what you have discovered about elevation to revise your predictions about the surface temperatures on *Planet X*. Use the data you collected in your elevation investigations to help you decide what changes to make. You can then identify which areas of *Planet X* are habitable based on this final prediction.

You will modify your *Planet X* temperature map based on the information you have about elevation from your investigations, readings, and the explanations you created. You will use the elevations reported for *Planet X* to help you decide how to adjust your habitability map. Once you have updated your prediction, modify your prediction of habitable areas on *Planet X* to reflect the new global temperatures.

Procedure: Prepare the January Field

1. **Open your *Planet X* project file in *My World*.** Select "Open Project" in the File drop-down menu.

2. **Show habitable and non-habitable areas.** In the "Visualize" tab, turn off the "LandWater Habitability" selection by selecting "All (highlighting off)" radio button in the *Planet X* layer. This will show your prediction for the whole planet, including both habitable and non-habitable areas.

3. **Duplicate the *Planet X* "LandWater January" field.**

   a) **Go to the "Edit" tab. Select the *Planet X* layer to edit that layer.** Be sure "LandWater January" is selected from the Edit Field drop-down menu.

   b) **Click "Add Field..." in the bottom right corner of the screen.** Select "Duplicate an Existing Field."

Learning Set 5

Back to the Big Challenge

< 5 min.

Students create temperature maps for January and July, and identify areas of habitability using My World.

○ **Engage**

Engage students by having them consider how they would revise their average January temperature prediction map for *Planet X*. Record students' responses.

*A class period is considered to be one 40 to 50 minute class.

❝How would you revise your January temperature prediction map for *Planet X* to include what you now know about elevation, and what information would you use to help you? ❞

△ **Guide**

Briefly review what students have written in Column 3 (*What are we learning?*), Column 4 (*What is our evidence?*), and Column 5 (*What does it mean for the challenge or question?*) of the class *Project Board*. If you have not updated the *Project Board,* review the class explanation constructed in the previous section and ask how it would affect their temperature prediction maps of *Planet X*.

Let students know they will be revising the temperature prediction maps they created at the end of the previous *Learning Set.*

Procedure: Prepare the January Field

20 min.

Students observe a demonstrate of My World *and then make their own maps for January.*

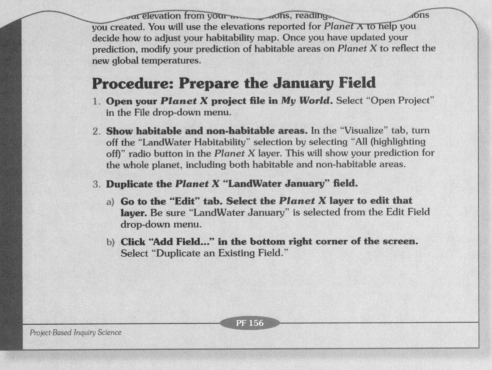

...ut elevation from your in......ions, reading......ions you created. You will use the elevations reported for *Planet X* to help you decide how to adjust your habitability map. Once you have updated your prediction, modify your prediction of habitable areas on *Planet X* to reflect the new global temperatures.

Procedure: Prepare the January Field

1. **Open your *Planet X* project file in *My World*.** Select "Open Project" in the File drop-down menu.

2. **Show habitable and non-habitable areas.** In the "Visualize" tab, turn off the "LandWater Habitability" selection by selecting "All (highlighting off)" radio button in the *Planet X* layer. This will show your prediction for the whole planet, including both habitable and non-habitable areas.

3. **Duplicate the *Planet X* "LandWater January" field.**

   a) **Go to the "Edit" tab. Select the *Planet X* layer to edit that layer.** Be sure "LandWater January" is selected from the Edit Field drop-down menu.

   b) **Click "Add Field..." in the bottom right corner of the screen.** Select "Duplicate an Existing Field."

△ **Guide**

Using the procedures described in the student text, demonstrate for students how to open their project file and turn off all highlighting to complete Steps 1 and 2.

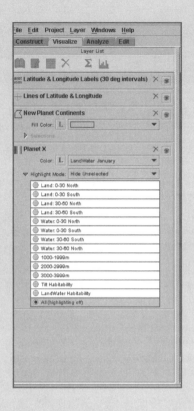

Show students how to duplicate their map following Step 3, which should look like the image shown below.

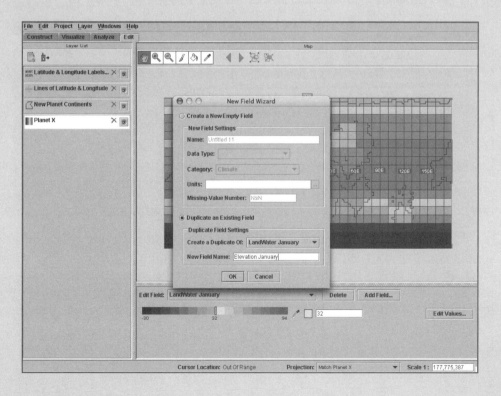

c) **Make a duplicate of "LandWater January."** Name the new field "Elevation January." Click OK. You now have a new field to edit called "Elevation January."

4. **Change the "Elevation January" visualization to represent predicted temperature changes due to elevation.** In *Learning Set 5.2*, you calculated the average temperature change per 1000 m of elevation. *For example, you may have found that for every 1000 m the elevation increases, the temperature will decrease 12°F.* You also calculated the temperature decrease for several elevations above sea level. Use the following steps and those calculations from *Learning Set 5.2* to change the average temperature to represent these changes in elevation.

a) **Focus on an elevation range.** Click on the "visualize" tab. Select an elevation range using the radio buttons in the *Planet X* layer.

   Example: 1000-1999 m. Select the "1000-1999 m" radio button in the Planet X *layer.*

   Your average predicted January temperatures at that latitude will be displayed and all other temperatures hidden.

b) **Determine how much the temperature will need to change if you traveled to an elevation in the middle of that elevation range.** Use your calculations from *Learning Set 5.2*.

   Example: For a distance of 1000-1999 m, the middle is 1500 m. We found that if we traveled 1500 m above sea level, the temperature would decrease 18°F. 12°F for the first 1000 m and then 6°F for the next 500 m.

   Example: For a distance of 2000 to 2999 m, the middle is 2500 m. We have now traveled another 1000 m above sea level, 18°F for the first 1500 m, and 12°F for the next 1000 m for a total decrease of 30°F.

c) **Subtract a constant value from the temperatures at that elevation.**

   • Go to the "Analyze" tab. Go to "Add Fields to Layer," and select "By Math Operation."

   • Add a Field to the Table of *Planet X* by computing a "Difference (subtraction)."

PF 157

PLANETARY FORECASTER

Show students how to change the predicted temperatures using their data. Emphasize that they should use the average temperature change they calculated for every 1000 m and subtract one and a half times this amount for each 1000 m range. Draw students' attention to the image in the student text that shows them how to complete Step 6 and demonstrate it to them.

Let students know they will be following similar procedures for the July fields and will be recalculating the habitable areas.

Example: *If I travel 1500 m above sea level, the temperature will decrease 18°F.*

- You are going to subtract a constant value from the Elevation January field. In the next section of the screen, select "Elevation January" from the first drop-down menu. Select "Constant Value" from the second drop-down menu.

- The "Constant Value" is the temperature difference you calculated in *Learning Set 5.2*. Enter this value in the space to the right of "Constant Value."

Example: *"18" would be entered in that box.*

- Select the focus elevation from the "Compute for:" drop down menu. The constant value will only be added to or subtracted from those elevations.

Example: *1000-1999 m*

- Check the box marked "Copy Results Into Existing Field" and select "Elevation January" from the drop-down menu.

- "Results Name" should follow the model in the example. Click "OK"

Example: *1000-1999 m January*

The cells you changed should now be a different color or at least represent different values. You may want to look at the entire *Planet X* temperature visualization. Select the "All (highlighting off)" radio button in the *Planet X* layer.

Example: *Analyze field for 1000–1999 m in January.*

5. **Save your changes.** "Save Project" in the File menu.
   Note: "Below 1000 m" and "Arctic" are separate categories. You don't have to do anything for these. The Arctic regions are being excluded here because there is so much ice there it is hard to determine the effects of elevation. Elevations ranges below 1000 m are also being excluded because the effects of elevation on temperature are very small at such low elevations.

PF 158

◯ Get Going

Emphasize to students they should complete their prediction map for January, July, and the habitable areas. Let students know how much time they have.

△ Guide and Assess

Monitor students' progress as they are revising their maps. Check that they are referring to their data from *Section 5.2* and all group members are participating. Assist students as needed with the computer. Check to see if students are using one and a half times their average change in temperature value for the 1000-1999 m range, and adding one more average change in temperature value to this value for the 2000-2999 m range as they did when constructing the second data table on the *Elevation and Temperature Data 2* page.

As students are completing their January maps have them print out a map for the *Solution Briefing*. Have them start to work on their July maps. The January maps should look similar to the following.

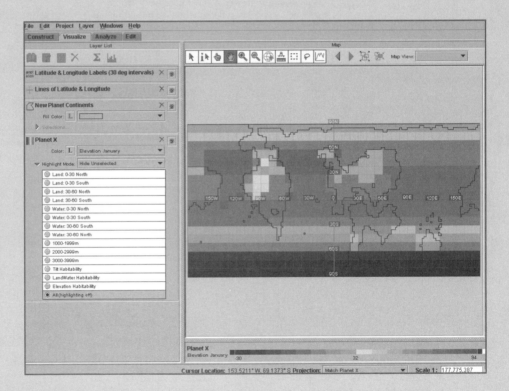

6. **Return to the "Analyze" tab.** Repeat Step 4 and Step 5 for the remaining elevations bands on the "Elevation January" map. Below is a list to help you keep track of those you have completed.

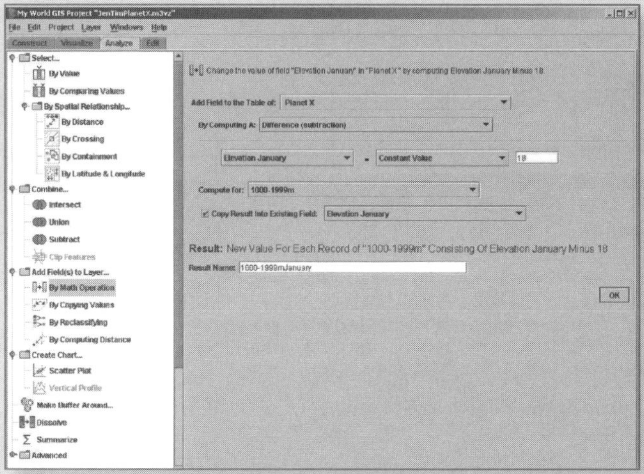

1000-1999 m; Result Name "1000-1999 m January"
2000-2999 m; Result Name "2000-2999 m January"
3000-3999 m; Result Name "3000-3999 m January"

Procedure: Prepare the July field

1. **Open your *Planet X* project file in *My World*.** Select "Open Project" in the File drop-down menu. If you have not closed your project file after creating the "Elevation January" field, skip to **Step 3**.

2. **Show habitable and non-habitable areas.** In the "Visualize" tab, turn off the "LandWater Habitability" selection by selecting "All (highlighting off)" radio button in the *Planet X* layer. This will show your prediction for the whole planet, including both habitable and non-habitable areas.

3. Duplicate the *Planet X* "LandWater July" field.

Procedure: Prepare the July Fields

10 min.

Groups follow the procedures to complete their July maps.

△ Guide and Assess

Monitor students' progress and guide them as needed. Students' July maps should look similar to the map shown below. Remind students to print out the map if needed and to continue on to complete their habitability map.

a) **Go to the "Edit" tab. Double click the *Planet X* layer to edit that layer.** Be sure "LandWater July" is selected from the Edit Field drop-down menu.

b) **Click "Add Field..." in the bottom right corner of the screen. Select "Duplicate an Existing Field."**

c) **Create a duplicate of "LandWater July."** Name the new field "Elevation July." Click OK! You now have a new field to edit called "Elevation July."

4. **Change the "Elevation July" visualization to represent temperature changes due to elevation.** In *Learning Set 5.2*, you calculated the average temperature change per 1000 m of elevation. *For example, you may have found that for every 1000 m the elevation increases, the temperature will decrease 12°F.* You also calculated the temperature decrease for several elevations above sea level. Use the following steps and those calculations from *Learning Set 5.2* to change the average temperature to represent these changes in elevation.

a) **Focus on an elevation range. Click on the "Visualize" tab. Select an elevation range using the radio buttons in the *Planet X* layer.**

Example: 1000-1999 m. Select the "1000-1999 m" radio button in the Planet X layer. Your average predicted January temperatures at that latitude will be displayed and all other temperatures hidden.

b) **Determine how much the temperature will need to change if you traveled to an elevation in the middle of that elevation range.** Use your calculations from *Learning Set 5.2.*

Example: For a distance of 1000-1999 m, the middle is 1500 m. We found that if we traveled 1500 m above sea level, the temperature would decrease 18°F to 12°F for the first 1000 m and then 6°F for the 500 m.

Example: For a distance of 2000 to 2999 m, the middle is 2500 m. We have now traveled another 1000 m above sea level. 18°F for the first 1500 m and 12°F for the next 1000 m for a total decrease of 30°F.

PF 160

NOTES

c) **Subtract a constant value from the temperatures at that elevation.**

- Go to the "Analyze" tab. Go to "Add Fields to Layer," and select "By Math Operation."

- Add a Field to the Table "*Planet X*" by computing a "Difference (subtraction)."

  Example: If I travel 1500 m above sea level, the temperature will decrease 18°F.

- You are going to subtract a constant value from the Elevation July field. In the next section of the screen, select "Elevation July" from the first drop-down menu. Select "Constant Value" from the second drop-down menu.

- The "Constant Value" is the temperature difference you calculated in *Learning Set 5.2*. Enter this value in the space to the right of "Constant Value."

  Example: "18" would be entered in that box.

- Select the focus elevation from the "Compute for:" drop-down menu. The constant value will only be added to or subtracted from those elevations.

  Example: 1000-1999 m

- Check the box marked "Copy Results Into Existing Field" and select "Elevation July" from the drop-down menu.

- "Results Name" should follow model in the example. Click "OK".

  Example: 1000-1999 m July

The cells you changed should now be a different color or at least represent different values. You may want to look at the entire *Planet X* temperature visualization. Select the "All (highlighting off)" radio button in the *Planet X* layer.

Example: Analyze field for 1000–1999 m in July.

NOTES

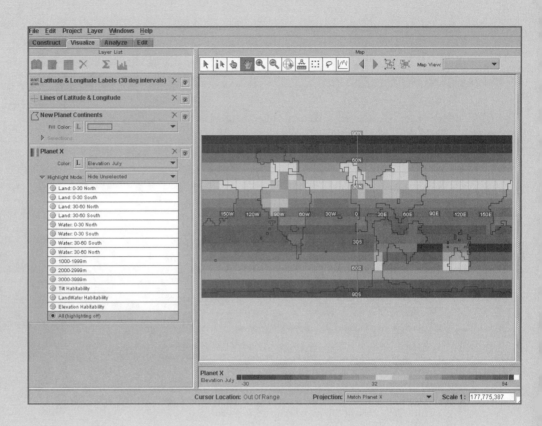

NOTES

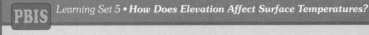

5. **Save your changes.** "Save Project" in the File menu.

Note: "Below 1000 m" and "Arctic" are separate categories. You do not have to do anything for these. The Arctic regions are excluded here because there is so much ice there it is hard to determine the effects of elevation. Elevations ranges below 1000 m are also excluded because the effects of elevation on temperature are very small at such low elevations.

6. **Return to the "Analyze" tab and repeat Steps 4 and 5 for the remaining elevation bands on the "Elevation July" map.** Below is a list to help you keep track of those you have completed.

    1000-1999 m; Result Name "1000-1999 m July"
    2000-2999 m; Result Name "2000-2999 m July"

Procedure: Identify Habitable Areas

You have made (and saved) a January and July prediction map for *Planet X*. Your prediction map now represents the shape, tilt, land/water differences, and elevation factors. The Cooperative Space Agency wants to know what areas on *Planet X* are habitable all year. Use the January and July temperature maps to create a new habitability map.

1. **Open your *Planet X* project file in *My World*.** Select "Open Project" in the File drop-down menu. This project file may still be open after making the Elevation January and July fields.

PF 162

Project-Based Inquiry Science

**Procedure:
Identify
Habitable Areas**

5 min.

Groups inform the CSA *of habitable areas on* Planet X.

△ Guide and Assess

Monitor students' progress and assist them as needed. Remind students to save their work. Have students print out maps if needed. Habitability maps should look similar to the map shown on the next page.

2. **Identify ranges for areas that are habitable in both January and July.**

   a) **Go to the Analyze tab.** Go to the Select folder and select by Value.

   b) **Under the "Select Records From:" drop-down menu, choose *"Planet X."*** Under the "Whose" drop-down menu, choose "Elevation July." Check "Less Than" and enter 85. Select "Greater Than or Equal To" and enter 25.

   c) **Click the button marked with a small plus sign to the right of the screen.** This will allow you to add a second set of requirements for your selection.

   d) **Under the second "Whose" drop-down menu, choose "Elevation January."** Check "Less Than" and enter 85. Select "Greater Than or Equal To" and enter 25.

   e) **Under "Results Name," type in the title "Elevation Habitability."** *Do not check the box called "Make Selection a New Layer."*

   f) **After you have filled out the page to select by value, click OK.**

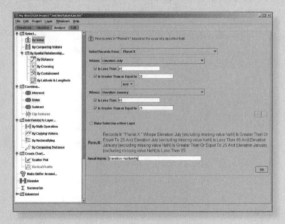

NOTES

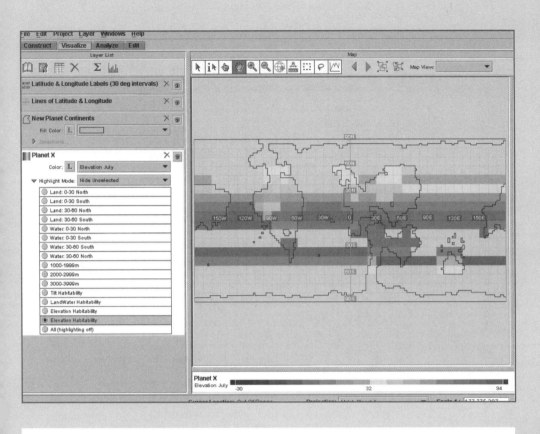

NOTES

Communicate Your Solution: Solution Briefing

20 min.

Students discuss the class's ideas on temperature predictions and habitability for Planet X.

---

3. **Show habitable areas.**

a) **Go to the "Visualize" tab to observe the selection titled "Elevation Habitability."** In this selection, places where you predicted the temperature to be too hot (above 85°F) or too cold (below 25°F) to be habitable in either January or July, have been hidden.

b) **You may have to modify your visualization screen to see your selection. In the Layer List, select the "Planet X" layer.** In the bottom left corner, find the small arrow and be sure this arrow is pointing down. If the arrow is pointing to the right, click on it to turn it. Under "Highlight Mode," select "Hide Unselected." Select the "Elevation Habitability" radio button to view only the areas you have predicted will be habitable.

4. **Save Your Solution.** "Save Project" in the file drop-down menu.

Communicate Your Solution

Solution Briefing

The goal of a *Solution Briefing* is for everyone to better understand how a particular group approached the challenge. You will get the opportunity to see a variety of solutions that might work. You will also have a chance to think about and discuss the merits of each solution.

Your *Solution Briefing* should focus on the following points:

• Present the general look of your solution. Explain the locations of the temperature differences that appear on your map.

• Tell others how the data you collected and the science content you gained during this *Learning Set* support the temperature design of your *Planet X*.

• Discuss how the class explanation of elevation supports your solution so far. If your design purposely does not match the explanation, tell your audience why this is so. Provide them with an explanation that better fits your idea.

△ Guide

Remind students that the goal of a *Solution Briefing* is for everyone to hear how other students approached the challenge and to see a variety of solutions that might work.

Emphasize that they will need to address each of the three bullets listed in the student text. Point out that as they listen they will need to look at each map and consider if the maps fit what they understand about how elevation effects a planet's surface temperature. Emphasize to the class that they should be prepared to ask and answer the five bulleted items in the student text. Remind students they will be taking notes using the *Solution-Briefing Notes* page as they listen to presentations.

NOTES

META NOTES

Students will need a way to project their maps. Use either a projection of an electronic version or a printed copy.

As you listen, it will be important to carefully look at each map. You should ask questions about how the map matches up with your ideas and knowledge from this *Learning Set.* Be prepared to ask (and answer) questions, such as the following:

- As the map was being made, what changes did you make that you do not see in the final map?
- How well does the map match up with the class's explanation of how elevation affects temperature?
- What areas do not seem to match the explanation?
- What areas seemed difficult to map? What areas were easy to map?
- Are there any changes this person might want to make on their map at this time? If so, why?

Be sure to fill out a *Solution-Briefing Notes* page as you listen to everyone's presentation.

Reflect

Answer the following questions. Be prepared to share your answers with the class.

1. How did you use the class elevation explanation to determine the temperature of *Planet X*?

2. How is the location and size of the habitable areas different than it was for shape, tilt, and land and water differences? Why?

3. Think back to the initial list of factors in *Learning Set 1.* Identify the ones that have something to do with elevation. Describe how each of those factors would affect surface temperatures.

Update the *Project Board*

Now that you have completed this *Learning Set,* you know more about how changes in elevation affect surface temperature. You are now ready to fill in the *Project Board* more completely.

PF 165

PLANETARY FORECASTER

⭕ Get Going

Distribute the *Solution-Briefing Notes* page and let groups know how much time they have to prepare their presentations and how much time they have for their presentations.

△ Guide and Assess

Have groups present. As each group is presenting, check that they have addressed the three bulleted points in the student text.

After each presentation, encourage students to ask questions especially if anything was not clear or if any bulleted items were not addressed. Students should ask the suggested questions listed in the student text and/or any other questions they may have.

Remind students to take notes as they are listening to the presentation and the responses to questions.

After each group has presented, discuss the similarities and differences between groups' ideas.

⬡ Get Going

Let students know they will be sharing their answers to the questions with their groups and then with the class. Let students know how much time they have.

△ Guide and Assess

Have a class discussion on students' responses.

1. Students should describe how they used their class's elevation explanation to determine their prediction for the temperatures of *Planet X*.

2. Students should compare and contrast the habitable area maps they created. Students should have areas within the continents that are no longer considered habitable because their temperatures dropped below 25°F.

3. Students should state that all the factors contribute to how elevation affects surface temperature. The air above high-elevation land is warmed by the land's energy. The land has energy to transfer because it absorbed energy from the sunlight striking it. The more sunlight that strikes the surface, the more the land can absorb. The amount of sunlight striking the surface is related to shape and tilt. Temperature is also dependent on how much the land and water absorbs the Sun's radiation and then transfers it to the atmosphere. Elevation further affects the temperature at higher elevations because the air is less dense and there is less air above it pushing down on it because of gravity. When the air is less dense, it does not absorb as much energy transferred to it from the land.

Reflect

10 min.

Students participate in a class discussion on their responses.

Update the Project Board

5 min.

Students update the Project Board *with new ideas and questions.*

You will focus on the two columns *What are we learning?* and *What is our evidence?* When you record your new knowledge in the third column, you will be answering a question or set of questions from the *What do we need to investigate?* column. You should describe what you gained from the investigation you just did. Make sure to provide evidence for your new knowledge.

As the class fills in the *Project Board*, record the same information on your own *Project Board* page.

Which regions of a newly discovered planet have surface temperatures appropriate for a human colony?				
What do we think we know?	What do we need to investigate?	What are we learning?	What is our evidence?	What does it mean for the challenge or question?

What's the Point?

You have just studied the final of the four major factors that influence surface temperatures. You now have a final predicted temperature map for *Planet X* that includes all of these factors. You have also just made a visualization that shows the regions of *Planet X* that have appropriate surface temperatures for a human colony. You will use this information to make and explain final recommendations for colony locations.

PF 166

△ Guide

Have a class discussion after the *Solution Briefing* and update the *Project Board* if needed. Add information to Column 5: *What does it mean for the challenge or question?*

◇ Evaluate

Students should have something similar to the information below on their *Project Boards*. They may have this information in multiple claims or they may combine claims.

Column 3 (claim): Temperature decreases as pressure decreases for a given air mass.

Column 4 (evidence): When a higher-pressure air mass is allowed to expand it has to do work to push away the surroundings as it is expanding. It transfers energy to its surroundings and decreases its average kinetic energy or temperature. We measured this in an experiment in which high pressured gas was released from a bottle and the remaining gas had a lower temperature. We also read how this occurs when warmed air rises, pushing air above it out of the way and transferring energy to that air. The rising and expanding warm air cools in this manner. This method of heat transfer is known as convection.

Column 3 (claim): Temperature decreases with elevation.

Column 4 (evidence): We analyzed data from *My World* and found that, on average, the temperature decreases 11.25°F for every increase of 1000 m. The air is less dense as the elevation increases and it does not warm up by the land as readily as the air at sea level. This is due to the fact that there are fewer particles of air that interact with the surface and collide with each other in a given area, so heat is not readily transferred from the land to the air or between air particles.

Column 3 (claim): Air pressure decreases with elevation.

Column 4 (evidence): We analyzed data from *My World* and found that air pressure decreases as the elevation of land increases. We also read that the air pressure is greater closer to sea level because there is more air above it pushing down on it.

△ Guide

Ask students what they would like to enter in Column 5 (*What does it mean for the challenge or question?*). Remind students the challenge is to determine which regions of *Planet X* have appropriate temperatures for a human colony.

Students must include elevation information that effects the range of temperatures a planet experiences and how it affects the temperature. Students should note that the surface temperatures at higher elevations are lower and they should describe why.

Teacher Reflection Questions

- What difficulties did students have applying the information they learned to create the computer models at the end? How did you guide them?

- How did students use the class explanation?

- What went well during the class discussions? What would you like to do differently next time?

NOTES

Address the Big Challenge I

Which Regions of a Newly Discovered Planet Have Surface Temperatures Appropriate for a Human Colony?

◀ *1 class period*

A class period is considered to be one 40 to 50 minute class.

Overview

Students apply what they know about the factors that effect temperature to make a recommendation of habitability locations on *Planet X*. Students receive another bulletin from the *CSA* asking to finish their recommendations on habitability. Students begin by organizing what they know about shape, tilt, land and water differences, and elevation into a single chart to help them organize their ideas. They prepare a recommendation that identifies a habitable location and a location that is uninhabitable. Their completed recommendation describes how both locations are effected by each of the four factors they studied.

Targeted Concepts, Skills, and Nature of Science	Performance Expectations
Scientists must keep clear, accurate, and descriptive records of what they do so they can share their work with others and consider what they did, why they did it, and what they want to do next.	Students should use their records to construct their first recommendation to *CSA*.
Graphs, maps, and tables are an effective way to analyze and communicate results of scientific investigation.	Students should use a chart to help them organize the information they need to construct their recommendation to *CSA*.

Targeted Concepts, Skills, and Nature of Science	Performance Expectations
Explanations are claims supported by evidence, accepted ideas and facts.	Students should explain how and why each factor (shape, tilt, land and water differences, and elevation) affect surface temperature. Students' explanations should include the application of the ideas listed. Students should then apply these ideas to make a recommendation for a location of *Planet X* they think a human colony should be formed and a location on *Planet X* where they do not think a human colony should not be formed. Students should support their recommendations with evidence and science knowledge.
The intensity of light on an object depends on its shape and the angle it strikes the object at. As the curvature of the object's surface increases the angle at which the light strikes increases, and the intensity of light on the object decreases.	
The average amount of solar energy that strikes Earth's surface over a year is highest near the Equator and the intensity of the solar energy that strikes the surface decreases as you move farther away from the Equator, whether you are moving north or south.	
Earth makes one complete rotation every day about its axis that is tilted with respect to the Sun. It takes a year for the planet to revolve around the Sun.	
Earth's tilted axis causes differences in how solar energy strikes its surface as it moves in an orbit around the Sun.	
Seasons experienced on Earth are caused by its rotation on a tilted axis. The tilt causes either the Northern or Southern Hemisphere to have more direct sunlight and an increase in the exposure time to the Sun, creating summer conditions. The other hemisphere receives less direct sunlight and less exposure time to the Sun and experiences winter.	
Different substances (such as soil and water) transfer heat energy at different rates and require different amounts of energy to raise their temperatures. The amount of energy needed to raise the temperature of a substance is described by its specific heat capacity.	

Targeted Concepts, Skills, and Nature of Science	Performance Expectations
The atmosphere is made up of molecules. The density and pressure of air decreases with increasing elevation.	Students should explain how and why each factor (shape, tilt, land and water differences, and elevation) affect surface temperature. Students' explanations should include the application of the ideas listed. Students should then apply these ideas to make a recommendation for a location of *Planet X* they think a human colony should be formed and a location on *Planet X* where they do not think a human colony should not be formed. Students should support their recommendations with evidence and science knowledge.
Surface temperature changes with changes in elevation and air pressure. As elevation increases, the air pressure and temperature decrease. As the pressure increases the temperature increases.	
Warm air rises and molecules of air spread out and cool as they reach higher, less-dense elevations. This results in heat being transferred through the atmosphere by the convection process.	

Materials

1 per student	*Four Factors Chart* page Blank copy of a *Planet X* map
1 per group	Computers with *My World* and printers, if students did not print out the maps they created in the last section.
2 per student	*Create Your Explanation* page
1 per class	Class *Project Board*

NOTES

Activity Setup and Preparation

Students will need printed copies of their January, July, and habitability elevation maps. If students have not yet printed these, consider printing these for students prior to class, or having a computer with *My World* and printers available.

Homework Options

Reflection

- **Science Process:** How is a recommendation like an explanation? *(Students' responses should include that a recommendation is a suggested claim based on evidence and science knowledge. An explanation is a claim supported by evidence and science knowledge.)*

Preparation for Learning Set 6

- **Science Content:** What do you think causes the differences in weather? *(The purpose of this is to elicit students' initial ideas about weather.)*

NOTES

....

....

....

....

....

....

....

....

....

Address the Big Challenge I

Which Regions of a Newly Discovered Planet Have Surface Temperatures Appropriate for a Human Colony?

You have discovered how elevation, land and water differences, tilt, and shape affect surface temperatures at different locations on Earth. These factors cause Earth to be heated unequally. Because of the similarities between Earth and *Planet X*, you can begin to apply what you have discovered to your challenge of recommending regions that would be suitable for human colony.

Get Started

You will get started by summarizing what you have discovered about the four factors that affect surface temperatures. Throughout this *Unit*, you have written a *Create Your Explanation* page for each of these factors. You have described the data and investigations that have supported these explanations.

Gather any maps or data that would support your explanation. For example, you will probably want to use the "Tilt January" and "Tilt July" maps.

Using these data and explanations, summarize what you have learned on a chart similar to the one shown on the next page. Record your explanations next to each factor.

CSA

TO: Scientific Research Team
FROM: The Cooperative Space Agency
SUBJECT: Request for Habitable Site Recommendation

You are approaching the end of your challenge. The CSA would like you to summarize what you have learned about each of the surface temperature factors and recommend *Planet X* locations appropriate for human colony. Based on your work, CSA is confident that your recommendation will be a good one.

As you are reading this message, potential colonists are undergoing a screening process to select them for their journey. Governments around the world are waiting for your recommendation before making final preparations for this incredible journey into a new frontier.

Thank you for your efforts in conducting this critical part of the investigation for the missions. We look forward to receiving your recommendation.

Address the Big Challenge I

Which Regions of a Newly Discovered Planet Have Surface Temperatures Appropriate for a Human Colony?

5 to 10 min.

Students make their recommendations to the CSA *based on their experiences with* My World.

△ Guide

Remind students they are supposed to make a recommendation to the *CSA* on habitability for *Planet X*. Remind students they now have information on the four identified factors (shape, tilt, land and water differences, and elevation) that affect surface temperature, and they have made prediction maps for the surface temperature and habitability of *Planet X*.

Remind students about recommendations and review updating the class *Project Board* as needed.

*A class period is considered to be one 40 to 50 minute class.

❝A recommendation is a type of claim based on evidence and science knowledge that suggest what to do if a certain situation exists.

Recommendations usually take the form: When some situation occurs, then do or try or expect something.

Sometimes recommendations can be in the form: If something… then something…

All the information you need for your recommendation should be in the class *Project Board*. Before you begin writing your recommendations, together we will review the *Project Board* to see if the class wants to add anything. You should review the *Project Board* and consider what each factor means for the challenge (what you have listed in Column 5), based on what you have listed in Column 3 and Column 4.❞

Review the *Project Board* with the class. Column 5 (*What does it mean for the challenge or question?*) should have something listed for each of the four factors. These should be similar to their explanations of how each factor affects surface temperature. Update the *Project Board* if needed.

Let students know that they will put together recommendations based on all the factors when they write letters of recommendation to the *CSA*. Then review the letter from the *CSA* and emphasize that students will need to include a summary of each factor, a location that would be suitable for a human colony with the reasons why, and a location that would not be suitable for a human colony and why.

NOTES

....

....

....

....

....

....

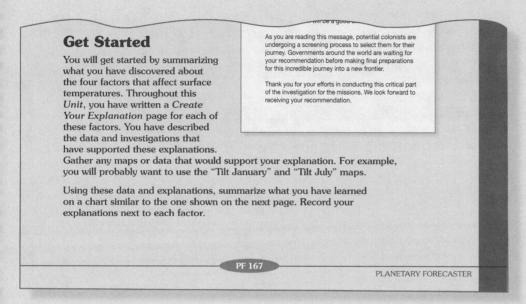

Get Started

You will get started by summarizing what you have discovered about the four factors that affect surface temperatures. Throughout this *Unit*, you have written a *Create Your Explanation* page for each of these factors. You have described the data and investigations that have supported these explanations.
Gather any maps or data that would support your explanation. For example, you will probably want to use the "Tilt January" and "Tilt July" maps.

Using these data and explanations, summarize what you have learned on a chart similar to the one shown on the next page. Record your explanations next to each factor.

As you are reading this message, potential colonists are undergoing a screening process to select them for their journey. Governments around the world are waiting for your recommendation before making final preparations for this incredible journey into a new frontier.

Thank you for your efforts in conducting this critical part of the investigation for the missions. We look forward to receiving your recommendation.

PF 167

PLANETARY FORECASTER

Get Started

15 min.

Students summarize the four factors that affect surface temperature.

◯ Get Going

Let groups know they will be explaining how each of the four factors affect surface temperature on a chart to help organize the information they will need for their explanation. Emphasize that they should collect any maps or other materials they will need to support their claims, including those listed in the student text. Distribute the *Four Factors Chart* page and let students know how much time they have.

NOTES

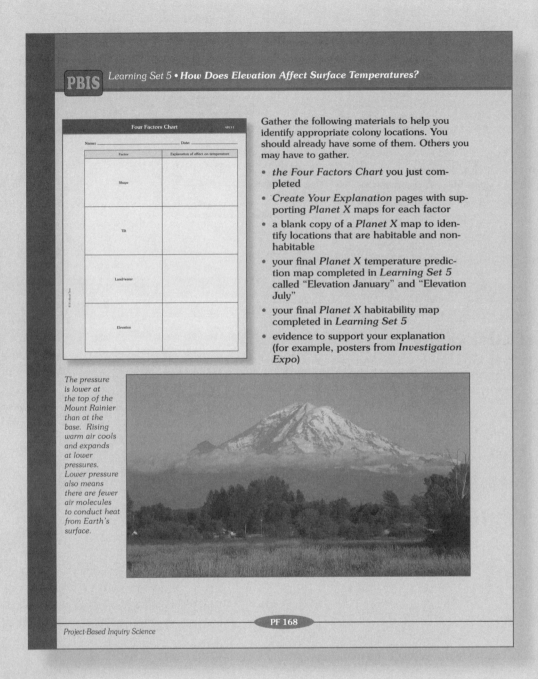

Four Factors Chart

Name: _____ Date: _____

Factor	Explanation of effect on temperature
Shape	
Tilt	
Land/water	
Elevation	

Gather the following materials to help you identify appropriate colony locations. You should already have some of them. Others you may have to gather.

- *the Four Factors Chart* you just completed
- *Create Your Explanation* pages with supporting *Planet X* maps for each factor
- a blank copy of a *Planet X* map to identify locations that are habitable and non-habitable
- your final *Planet X* temperature prediction map completed in *Learning Set 5* called "Elevation January" and "Elevation July"
- your final *Planet X* habitability map completed in *Learning Set 5*
- evidence to support your explanation (for example, posters from *Investigation Expo*)

The pressure is lower at the top of the Mount Rainier than at the base. Rising warm air cools and expands at lower pressures. Lower pressure also means there are fewer air molecules to conduct heat from Earth's surface.

PF 168

Project-Based Inquiry Science

☐ Assess
Check that students have all the needed items from the bulleted list in the student text.

Check students' explanations of the four factors. Below is an example of explanations with supporting evidence and science knowledge.

Four Factors Chart

Name: _____ Date: _____

Factor	Explanation of effect on temperature
Shape	Because Earth is curved, light energy strikes Earth most directly at the Equator and at smaller angles farther north and south. In our experiments, we shined a light on a sphere and a cube. When we moved the light up and down, it did not spread differently along the cube. Light struck the sphere at different angles because the surface is curving away, causing the amount of light to be spread over a greater area. This also means the amount of heat energy transferred per area was less, resulting in overall lower temperatures. Using My World, we analyzed the average yearly incoming solar energy per area. For Earth, we observed the average yearly incoming solar energy decreased from 391 units/m² at the Equator to about 179 units/m² at the poles, with the greatest change occurring near the Equator.
Tilt	A planet's tilt affects the angle at which sunlight strikes the Earth's surface and the amount of time the sunlight shines on its surface. Earth's tilt is always pointed in the same direction. In July, the Northern Hemisphere is tilted toward the Sun, it receives more direct solar energy over a longer amount of time during a day, making it warmer. This is summer. The Southern Hemisphere is tilted away from the Sun in July and receives less sunlight for a less amount of time each day. During this time, it is winter. In January, when the Earth is on the other side of the Sun, the Southern Hemisphere is tilted toward to the Sun and experiences summer. The Northern Hemisphere is tilted away from the Sun and experiences winter. We observed this qualitatively in models we ran using a globe and a light source. Using My World, we observed monthly average temperatures around the world. From the data table in the text, we analyzed average hours of daylight for each month at various locations.
Land/Water	The surface temperatures above water or near a coastline are warmer in the winter and cooler in the summer. This is because water requires more than five times the energy land does to raise its temperature, and requires more energy than land to lower its temperature. As a result, land warms and cools more quickly than water does. We observed that water did not change its temperature as much or as rapidly as sand when heated or cooled over a duration of 12 minutes of heating and 12 minutes of cooling. Using My World, we observed land and water differences varying with latitude.
Elevation	It is colder at higher elevations because there is less air pressure and the air is more spread out. Using My World, we analyzed data showing that temperature decreases an average of 11.5°F with each 1000 m increase in elevation and that pressure decreases as elevation increases. There is less air pressure because there is less air pushing down from above at higher altitudes. Warm air rises and expands because its molecules have more average kinetic energy. As it rises and expands, the molecules bump into and transfer energy to other molecules. In our experiment, we released compressed air from a bottle and measured a decrease in temperature of the gas remaining in the bottle after it was allowed to expand. The air remaining in the bottle had a lower temperature because it transferred energy to the surrounding molecules as it pushed them out of the way.

Recommend

5 min.

Groups select their habitable and uninhabitable locations on Planet X *to recommend to the* CSA.

Recommend

Using your final and most complete habitability map as a guide, select at least one location on *Planet X* that might be appropriate for a human colony. Identify this location on the blank *Planet X* map. Think about why this area is habitable and how the four factors combine to influence surface temperatures. (You may wish to select more than one location.)

The CSA would also like you to identify at least one location that would not be appropriate for a human colony. Think about the way this area is not habitable and how the four factors combine to influence surface temperatures at this place. Identifying these non-habitable places will strengthen your position and prepare you to discuss other student recommendations.

Explain

Using the *Four Factors Chart* and supporting maps, develop a final explanation about how shape, tilt, land and water differences, and elevation affected the surface temperatures at the locations you are recommending and not recommending. You and your group should agree on several points, such as the following:

- How did each factor affect surface temperatures?
- Why did it affect surface temperatures that way?

Remember that claims are based on your results from investigations and research. They must be supported by evidence, such as data and observations. For some of these factors, you can give actual data, or values. For others, you may have to rely on observations or comparisons. For example, you might state, "It makes little difference at the Equator and a big difference near the poles" for one of the factors. Use a *Create Your Explanation* page for each location to help you make a claim and describe evidence.

Remember that this is your official recommendation. The Cooperative Space Agency officials from all over the world will read it. You have some very important information to communicate. Your explanations should include maps. For example, your explanation of tilt as a factor could be matched with your Tilt January and Tilt July temperature maps.

Save your recommendations, explanations, and supporting data. You will need these to prepare a final summary and location recommendation to the CSA.

PF 169

PLANETARY FORECASTER

△ Guide

Let students know they should work with their group members to select one location on *Planet X* they think would be a good place to start a colony and one location that they think would not be a suitable place. Emphasize that they will need both locations in their recommendations. By also identifying these two locations, they will provide *CSA* with information about what is and what is not suitable.

During your investigation, you may have identified other important factors that need to be considered. Write a brief paragraph describing your thoughts about those factors, as well. You might label this paragraph "Suggestions for Additional Research."

What's the Point?

You have now started to summarize how tilt, shape, land and water differences, and elevation influence surface temperatures. You have also used evidence to recommend regions of *Planet X* you think are appropriate for a human colony. You have also gathered maps and data to support your claims. You are ready to prepare a final report and summary to the CSA. In the next *Learning Set*, you will learn about the factors that influence weather. You will write a description of possible weather patterns for the *Planet X* locations you are recommending and add this information to your final recommendations.

Explain
20 min.

Groups explain how each of the factors affects the surface temperatures at the locations they selected and write up their recommendations.

△ Guide

Let groups know they should write up their recommendations and an explanation for why each of locations is or is not suitable for a colony. Emphasize that they should describe how and why each of the four factors affected the surface temperature at each location. Students should use a *Create Your Explanation* page for each location. They should also write a paragraph of factors they have identified that still need to be researched.

Let students know because a location is considered uninhabitable, it does not mean that it would be uninhabitable due to all of the factors. One or more of the factors may make the location favorable. However, students should realize that only one factor's affect on surface temperature is needed to make the location completely uninhabitable.

Encourage students to include any questions or uncertainties in their explanation.

Emphasize to students that this is for their final recommendation, which should include the recommendations, explanations, and supporting data.

◇ Evaluate
Make sure students are supporting their claims with evidence and science knowledge from this Unit.

△ Guide
Consider having students present their recommendations to the class.

Teacher Reflection Questions
- What difficulties did students have with the content while constructing their recommendations?
- What difficulties did students have with recommendations and explanations? How did they utilize the class *Project Board?*
- What issues arose during this section and what would you do next time?

NOTES

LEARNING SET 6 INTRODUCTION

Learning Set 6

◀ **10 class periods**

A class period is considered to be one 40 to 50 minute class.

What Types of Weather Might the Planet X Colony Experience?

Students explore factors that interact to cause changes in weather and explain what causes weather changes. Students apply what they know to predict weather patterns for Planet X.

Overview

Students explore factors that interact to cause weather changes by considering weather maps for a part of North America. Groups analyze data for a location over several days and share their results with the class to find trends in weather patterns. Students further familiarize themselves with some of the factors that affect weather by building and using the tools meteorologists use to measure precipitation, temperature, air pressure, and wind velocity. Students observe a demonstration that simulates how the water cycle works and read more about the water cycle. Building on this knowledge, students read about how the water changes state and how water gets into the atmosphere and forms clouds. Students explain how the Sun's energy drives the water cycle. Students read about local and global wind patterns and what affects these. With information about wind, air pressure, the water cycle, and warming and cooling trends, students explain what causes the changes in weather for the location they were initially asked to analyze, and read about severe storms. Students apply what they know to describe the weather of *Planet X* for two locations near its equator and two locations far from its equator. Students also describe the weather patterns for the location they recommended for a colony and the location they recommended against colonizing. Students conclude the Unit by showcasing their completed recommendations to the class and making recommendations to the *CSA* for the best two or three locations that were suggested.

Targeted Concepts, Skills, and Nature of Science	Section
Scientists often work together and share their findings. Sharing findings makes new information available and helps scientists to refine their ideas and build on others' ideas. When another person's or group's idea is used, credit needs to be given.	6.1, 6.4, 6.5, 6.6, BBC, ABC II
Scientists must keep clear, accurate, and descriptive records of what they do so they can share their work with others and consider what they did, why they did it, and what they want to do next.	6.1, 6.3, 6.4, 6.5, 6.6, BBC, ABC II
Graphs, maps, and tables are an effective way to analyze and communicate results of scientific investigation.	6.1, 6.6, ABC II
Identifying factors that lead to variation is an important part of scientific investigation.	6.1
Scientists make claims (conclusions) based on evidence obtained (trends in data) from reliable investigations	6.3
Explanations are claims supported by evidence, accepted ideas and facts.	6.4, 6.6, BBC, ABC II
Temperatures around the Earth's surface vary widely, but can be predicted somewhat by location and season.	6.6, BBC, ABC II
Weather moves in patterns that can be identified and tracked. Weather maps allow scientists to observe weather patterns and make predictions. Some factors that weather depends on are temperature, air pressure, wind direction, and wind speed.	6.1, 6.2, BBC, ABC II
Trends in weather data show Earth's climate is changing. Scientists believe these changes caused by an increase in global warming due to an increase in greenhouse gases in the atmosphere.	6.2
Energy from the Sun drives Earth's water cycle. Water moves between different physical states in a continuous cycle of evaporation, condensation, and precipitation.	6.3, 6.4, BBC, ABC II
Water changes state (solid, liquid, gas) by adding or removing heat energy.	6.4, BBC, ABC II
Wind results from the Sun's energy heating Earth. Solar energy heats air molecules and creates areas of high and low pressure. Wind is created as air molecules move from high to low pressure areas. This is affected greatly by landforms and water on a local scale.	6.5, BBC, ABC II

Targeted Concepts, Skills, and Nature of Science	Section
Changes in weather are caused when air fronts of different temperatures interact with each other. The different pressures of the fronts cause air masses to move and create precipitation and other forms of weather. Special conditions are needed to develop storms, tornadoes, and hurricanes.	6.6, BBC, ABC II
The intensity of light on an object depends on its shape and the angle it strikes the object at. As the curvature of the object's surface increases, the angle at which the light strikes increases and the intensity of light on the object decreases.	ABC II
The average amount of solar energy that strikes Earth's surface over a year is highest near the Equator. The intensity of the solar energy that strikes the surface decreases as you move farther away from the Equator, either north or south.	ABC II
Earth makes one complete rotation every day about its axis that is tilted with respect to the Sun and takes a year to revolve around the Sun.	ABC II
Earth's tilted axis causes differences in how solar energy strikes its surface as it moves in an orbit around the Sun.	ABC II
Seasons experienced on Earth are caused by its rotation on a tilted axis. The tilt causes either the Northern or Southern Hemisphere to have more direct sunlight and an increase in the exposure time to the Sun, creating summer conditions. At the same time, the other hemisphere receives less direct sunlight, less exposure time to the sun, and experiences winter.	ABC II
Different substances, such as soil and water, transfer heat energy at different rates and require different amounts of energy to raise their temperatures. The amount of energy needed to raise the temperature of a substance is described by its specific heat capacity.	ABC II
The atmosphere is made up of molecules. The density and pressure of air decreases with increasing elevation.	ABC II
Surface temperature changes with changes in elevation and air pressure. As elevation increases, the air pressure and temperature decrease. As the pressure increases, the temperature increases.	ABC II
Warm air rises and air molecules spread out and cool as they reach higher, less-dense elevations. This results in heat energy being transferred through the atmosphere by the convection process.	ABC II

Students' Initial Conceptions and Capabilities

There are many different ideas students may have initially that pertain to weather, some of which are listed below.

- Students may believe that weather is a random phenomenon that has no direct cause and/or does not follow patterns.

- Students might think warm weather is caused by warm energy and cold weather is caused by cold energy. Students may not understand that temperature changes result from a transfer of heat energy to or from an object.

- Students may think weather is caused by local conditions, such as thinking rain comes from locations near bodies of water.

- Students may not understand air has mass and different air masses react with each other in ways similar to solid or liquid materials.

- Students may not understand ice, water, and water vapor are all the same substance in different physical states.

- Students may think when water evaporates it no longer exists, or that it is still a liquid but is relocated, or that it is transformed into water vapor (Bar, 1989; Russell, Harlen, & Watt, 1989; Russell & Watt, 1990).

- Students may have difficulty understanding condensation. They often believe condensation occurs because a liquid has passed through its solid container (Ewings & Mills, 1994; Osborne & Cosgrove, 1983). Some students may believe condensation is air turning into liquid (Lee, et al., 1993; Osborne & Cosgrove, 1983).

- Some students may not realize molecules in ice vibrate less than molecules in liquid water because they have less kinetic energy when their temperature is lower (Lee, et al., 1993).

- Students may believe clouds block wind and slow it down (Dove, 1998).

- Some students may believe cold temperatures produce fast winds (Dove, 1998).

- Some students may believe clouds are refilled by the sea and the water stays in its liquid state during the entire process (Bar, 1989; Philips, 1991).

- Some students may think clouds are formed by steam from boiling water, or the sun boiling the sea (Philips, 1991). Others may think clouds are made of cold, heat, fog, snow, smoke, cotton or wool, or bags of water (Philips, 1991). Some students may believe clouds are water vapor or dust particles (Henriquez, L, 2000).

Students' Initial Conceptions and Capabilities	• Some students may believe thunder is caused by two clouds colliding (Dove, 1998). • Some students may think clouds and rain are independent of each other, or that clouds foretell rain (Bar, 1989). • Some students may think rain comes from evaporating clouds (Stepans & Keuhn, 1985). Others may believe rain comes from holes or funnels in clouds, or from clouds sweating (Philips, 1991; Stepans & Keuhn, 1985) or melting (Dove, 1998). • Some students might think rain occurs when wind shakes the cloud (Bar, 1989; Philips, 1991) or when two clouds collide (Bar, 1989). • Some students may believe rain occurs when clouds become too heavy (Bar, 1989; Stepans & Keuhn, 1985).

Understanding for Teachers

Although many students may believe weather conditions are mostly random occurrences, they should know about the forces that cause weather from the previous *Learning Sets*. Students have been introduced to the concepts of uneven heating on Earth's surface as well as general temperature differences and air pressure. In this *Learning Set,* students will use much of what they know about surface temperatures to investigate the forces and conditions that create weather. Students will learn weather occurs in patterns and will gain experience interpreting weather maps and using tools to measure weather conditions.

Weather

Weather systems are the combination of warm and cold areas, and rising and sinking air. When an air mass gets too warm, it rises until it is the same temperature as the surrounding air. When an air mass cools, it sinks. Land and water affect local weather patterns greatly because land warms and cools faster than water.

Winds

Air masses that have high pressure are called Highs. Highs are composed of air masses that tend to be cold and sink. Highs produce clear skies and fair weather. Air masses that are warm and have low pressure are called Lows. Lows are composed of air masses that rise. Lows can cause clouds to form, rain to fall, and storms to occur. Weather systems in the United States and within the mid-latitudes, between 30° N and 60° N and between 30° S and 60° S, usually move from west to east. Weather systems in other latitudes move from east to west. For example, most winds over Northern Africa move from east to west. Local winds may also move from east to west due to local features, such as the jet stream in the Gulf of Mexico.

Clouds

When warm, moist air meets colder, drier air, the warm air rises and the water vapor condenses, usually on a dust particle or some other particle in the air. This forms a cloud. As the water vapor condenses, it releases energy and warms its surroundings. A visible cloud is composed of tiny water droplets and/or tiny ice crystals; it is not water vapor. Rain begins to fall when water drops in the cloud are too heavy to remain airborne.

Thunderstorms

The atmosphere releases energy during thunderstorms. A large amount of a thunderstorm's energy comes from the condensation process that forms the thunderstorm clouds. As the thunderstorm progresses, the rain transfers energy away from the cloud.

There is always a steady current of electrons flowing upwards from the entire surface of Earth into its atmosphere. Thunderstorms help transfer the negative charges back to Earth's surface (lightning is generally negatively charged). Without thunderstorms and lightning, the electrical balance between Earth and its atmosphere would quickly disappear. Scientists are not sure of what the consequences of this would be. Thunderstorms are not the only way the atmosphere conducts electricity — solar wind and ionospheric wind play a role, too.

Thunder and Lightning

Thunder and lightning are the visible and auditory effects of a massive charge transfer that occurs. Lightning is not completely understood. The typical lightning bolt begins with a charge formation in a cloud that induces a charge on the ground. Then a stream or channel of negative charge, called a stepped leader, zigzags downward in roughly 46-m (50-yd) segments in a forked pattern. This stepped leader is invisible to the human eye and shoots to the ground in less time than it takes to blink. As it nears the ground, the negatively charged stepped leader attracts a channel of positive charge reaching up from the ground known as streamers. The streamer normally stems from something tall, such as a tree, house, or telephone pole. When the oppositely-charged leader and streamer connect, a powerful electrical current begins flowing. A return stroke of bright luminosity, which we see, travels about 60,000 miles per second back towards the cloud. The actual diameter of a lightning channel is 2.5 cm to 5 cm (one-to-two inches). Lightning can strike from the sky down or the ground up. Cloud-to-ground lightning comes from the sky down, but the part you see comes from the ground up. A typical cloud-to-ground flash lowers a path of negative electricity (that we cannot see) towards the ground in a series of spurts. Objects on the ground generally have a positive charge. Since opposites attract, an upward streamer is sent out from the object about to be struck. When these two paths meet, a return stroke zips back up to the sky. The return stroke produces the visible flash, but it happens so fast (in about one-millionth of a second) the human eye does not see the actual formation of the stroke.

Thunder is a direct result of lightning caused by the sudden increase in pressure and temperature lightning produces. When a bolt of lightning strikes, it causes a rapid expansion of the surrounding air. Within a bolt of lightning, heat energy is transferred to the air, heating the air anywhere between 18,000 °F to 60,000 °F. This rapid expansion of air creates a sonic shock wave that produces the sound of thunder.

NOTES

....

....

....

....

....

....

....

....

....

....

....

NOTES

LEARNING SET 6 IMPLEMENTATION

Learning Set 6

What Types of Weather Might the Planet X Colony Experience?

TO: Scientific research team
FROM: The Cooperative Space Agency
SUBJECT: Planetary Weather

Congratulations on a job well done. You have completed your research into the four factors affecting temperature variations on Earth. Using this information, you can make a very strong recommendation about habitable areas on *Planet X*.

However, due to the similarities between Earth and *Planet X*, we are concerned about possible weather conditions that the colonists may need to be prepared for. If it is anything like Earth, they will have to be prepared for severe weather in some places, including hurricanes and tornadoes. What you have discovered about temperature will help you advise them about weather conditions. Therefore, when you make your final recommendation about habitable areas on *Planet X*, we are asking that you also give some advice about the types of weather the colonists may experience so they can be prepared for it.

Weather influences when farmers can plant, and how successful their crops are going to be.

Weather is constantly changing. It affects many things in people's daily lives, such as transportation, energy use for heating and cooling, agriculture, and daily activities. Sometimes the weather can become severe, causing property damage and putting people's lives in danger. People often choose to live or not live in an area because of weather conditions.

PF 171

Learning Set 6

What Types of Weather Might the Planet X Colony Experience?

5 min.

Students are introduced to the Learning Set.

○ Engage

Ask students if they can think of any other factors affecting the surface temperatures the colonists might need to prepare for. Record students' ideas.

Discuss the bulletin. Consider having students read the bulletin aloud.

Have the students look at the picture of the farm in the student text. Ask them to think about the different types of weather experienced on the farm. Ask them to describe several examples and how it might affect the successfulness of the crops planted.

*A class period is considered to be one 40 to 50 minute class.

Ask students if they know of any places where weather can be severe. The class should discuss how Florida experiences severe thunderstorms and hurricanes, and is the lightning capital of the United States, the Midwest and Southeast experience many tornadoes, and the dry Southwest experiences flash flooding and dry spells that lead to fires.

Conclude by having students discuss how weather can make a place more or less habitable, and ask students what kind of weather might be best for starting a human colony on *Planet X*.

NOTES

SECTION 6.1 INTRODUCTION

6.1 Understand the Challenge

What Factors Interact to Cause Weather?

◀ *1 class period*

A class period is considered to be one 40 to 50 minute class.

Overview

Students consider what factors affect weather. Each group explores weather maps and data for one of four locations in North America. The groups analyze data for their location over three days to determine weather patterns in their location. Groups share their results with the class to find trends in weather patterns. Based on this information, students consider what factors cause different types of weather. Students update the class *Project Board* with what they think they know about weather and what they think they need to investigate.

Targeted Concepts, Skills, and Nature of Science	Performance Expectations
Scientists often work together and share their findings. Sharing findings makes new information available and helps scientists to refine their ideas and build on others' ideas. When another person's or group's idea is used, credit needs to be given.	Students should work in groups to analyze weather data and weather maps for a specific location, then groups should share their results with the class and the class should look for trends in weather patterns across the four locations. The class should update their *Project Board* with what they think they know and discuss questions they think they should investigate.
Scientists must keep clear, accurate, and descriptive records of what they do so they can share their work with others and consider what they did, why they did it, and what they want to do next.	Students should keep clear and descriptive records of their ideas and questions to build upon during this *Learning Set*.
Graphs, maps, and tables are an effective way to analyze and communicate results of scientific investigation.	Students should read and analyze the maps and tables provided and use them when sharing their ideas about the trends they find.

Targeted Concepts, Skills, and Nature of Science	Performance Expectations
Identifying factors that lead to variation is an important part of scientific investigation.	Students should identify factors they think affect weather.
Weather moves in patterns that can be identified and tracked. Weather maps allow scientists to observe weather patterns and make predictions. Some factors that weather depends on are temperature, air pressure, wind direction, and wind speed.	Students should identify patterns they see in a given location and across the locations being analyzed.

Materials	
1 per class	Class *Project Board*
1 per student	*Project Board* page
1 per group	Presentation materials

NOTES

....

....

....

....

....

....

....

....

....

Activity Setup and Preparation

Consider obtaining three days of weather data for a specific location and going through it as a class, or assigning it to a group to analyze.

There are many interesting satellite images on the Internet showing current wind patterns, cloud coverage, and animations of cloud coverage. Consider exploring some of these and sharing with the class.

Homework Options

Consider assigning students or groups a project for the *Learning Set* constructing a weather journal to include observations from weather maps and/or weather forecasts for your local area, observations of the weather using their senses, and measurements made using instruments they will be constructing in the next section. Students should look for patterns in the data to help support causes for change in weather.

Reflection

- **Science Content:** Describe the symbols used on a weather map. *(Students should explain that warm air is represented by a red line with semi-circles showing the direction it travels and cold air is represented by a blue line with triangles showing the direction it travels. The H represents areas with high atmospheric pressure and L represents areas with low atmospheric pressure.)*

Preparation for 6.2

- **Science Content:** What factors affect weather and what types of instruments do you think meteorologists use to measure factors that affect weather? *(The purpose of this question is to get students thinking about the factors that affect weather and how they are measured before building instruments to collect weather data.)*

NOTES

SECTION 6.1 IMPLEMENTATION

6.1 Understand the Challenge

What Factors Interact to Cause Weather?

You have lots of experience with the weather. Perhaps you have had an outdoor activity cancelled due to rain or snow. You may have had to decide what to wear on a cold or very hot day. Think about what weather actually means. In this *Learning Set*, you will investigate the factors that inluence weather.

Get Started

In this section, you will begin to think about weather more scientifically than you have in the past. You will discover a lot about different weather patterns. You will discover why they happen. You will also discover how they move around Earth. To do this, you are going to look at three different weather maps of the United States. These maps show typical weather over a three-day period in the fall. The maps will help you understand more about the weather and the factors that influence weather.

PF 172

Project-Based Inquiry Science

6.1 Understand the Challenge

What Factors Interact to Cause Weather?

< 5 min.

Students study and analyze the weather patterns of four locations.

Get Started

< 5 min.

Students are introduced to weather maps.

○ Engage

Have a discussion about how weather affects students' daily lives.

△ Guide

Let students know they will study weather maps that show typical weather over a three-day period in the fall. Have them briefly look over the maps in the student text and discuss them.

*A class period is considered to be one 40 to 50 minute class.

"Weather maps are visualizations of all data meteorologists collect. What types of information do you see that are provided by the weather map? What factors do you think affect weather?"

NOTES

6.1 Understand the Challenge

Tornadoes form when cold air and warm air combine—the cold air goes down as the warm air rises. The warm air twists into a spiral and forms a funnel cloud, or tornado.

You have probably seen maps on television, in the newspaper, or on the Internet like the ones on the next page. They show a lot of information about the weather. All of the information comes from data that weather scientists, called **meteorologists,** collect. The data include factors like temperature, air pressure, wind speed and direction, and rainfall. People use these maps to find out what the weather is and what it will be like.

> **meteorologist:** a scientist who studies weather.

Explore

Your group will be assigned one of the locations on the maps—A, B, C, or D. Describe the weather at your assigned location over the three days. Use the maps and the key to answer the questions for your location. Some of the questions are the same across all groups and some are different. This is because each location has a different weather pattern occurring over the three days.

This may be the first time you will have looked carefully at a weather map. You may have questions you cannot answer right now. That is okay. Read all the questions and make notes about the questions you could not answer. You will return to those questions throughout the *Learning Set* as you read more about each of the symbols on the map and how the factors they represent influence the weather.

PF 173

PLANETARY FORECASTER

Explore

15 min.

Groups analyze weather conditions in specific locations over three days.

META NOTES

It is not expected for students to be able to answer all the questions. Questions that students are uncertain of should provide discussion topics and hooks for information presented later.

△ Guide

Let students know there are four different locations that will be analyzed. Each group will only analyze weather conditions for one location. Groups will share their results with the class and the class will look for trends in weather patterns across the locations.

Emphasize that there are questions for each location they should answer, although they may not be able to answer all the questions. Let them know they should make notes about the questions they are not sure about.

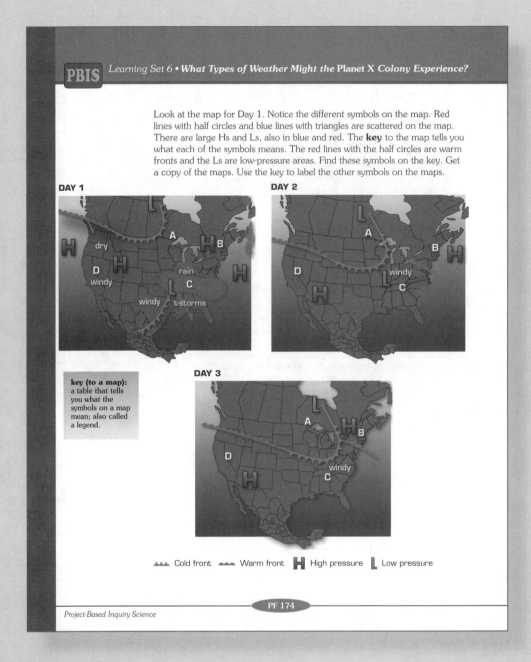

Look at the map for Day 1. Notice the different symbols on the map. Red lines with half circles and blue lines with triangles are scattered on the map. There are large Hs and Ls, also in blue and red. The **key** to the map tells you what each of the symbols means. The red lines with the half circles are warm fronts and the Ls are low-pressure areas. Find these symbols on the key. Get a copy of the maps. Use the key to label the other symbols on the maps.

DAY 1

DAY 2

key (to a map): a table that tells you what the symbols on a map mean; also called a legend.

DAY 3

▲▲▲ Cold front   ◠◠◠ Warm front   **H** High pressure   **L** Low pressure

PF 174

Project-Based Inquiry Science

Consider reviewing the symbols on the weather maps with the class using the information in the student text. Consider having students identify which cities they are monitoring. Accept any close estimates reasonably matching the maps in the student text.

6.1 Understand the Challenge

Location A

Information	Day One	Day Two	Day Three
High Temperature	55	48	50
Low Temperature	34	30	31
Wind Direction	Northwest	Northwest	Northwest
Air Pressure	30.20 Rising Slowly	30.23 Rising Slowly	30.24 Rising Slowly
Humidity	62%	56%	50%

Location B

Information	Day One	Day Two	Day Three
High Temperature	60	61	63
Low Temperature	45	47	39
Wind Direction	Southwest	Southwest	Southwest
Air Pressure	30.10 Falling Slowly	29.86 Falling Slowly	29.75 Steady
Humidity	65%	70%	86%

Location C

Information	Day One	Day Two	Day Three
High Temperature	65	74	76
Low Temperature	55	57	55
Wind Direction	Southwest	Southwest	West
Air Pressure	29.86 Falling Slowly	29.65 Rising Slowly	30.00 Rising Slowly
Humidity	89%	89%	80%

Location D

Information	Day One	Day Two	Day Three
High Temperature	77	82	77
Low Temperature	60	55	55
Wind Direction	Northwest	Northwest	West
Air Pressure	30.10 Steady	30.14 Steady	30.12 Steady
Humidity	72%`	73%	70%

PF 175

PLANETARY FORECASTER

○ Get Going

Assign one of the locations to each student group. Emphasize that they should answer the questions coordinating with the location assigned to them and distribute the maps. Let students know how much time they have.

☐ Assess

Monitor students' progress to determine where they are having difficulty. Note these to be areas of discussion during the class discussion. Check that students are writing notes about questions they are not sure of.

It is not expected for students to have all the answers on the next page.

Location A

1. Briefly describe the weather on each day. Try to include as many details as possible.

2. Use the map key. What symbols appear on the maps at location A? Label each map symbol at this location on your copy of each map.

3. Look carefully at the air-pressure readings for this location. What do you notice about the changes in the air-pressure readings over the three days?

4. How do the high and low temperatures change over the three days?

5. Compare the changes in the air-pressure readings and the temperature readings to the movement of the symbols at location A over the three days. What happens to the air-pressure and temperature readings as the blue line moves?

6. In what direction does the blue line move near location A?

Location B

1. Briefly describe the weather on each day. Try to include as many details as possible.

2. Use the map key. What symbols appear on the maps at location B? Label each map symbol at this location on your copy of each map.

3. Look carefully at the air-pressure readings for this location. What do you notice about the changes in the air-pressure readings over the three days?

4. How do the high and low temperatures change over the three days?

5. Using the three maps, determine the direction in which the weather is moving near location B.

Location C

1. Briefly describe the weather on each day. Try to include as many details as possible.

2. Use the map key. What symbols appear on the maps at location C? Label each map symbol at this location on your copy of each map.

3. At location C, a blue line and a red line are shown together. Label the blue and red lines. What is happening at the place where these two lines are near each other?

PF 176

Project-Based Inquiry Science

Location A

1. Day 1: A cold front was moving in that was in front of a low-pressure area. The high temperature was 55°F, the low was 34°F, and the winds blew from the northwest and headed southeast. The air pressure was rising slowly and the humidity was 62%.

Day 2: The cold front had passed, the high temperature was 48°F, and the low temperature was 30°F. The winds were still blowing from the northwest, the air pressure was 30.23 and slowly rising, and the humidity dropped to 56%.

Day 3: The temperature range was 50°F to 31°F. The winds were still from the northwest and the air pressure was 30.24 and slowly rising. The humidity dropped to 50%.

2. Students should describe the cold front moving through Location A.

3. The air pressure is increasing over the three-day period. It increases by 0.03 on Day 2 and by 0.01 from Day 2 to Day 3.

4. The high temperature dropped seven degrees from Day 1 to Day 2, and increased two degrees from Day 2 to Day 3.

5. As the cold front was passing, the temperatures dropped and the air pressure increased. After it passed, the temperatures started to increase and the air pressure increased slightly.

6. The blue line moved from the northwest to the southeast, in the same direction as the wind.

Location B

1. Day 1: A high-pressure area was at this location. The high temperature was 60°F, the low was 45°F, and the winds blew from the southwest to the northeast. The air pressure was falling slowly and the humidity was 65%.

   Day 2: A warm front was closer, the high temperature was 61° and the low temperature was 47°F. The winds were still blowing from the southwest, the air pressure was 29.86 and slowly falling. The humidity increased to 70%.

   Day 3: The temperature range was from 63°F to 39°F. The winds were still blowing from the southwest and the air pressure was 29.75 and steady. The humidity increased to 86%.

2. Students should describe the H, high pressure, for Day 1. For Day 2, students should indicate that a warm front was moving in from the southwest and there was high pressure to the southeast of Location B. For Day 3, students should describe how the warm front was closer and there was high pressure to the northwest of Location B.

3. The air pressure decreased by 0.24 on Day 2 and by 0.09 from Day 2 to Day 3.

4. The high temperature increased one degree from Day 1 to Day 2 and increased two degrees from Day 2 to Day 3. The low temperature decreased four degrees from Day 1 to Day 2 and increased one degree from Day 2 to Day 3. The low temperature increased two degrees from Day 1 to Day 2 and decreased eight degrees from Day 2 to Day 3.

5. The weather seems to be moving in the direction of the cold front and the winds moved from the southwest towards the northeast.

6.1 Understand the Challenge

4. How does the air pressure change over the three days? When is the air pressure highest? When is it lowest? What is the weather at the highest and lowest points?

5. Using the three maps, determine the direction in which the weather is moving near location C.

Location D

1. Briefly describe the weather on each day. Try to include as many details as possible.
2. Use the map key. What symbols appear on the maps at location D? Label each map symbol at this location.
3. On which day does the weather begin to change? Where are the symbols on that day?
4. Use the information table next to the maps. How does the air pressure change over the three days at this location? Compare the air pressure to the weather symbols on the maps. When is the air pressure highest? What is the weather on that day? When is the air pressure lowest? What is the weather on that day?
5. Using the three maps, determine the direction in which the weather is moving near location D.

Communicate

Each group in the class examined only one location on the weather maps. However, to really understand weather patterns, you need to know about the weather patterns in a variety of different places. Therefore, each group will share the data and descriptions of their location by making a poster and presenting it to the class. The posters should include a weather table, filled in as completely as possible, for each location. During your presentation, make sure you answer all the questions about your location. If there were things you did not understand about the weather in your location, you should report them to the class, as well.

- Over the next few days, you might want to look at the weather maps in your local newspaper or on the Internet. Look for any patterns in the way weather systems move. Keep a weather journal. Compare the maps to your observations. Record any questions you may have about changes in the weather.

Location C

1. Day 1: It was raining. There was a low-pressure area to the southwest of Location C. A warm front from the southwest and a cold front from the west were moving in. The high temperature was 65°F; the low was 55°F. The winds blew from the southwest and headed northeast. The air pressure was 29.86 and falling slowly, and the humidity was 89%.

Day 2: The warm front had passed and the low-pressure air was to the northwest. It was no longer raining. The high temperature was

74°F and the low temperature was 57°F. The winds still blew from the southwest, the air pressure was 29.65 and slowly rising, and the humidity increased to 89%.

Day 3: A cold front was moving in from the northwest. The temperature range was from 76°F to 55°F. The winds were from the west and the air pressure was 30.00 and rising slowly. The humidity decreased to 80%.

2. Students should describe the rain shown in green, the warm front headed to the northeast, and the cold front moving to the southeast, which seem to intersect under the rain area to the left of Location C. There was also nearby low pressure to the southwest of Location C for Day 1. For Day 2, there was low pressure to the northwest of Location C. On Day 3, there was a cold front approaching Location C from the northwest.

3. It was raining where the blue line (cold front) and the red line (warm front) met.

4. The air pressure dropped 0.21 from Day 1 to Day 2, and rose 0.45 on Day 3. The air pressure was highest on Day 3 as a cold front moved in. The air pressure was lowest on Day 2 after the rain and the warm front passed.

5. The weather seems to move toward the northeast with moving warm fronts. Some students may note the cold front on Day 3 indicates weather moving toward the southwest or west.

Location D

1. Day 1: It was windy and there were two high-pressure air masses, one to the northeast and one to the northwest. The temperature ranged from 77°F to 60°F. The wind blew from the northwest. The air pressure was 30.10 and steady. The humidity was 72%.

Day 2: There was high pressure to the southeast. The high temperature was 82°F and the low temperature was 57°F. The winds blew from the northwest and the air pressure was 29.65 and rising. The humidity increased to 73%.

Day 3: The high pressure remained southeast of Location D; the temperature range was between 77°F and 55°F. The wind blew from the west; the air pressure was 30.12 and steady. Humidity was 70%.

2. Students should describe the high-pressure areas northwest and northeast on Day 1, and southeast on Days 2 and 3. Students should state it was windy on Day 1.

3. There is not much change in weather. It was windy on Day 1 and there were two high-pressure areas nearby (to the northeast and northwest), it was not windy after that, and only one high-pressure area was nearby to the southeast. The wind changed direction on Day 3.

4. The air pressure increased 0.04, from 30.10 to 30.14 between Day 1 and Day 2 and decreased 0.02, to 30.12 between Day 2 and Day 3. The change was slight and the air pressure remained steady at Location D. There were no cold fronts or warm fronts affecting the area, only some high-pressure air to the northeast and northwest on Day 1 and to the southeast on Days 2 and 3.

5. Students should note there is not a lot of information to determine the direction of the weather. The wind was moving from the northwest to the southeast, which followed the cold front and the high-pressure area moving south, and the wind was also to the west.

What is the weather on that day?

5. Using the three maps, determine the direction in which the weather is moving near location D.

Communicate

Each group in the class examined only one location on the weather maps. However, to really understand weather patterns, you need to know about the weather patterns in a variety of different places. Therefore, each group will share the data and descriptions of their location by making a poster and presenting it to the class. The posters should include a weather table, filled in as completely as possible, for each location. During your presentation, make sure you answer all the questions about your location. If there were things you did not understand about the weather in your location, you should report them to the class, as well.

- Over the next few days, you might want to look at the weather maps in your local newspaper or on the Internet. Look for any patterns in the way weather systems move. Keep a weather journal. Compare the maps to your observations. Record any questions you may have about changes in the weather.

PF 177

PLANETARY FORECASTER

Communicate

20 min.

Groups present their results to the class and have a discussion to find trends in weather patterns.

△ Guide

Let students know each group will be presenting their results and will need to answer all the questions for their location during their presentations. They will also need to include anything they did not understand. Let them know they will need to construct a poster containing a weather table filled in as completely as possible for each location.

◯ Get Going

Distribute the presentation materials and let groups know how much time they have to prepare their posters and how much time they will have to present.

△ Guide

Before a group presents, remind students to look at the questions the presenting group should answer. Emphasize that they should ask questions if they are not clear on an answer to any of the questions.

Model appropriate language as needed.

TEACHER TALK

"I don't understand how the science knowledge backs up your explanation. Could you walk me through it?

I don't see how ... is supported by your data. Could you show me?

This statement doesn't make sense to me. Could you state it another way?

I'm not sure if I understand this. Do you mean: ... (*state it in your own words*.)"

Have each group present in an order so that all groups that analyzed the same location present after another.

After each presentation, ask students what trends they found in the weather data over three days. Encourage the class to ask questions. Use the information in the previous segment to help guide and assess the discussion.

After all groups of a given location have presented, have a discussion on any differences the groups found.

After all groups have presented, have a class discussion on the similarities and differences between locations. Record these and ask students what trends they see based on these similarities and differences.

Encourage students to look at other weather maps or weather forecasts for your local area and to keep a weather journal with observations they make (including observations they make with instruments they will be constructing in the next section). Students should look for patterns.

META NOTES

As students try to find trends in weather patterns across locations, they should form questions. These questions should be included in the class *Project Board.*

Update the Project Board

10 min.

The class updates the Project Board.

Update the *Project Board*

Your class started a *Project Board* as you were investigating the factors that influence weather. Now, you are extending that thinking as you look at the factors, including temperature, that cause weather. The maps you investigated helped you begin to understand patterns of weather in the United States. You may have also been introduced to several new words while looking at the patterns. Think, too, about the most recent memo from the Cooperative Space Agency. It may have reminded you about other things you think you know about weather. Record your ideas about weather and weather patterns under *What do we think we know?* Record your questions and what you think you need to investigate to report back to the Cooperative Space Agency under *What do we need to investigate?* You will gather more information about each of these ideas and many of these questions during the rest of this *Learning Set*.

What's the Point?

Weather affects everyone. You probably have a lot of personal experience with weather. The weather helps you decide if you are going to wear a coat or carry an umbrella, walk to school or get a ride, play baseball or sit inside and read a book. You may have even read the weather forecasts to help you plan an activity. Meteorologists use different tools and models to help report and forecast weather. Meteorologists collect information about temperature, air pressure, wind speed and direction, and rainfall to help them predict and describe the weather. In this section, you looked at weather maps with representations of some of these factors. You tried to figure out what those factors and those symbols mean. You also tried to figure out how those factors influence the weather. Using these symbols and factors you described the weather patterns at four different locations. You also shared with your class what you think these weather maps mean. You and your class probably have a lot of questions about these factors and weather maps. In this *Learning Set*, you are going learn about these factors and how they influence weather.

△ Guide

Ask students what they think they know about weather patterns. Record students' responses in the first column of the *Project Board*.

Update the Project Board

10 min.

The class updates the Project Board.

Update the *Project Board*

Your class started a *Project Board* as you were investigating the factors that influence weather. Now, you are extending that thinking as you look at the factors, including temperature, that cause weather. The maps you investigated helped you begin to understand patterns of weather in the United States. You may have also been introduced to several new words while looking at the patterns. Think, too, about the most recent memo from the Cooperative Space Agency. It may have reminded you about other things you think you know about weather. Record your ideas about weather and weather patterns under *What do we think we know?* Record your questions and what you think you need to investigate to report back to the Cooperative Space Agency under *What do we need to investigate?* You will gather more information about each of these ideas and many of these questions during the rest of this *Learning Set*.

What's the Point?

Weather affects everyone. You probably have a lot of personal experience with weather. The weather helps you decide if you are going to wear a coat or carry an umbrella, walk to school or get a ride, play baseball or sit inside and read a book. You may have even read the weather forecasts to help you plan an activity. Meteorologists use different tools and models to help report and forecast weather. Meteorologists collect information about temperature, air pressure, wind speed and direction, and rainfall to help them predict and describe the weather. In this section, you looked at weather maps with representations of some of these factors. You tried to figure out what those factors and those symbols mean. You also tried to figure out how those factors influence the weather. Using these symbols and factors you described the weather patterns at four different locations. You also shared with your class what you think these weather maps mean. You and your class probably have a lot of questions about these factors and weather maps. In this *Learning Set*, you are going learn about these factors and how they influence weather.

△ Guide

Ask students what they think they know about weather patterns. Record students' responses in the first column of the *Project Board*.

Review with students what they were unsure of when answering questions for their locations, and the differences they observed between the groups' presentations for the same location. Ask the class what they would like to record in Column 2 (*What do we need to investigate?*) of their class *Project Board*. Record students' investigative questions and remind them these are questions they will need to answer to help make weather-prediction maps for various locations on *Planet X*.

Assessment Options

Targeted Concepts, Skills, and Nature of Science	How do I know if students got it?
Identifying factors that lead to variation is an important part of scientific investigation.	
Weather moves in patterns that can be identified and tracked. Weather maps allow scientists to observe weather patterns and make predictions. Some factors that weather depends on are temperature, air pressure, wind direction, wind speed, and humidity.	**ASK:** What factors do you think affect weather and why? **LISTEN:** Students should identify factors based on trends they found that show an understanding of the targeted concepts.

Teacher Reflection Questions

- What difficulties did students have with the weather maps or identifying trends in the data?

- What content from previous lessons did students bring into discussions?

- Describe the class participation in the discussions of groups' analysis. If needed, how could participation improve?

NOTES

6.2 Build

How are Precipitation, Temperature, Humidity, Air Pressure, and Winds Measured?

◀ $1\frac{1}{2}$ *class periods*

A class period is considered to be one 40 to 50 minute class.

Overview

Students explore the factors of weather and the tools that measure these factors by building working weather instruments. Students read about five instruments meteorologists use to collect information to study weather: a rain gauge, a thermometer, a barometer, an anemometer, and a wind vane. Students build working models of these instruments and consider how these instruments measure factors that help with weather predictions. At the end of the section, students read about greenhouse gases and global warming.

Targeted Concepts, Skills, and Nature of Science	Performance Expectations
Weather moves in patterns that can be identified and tracked. Weather maps allow scientists to observe weather patterns and make predictions. Some factors that weather depends on are temperature, air pressure, wind direction, and wind speed.	Students should read about and build working models of rain gauges to measure precipitation, thermometers to measure surface temperature, barometers to measure air pressure, anemometers to measure wind speed, and weather vanes to measure wind direction.
Trends in weather data show that Earth's climate is changing. Scientists believe that these changes are being caused by an increase in global warming due to an increase in greenhouse gases in the atmosphere.	Students should read and discuss the trends in weather patterns meteorologists have observed, greenhouse gases, and global warming.

Materials

1 per group	Ruler
	Straight-sided clear jar
	Tape
	Thermometer
	Carton (e.g. a milk carton) or box
	Scissors
	String
	Small jar
	Food Coloring
	Clay
	Index Card
	One-hole paper punch
	Stapler
	Measuring tape
	Highly visible sticker (e.g. fluorescent colored dots), decal, or colored tape
	Triangle pattern
	Presentation materials
4 per group	Clear, plastic drinking straws (keep extras in classroom)
5 per group	Small paper cups
2 per group	Smooth cylindrical pencils with erasers, one sharpened and one unsharpened. (Pencils with straight edges for sides should not be used.)
	Straight pins
1 per group (optional)	Magnetic compass

Activity Setup and Preparation

Make sure the straws and jars are clean for the barometer.

The pencils used for the anemometer and wind vane should have smooth sides to reduce the amount of friction.

Assemble and test each instrument prior to demonstrating what the finished instrument looks like. Use the instructions on how to assemble the instruments in the student text. The instruments may have too much friction to be sensitive enough to be affected by slight wind speeds. If this occurs, check how level the instruments are (no tilting or angle of the cups or of the arrow) and how easily they spin.

Barometers may lose water over time due to evaporation. More water should be added to keep the barometers near the original level. Students should note when they have added water and how it affected the height of the water in the jar and in the straw.

Students should use the tools they constructed to measure the weather. The wind vane, anemometer, thermometer, and the barometer should be used during class after students have assembled the instruments. Determine how you want students to use the instruments. Students could take turns bringing the instruments home, taking measurements, and creating a weather map of the area for four or more days.

Consider setting up a weather station at the school, using the students' or your tools for the station. Each class could collect data each day during this Unit as a class project.

Consider grouping the materials for each tool and determine if you want to distribute the materials for all tools or the materials for one tool at a time after discussing the tool to be built.

Homework Options

Consider assigning students or groups a project for the *Learning Set* constructing a weather journal to include observations from weather maps and/or weather forecasts for your local area, observations of the weather using their senses, and measurements made using instruments they construct in this section. Students should look for patterns in the data to help support causes for change in weather.

Reflection

- **Science Content:** Describe what each tool you built measures. *(Students should state the rain gauge measures how much precipitation falls, the thermometer measures the temperature, the barometer measures the air pressure, the anemometer measures the wind speed, and the wind vane measures the direction of the wind.)*

- **Science Content:** Which weather instrument were you least familiar with before completing the exercise? *(The purpose of this if for students to think again about the instrument they were least familiar with.)*

Preparation for 6.3

- **Science Content:** What do you think causes rain? *(The purpose of this is to elicit students' ideas about the cause of rain.)*

NOTES

....

....

....

....

....

....

....

....

....

....

....

6.2 Build

How Are Precipitation, Temperature, Humidity, Air Pressure, and Winds Measured?

The Cooperative Space Agency has requested that you give the colonists on *Planet X* some advice about the weather. It may be helpful to have the ability to observe and measure each factor that makes up weather.

Build Weather Tools

Meteorologists use many different tools to help them collect weather information. This information allows meteorologists to predict the weather. They use weather stations, set up around the world, to collect weather information. Five tools are always part of a weather station. They are a rain gauge, a thermometer, a barometer, an anemometer, and a wind vane.

Build a Tool to Measure Precipitation

Precipitation is water in the form of rain, snow, sleet, or hail that falls in an area. Measuring the amount of precipitation is important. For example, if people know the amount of rain that has fallen, they will know whether a river will rise and cause floods. The amount of rainfall is also important to farmers' crops. In cold climates, road crews need to know how much snow may fall.

A **rain gauge** measures the amount of precipitation. In the U.S., precipitation is usually measured in inches. A rain gauge is very simple. It is usually just a tube with markings on the outside. As the precipitation falls into the tube, water collects inside. The amount of rain can be read from the marks on the outside of the tube. Because the rain gauge needs to collect

rain gauge: a tool used to measure precipitation. In the U.S., precipitation is usually measured in inches.

PF 179

PLANETARY FORECASTER

6.2 Build

How are Precipitation, Temperature, Humidity, Air Pressure, and Winds Measured?

< 5 min.

Elicit students' ideas about how to understand weather.

○ **Engage**

Remind students that the *CSA* has requested advice for how to prepare for the weather for suggested locations on *Planet X*. Ask students what they think would be a good way for them to understand weather more so that they could give advice about *Planet X*.

*A class period is considered to be one 40 to 50 minute class.

Build Weather Tools

Students are introduced to the tools commonly used to measure weather conditions.

Build a Tool to Measure Precipitation

10 min.

Students have a discussion on rain gauges and build one.

The Cooperative Agency has requested give the colonists on *Planet X* some advice about the weather. It may be helpful to have the ability to observe and measure each factor that makes up weather.

Build Weather Tools

Meteorologists use many different tools to help them collect weather information. This information allows meteorologists to predict the weather. They use weather stations, set up around the world, to collect weather information. Five tools are always part of a weather station. They are a rain gauge, a thermometer, a barometer, an anemometer, and a wind vane.

Build a Tool to Measure Precipitation

Precipitation is water in the form of rain, snow, sleet, or hail that falls in an area. Measuring the amount of precipitation is important. For example, if people know the amount of rain that has fallen, they will know whether a river will rise and cause floods. The amount of rainfall is also important to farmers' crops. In cold climates, road crews need to know how much snow may fall.

A **rain gauge** measures the amount of precipitation. In the U.S., precipitation is usually measured in inches. A rain gauge is very simple. It is usually just a tube with markings on the outside. As the precipitation falls into the tube, water collects inside. The amount of rain can be read from the marks on the outside of the tube. Because the rain gauge needs to collect

rain gauge: a tool used to measure precipitation. In the U.S., precipitation is usually measured in inches.

PF 179

PLANETARY FORECASTER

◯ Engage

Let students know one way to better understand weather is to consider all things about weather we observe every day (it feels warm, cold; it feels sticky, dry; it feels windy; etc.) and consider how to measure these things. Ask students how they would measure these aspects of weather and record their ideas.

△ Guide

Let students know each group will be building five working instruments: a rain gauge, a thermometer, a barometer, an anemometer, and a wind vane. Ask students what they think these instruments measure.

△ Guide

Using the student text, discuss precipitation, the importance of measuring it, and how it is measured using a rain gauge. Then let groups build a rain gauge.

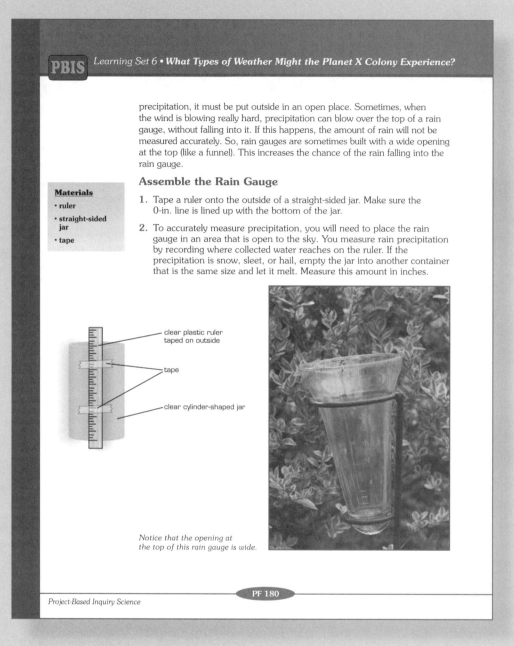

precipitation, it must be put outside in an open place. Sometimes, when the wind is blowing really hard, precipitation can blow over the top of a rain gauge, without falling into it. If this happens, the amount of rain will not be measured accurately. So, rain gauges are sometimes built with a wide opening at the top (like a funnel). This increases the chance of the rain falling into the rain gauge.

Assemble the Rain Gauge

Materials
• ruler
• straight-sided jar
• tape

1. Tape a ruler onto the outside of a straight-sided jar. Make sure the 0-in. line is lined up with the bottom of the jar.

2. To accurately measure precipitation, you will need to place the rain gauge in an area that is open to the sky. You measure rain precipitation by recording where collected water reaches on the ruler. If the precipitation is snow, sleet, or hail, empty the jar into another container that is the same size and let it melt. Measure this amount in inches.

clear plastic ruler taped on outside

tape

clear cylinder-shaped jar

Notice that the opening at the top of this rain gauge is wide.

PF 180

Project-Based Inquiry Science

⬡ Get Going

Show the class a finished rain gauge. Let students know that they will need to build the tool and record what the tool measures and how to use it. Distribute all the materials or the materials for only the rain gauge and let students know how much time they have.

☐ Assess

Monitor students' progress. As students are building the rain gauge, ask them to describe how various forms of precipitation are measured using the rain gauge. Students should realize sleet, snow, and hail should be emptied into another container, allowed to melt, and measured.

Ask the students to identify good locations to place a rain gauge. Students should describe locations that are open and can receive rain directly, and where wind is blocked or minimized.

NOTES

6.2 Build

Build a Tool to Measure Temperature

A thermometer gives meteorologists information about the temperature of the air. When you investigated temperature earlier in this Unit, you found out that air temperature is measured above ground level. Meteorologists mount a thermometer at about 1.5 m (about 5 ft) above the ground. They put the thermometer in a shelter to protect it from wind, direct sunlight, and moisture. Parking lots, roads, and pavements absorb and radiate a lot of heat. They can raise the temperature of the air around them. So, meteorologists place thermometers as far away as possible from these areas. Sheltering the thermometer and keeping it away from paved areas helps meteorologists be sure they are recording air temperatures as accurately as possible.

Assemble Your Thermometer Shelter

1. Carefully cut several small holes in the sides of the carton. This will allow air to circulate.

2. Make a hole in the top of the carton.

3. Pull a piece of string through the hole and make a knot in the end that is outside the carton. Make the knot big enough so it will not slip back through the hole.

4. Mount the carton on the wooden stick with duct tape.

5. Secure the thermometer to the string, so it is suspended inside the carton.

6. Place the shelter outdoors, at least 30 m (about 100 ft) from any paved areas.

A thermometer shelter helps make sure the air temperatures recorded are as accurate as possible.

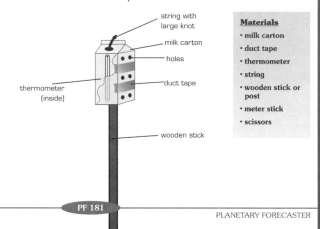

string with large knot
milk carton
holes
duct tape
thermometer (inside)
wooden stick

Materials
- milk carton
- duct tape
- thermometer
- string
- wooden stick or post
- meter stick
- scissors

PF 181

Build a Tool to Measure Temperature
10 min.

Students have a discussion on thermometer shelters and build one.

△ Guide

Discuss thermometers and thermometer shelters using the student text. Remind students the temperature data they analyzed using *My World* was surface temperature, which is measured about 1.5 meters above the ground. Let students know thermometers are put in a shelter to protect them. These thermometer shelters should be kept away from paved areas. Ask the students why. Students should make connections to specific heat capacity or describe how different materials absorb and re-emit energy differently, affecting the temperature of the air nearby.

◯ Get Going

Show students a thermometer shelter. Let students know they will need to build the thermometer shelter and record what the tool measures and how to use it. Distribute the materials, if needed, and let students know how much time they have.

☐ Assess

Monitor students' progress. Ask the students to explain why they think the thermometer must be suspended by a string and not taped to the inside of the box. Students should understand that the tool is supposed to measure the temperature of the air. They have seen different materials heat and cool differently from each other. A thermometer that is taped to the inside of the box will measure the temperature of the box material instead of the air.

NOTES

Build a Tool to Measure Air Pressure

You may have heard or seen the words "high pressure" or "low pressure" on a weather map or weather forecast. These words refer to air pressure. High pressure usually results in weather with sunny and clear skies. If the air pressure is low, rainy or stormy weather is coming.

You may think you can feel changes in air pressure, but the changes are very, very small. You cannot feel the differences. However, they have a huge effect on the weather.

barometer: an instrument used to measure air pressure.

History Connection

The barometer was invented by Evangelista Torricelli around 1643. He first made a water barometer, but it was very long and clumsy. It was so long it actually went out the roof of his house. Using a suggestion from another well-known scientist, Galileo, he replaced the water with mercury. This allowed Torricelli to use a much shorter tube. Mercury barometers are still used today.

Meteorologists measure air pressure with a tool called a **barometer.** There are different types of barometers. You may have seen a "weather glass" in someone's home. This is a sealed container with an open spout. High air pressure pushes down more on the water in the spout. This pushes the water down. As the water in the spout is pushed down, it forces the water in the container up. As air pressure decreases, it pushes down less on the water in the spout. This allows the water in the spout to move up. As the water in the spout moves up, the water in the body of the barometer moves down.

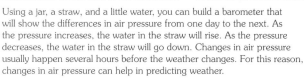

Another type of barometer is called an aneroid barometer. It is made of an airtight metal box from which most of the air has been removed. The box is squeezed as air pressure increases. It expands as air pressure decreases. Levers attached to the box transfer this movement to a needle. The needle moves to the corresponding air-pressure measurement on the face of the barometer.

Using a jar, a straw, and a little water, you can build a barometer that will show the differences in air pressure from one day to the next. As the pressure increases, the water in the straw will rise. As the pressure decreases, the water in the straw will go down. Changes in air pressure usually happen several hours before the weather changes. For this reason, changes in air pressure can help in predicting weather.

PF 182

Project-Based Inquiry Science

Build a Tool to Measure Air Pressure
15 min.

Students have a discussion on barometers and build one.

△ Guide

Discuss barometers using the student text. Discuss how high pressures usually result in sunny and clear skies and low pressure may indicate rainy or stormy weather. Emphasize that these changes are very small and difficult to sense directly, but they have a big effect on the weather.

Let students know that barometers measure air pressure. Ask students of their experiences with barometers.

"Do any of you have a barometer in your home? What does it look like and how do you use it?"

If no one has a barometer, have the students look at the picture of a barometer in the student text.

Describe how the barometer works. When the air pressure is high, the water in the spout is pushed down. The water in the spout can rise higher because it is not being pushed down when the air pressure is low. Describe the aneroid barometer, which uses levers that move according to the air pressure on the box it is encased in.

META NOTES

Liquid barometers are usually open on the spout side to reduce evaporation. Students' barometers should not be placed in the Sun or by air vents to avoid an increase in the evaporation rate. The fluid in the barometer should be replaced as it evaporates to keep the volume of water constant. To do this, have students measure the heights of fluid in the straw and the jar. The volume could be calculated or estimated, if needed.

NOTES

....
....
....
....
....
....
....
....
....
....

6.2 Build

Barometers can be mounted inside or outside. When air pressure changes, the changes are the same both indoors and outdoors. When you make your barometer, record what the weather is like that day (clear skies or cloudy skies). This information will help you know if the air pressure is going up or down.

Assemble Your Barometer

1. Put some cold water into a jar so it is less than half full. Add some food coloring to make it easier to see the height of the water.

2. Put the straw into the jar and tape it to the inside. The bottom end of the straw should be in the water but not touching the bottom of the jar.

3. Suck the water halfway up into the straw. Pinch the straw to trap the water. The height of the water in the straw needs to be above the height of the water in the jar. Try not to get the water into your mouth.

4. When you take your mouth off the straw, keep pinching it until you put a piece of modeling clay over the top of the straw to seal it closed. The water should stay in the straw. If it does not, start over and make sure to seal the straw well with the clay.

Materials
- small jar
- clear drinking straw
- food coloring
- small piece of clay
- tape
- index card

Be sure the jar and water are clean, and use a new, clean straw.

5. Leave your barometer in a place where it is unlikely to get knocked over.

6. Develop a method of recording changes in the level of the water in the straw. You could attach an index card onto the outside of the jar and mark it each day. Or, you could put an elastic band around the jar, and move the band up or down each day to show the level of the water in the straw. Each time you measure, record the level of water in the straw and the date.

PF 183

○ Get Going

Show students a finished barometer. Let students know they will be building a barometer out of a glass jar and a straw. Distribute the materials, if needed, and let students know how much time they have. Emphasize to students that they should record what the barometer is used for, how the barometer works, and the initial height of the fluid in the straw and jar.

☐ Assess

Monitor students' progress. Check that students are recording information about the barometer and the initial height of the fluid in the straw. Ask the students if it would make a difference if the barometer was inside or outside. Students may believe air pressure may change from indoors to outdoors. Students may confuse the wind they feel with pressure. Let students know that although most buildings seem to be fully enclosed, air actually moves in and out of buildings freely. The air pressure does not change significantly between the inside and outside of a building.

NOTES

Build a Tool to Measure Wind Speed

anemometer:
a tool used by
meteorologists
to measure wind
speed.

Flags whipping or trash cans rolling down the street are common sights on very windy days. These things can be interesting or annoying. To a meteorologist, they can signal changes in the weather.

Meteorologists measure wind speed to help determine changes in the weather. They also use wind speed to inform people about wind chill, dangerous wind conditions, and the kind of sailing or flying conditions they can expect.

Meteorologists use a tool called an **anemometer** to measure wind speed. One common type is called a cup anemometer. The cups are pushed by the wind, and they spin as the wind pushes them. The faster the cups spin, the faster and harder the wind is blowing.

Anemometers need to be mounted out in the open in the wind. Think about a time when you have walked through a narrow place, like an alley or outdoor mall, where the wind was blowing very hard. Wind speed readings can be easily changed depending on where the anemometer is mounted. If you put it in an alley or between buildings, you will be measuring the wind in that small space. This information is not as useful as a reading that you could take in a field or on top of a building where other factors are not changing the wind.

Assemble Your Anemometer

1. Cut the rolled rims off four of the small paper cups.

2. Using a one-hole paper punch, make a hole in each cup. Make the hole about 1.5 cm from the top of the cup. Use the diagram to help you see where the hole should be placed.

3. Take one cup and push one end of a straw through the hole. The straw should go all the way in, to the other side. Bend about 1 cm of the straw at the end and staple it to

Materials
- 5 small paper cups
- scissors
- 2 straight plastic straws
- pencil with eraser
- straight pin
- one-hole paper punch
- stapler
- tape measure
- sticker or decal

Project-Based Inquiry Science

Build a Tool to Measure Wind Speed

15 mins.

Students have a discussion on anemometers and build one.

△ Guide

Discuss anemometers using the student text. Explain how they are used to measure wind speed. Discuss the importance of measuring wind speed in determining changes of weather, how cold it feels (wind chill factor), and dangerous conditions.

Ask the students to describe where anemometers should be placed. Students should understand anemometers should be placed in locations where the wind is not blocked or altered by buildings, trees, or other structures.

the opposite side of the cup. The straw should go all the way through the cup and be stapled to the other side. Repeat this procedure with the four cups.

4. Place an easily visible sticker, decal, or piece of colored tape on the side of one of the cups.

5. Punch four equally spaced holes about 1.5 cm from the top of the fifth cup. This is the cup that will go in the center. Another hole should be punched into the center of the bottom. Use the diagram to help you see where the holes should be placed.

6. Now attach the four cups from Step 3 to the center cup. Place each cup so it opens in a clockwise direction. Put the free end of each straw through a hole in the center cup. Push all the straws to the center of the cup.

7. Carefully push the straight pin through the straws where they cross in the middle of the center cup. Push the pin all the way through the straws so the point sticks out the bottom of the last straw.

8. Slide the eraser end of the pencil up through the hole in the bottom of the center cup. Push the straight pin into the eraser.

9. To read your anemometer, hold it up to the wind. Count the number of complete turns it makes in 30 s (seconds). Use the cup with the sticker to help you keep count of the complete turns.

Build a Tool to Measure Wind Direction

Wind speed is very important, but knowing wind speed does not give a meteorologist enough information to really understand what is happening with the wind. They also need to measure wind direction. Wind direction helps meteorologists understand the patterns of weather in smaller areas. Sometimes a change in wind direction signals a weather change, like a big storm. In severe weather, if meteorologists can tell people the speed and direction of the wind, they can actually save lives.

Ask students to think about why four cups are used to create the anemometer. Students should realize that with four cups, the hollow part of a cup should always be facing the direction the wind is coming from.

You may wish to point out because the anemometer uses four cups, one cup will always be pushed by the wind, and another cup will be pushing the other way at the same time. Point out this is why cups are used instead of flat surfaces. By using a cup shape, one cup experiences more force than the other cup, causing an imbalance of forces and allowing the anemometer to turn.

⬡ Get Going

Show students a finished anemometer and let them know they should use a sharpened pencil to punch a hole through the middle of the bottom of the cup. Let students know they will need to build an anemometer using the procedure in the student text and they should record what the tool measures and how to use it. Distribute the materials if needed and let students know how much time they have.

☐ Assess

Monitor students' progress and check that they have recorded information about what an anemometer measures and how to use it. Assist students as needed in the construction of the anemometer.

△ Guide

Discuss wind vanes using the student text. Explain that they are used to measure the direction of the wind. Let students know wind speed sometimes indicates a weather change.

Ask the students to describe where a wind vane should be placed. Students should understand wind vanes should be placed in locations where the wind is not blocked or altered by buildings, trees, or other structures.

Build a Tool to Measure Wind Direction

15 mins.

Students have a discussion about wind vanes and build one.

NOTES

Wind vanes are used to measure the direction of the wind. You may have seen wind vanes on the tops of buildings like skyscrapers, houses, or barns. Sometimes weather vanes look like farm animals. The one in the photo shows a rooster. Notice how there is an arrow and letters under the rooster in the picture. The letters show north, east, south, and west. These are used to read the direction the wind is blowing. The arrow shows the direction that the wind is blowing. The wind vane, like the anemometer, is mounted at the top of a pole. There it can spin around easily in the wind.

wind vane: a tool for measuring wind direction.

Also, the wind vane needs to be placed out in the open, on top of a house or barn or in a field. To be accurate it needs to measure the direction of the wind in an open space. In an enclosed space, wind speed and direction can be affected by walls or objects in the space, and so are different than out in the open.

Assemble Your Wind Vane

1. Trace the triangle pattern two times onto the poster board. Cut the two triangles from the poster board. This will be the "tail" of your wind vane.

2. Put one triangle on the table and lay the straw on top of it. The straw should extend about halfway into the triangle in the middle of one side. Follow the diagram for this part. Tape the straw to the triangle.

3. Sandwich the straw between the 2 triangles by putting the second triangle on top of the straw. Line up all the edges of the two triangles carefully.

4. Tape all three edges of the triangles together, covering the straw.

5. Find the place where the straw balances by putting the straw on your finger so it sits on your finger without tilting or falling. This place will be close to the triangle.

6. Mark the balance point on the straw with a marker.

7. Hold the straw so the back edge of the triangle is pointing up and down. Stick the straight pin from the topside, down through the straw, so it pokes all the way through.

Materials
- plastic drinking straw
- tape
- poster board
- marker
- triangle pattern
- new pencil with a new eraser
- one straight pin
- scissors
- clay

⬡ Get Going

Show students a finished wind vane. Let students know they will need to build a wind vane using the procedure in the student text and they should record what the tool measures and how to use it. Distribute the materials if needed and let students know how much time they have.

☐ Assess

Monitor students' progress and check that they have recorded information about what a wind vane measures and how to use it. Assist students as needed with constructing the wind vane. Ask students which way north, south, east, and west are, and how they could determine these locations at home. If needed, remind students that the Sun rises in the east and sets in the west.

NOTES

8. Push the pin into the center of the eraser at the end of the pencil. Make sure the straw spins smoothly around the pin.

To find the direction of the wind, you have to know where north, south, east, and west are in the location where you are going to place the wind vane. You can use a compass to do this. Or you can stretch out your arms and point your right hand toward where the Sun rises (east) and your left hand toward where the Sun sets (west). *The direction you will be facing is north.* When the wind vane spins in the wind, it will show you the way the wind, is blowing. The triangle pointer tells you the direction the wind is coming from. A south wind will be coming from the south, and that is the direction the pointer will be pointing.

Stop and Think

1. One of the important reasons for recording weather data is to be able to tell people about the weather in advance. Describe one time when weather predictions made life easier for you. What measuring tool was most helpful for making this prediction?

2. Five tools are described in this section: rain gauge, thermometer, barometer, anemometer, and wind vane. Pick two of the different meteorological tools. Describe how they measure factors that help with weather predictions. Include any information that is important to remember about where the tools should be placed to collect the most accurate and consistent data.

3. One of the tools you might not have known about before is a barometer. Describe what you have learned about the barometer.

What's the Point?

Meteorologists use many different tools to collect weather data. Each tool is used to collect one type of data. Temperature, wind speed, wind direction, amount of precipitation, and air pressure are all important in understanding and predicting the weather. Because meteorologists can use tools to understand the weather, they are able to give helpful information to people. The information they provide can save lives, food crops, or your outdoor party.

PF 187

PLANETARY FORECASTER

Stop and Think

15 mins.

Students have a class discussion on their responses.

⬡ Get Going

Let students know they should complete the questions on their own and a class discussion will follow.

△ Guide and Assess

Have a class discussion on students' responses. Use the information below to guide and assess students' understanding.

1. Students should describe a situation where the weather forecast assisted them. Students may not be sure which tool contributed directly to the weather prediction. Have students refer back to what they recorded about each instrument. Students might say the barometer helps predict clear, sunny skies or rainy or stormy weather.

2. Students should describe two of the instruments. Their responses should include the information below pertaining to the instruments they selected.

    Rain Gauge: *A rain gauge is used to measure how much precipitation reached the surface. A rain gauge is an open container that collects precipitation (rain, sleet, snow, hail). It should be placed outside in an open place. The precipitation can be measured using a ruler to measure how much fluid fell into the container. If the precipitation is sleet, snow, or hail, the contents of the rain gauge should be poured into another container of the same size and the height should be measured as soon as the contents melt. If the wind is strong, sometimes it is better to use a funnel shaped rain gauge.*

    Students may not know what to write about how the rain gauge helps with weather predictions. Some possible responses are: *By measuring the precipitation over many years, one can figure out the average precipitation for that location over a year, season, or month and use this value to make predictions about rainfall. By measuring the precipitation and other factors of the weather, one could predict similar amounts of precipitation for similar conditions.*

    Thermometer: *A thermometer is used to measure surface temperature. The thermometer should be placed about 1.5 m above the ground and about 300 m from paved surfaces. It needs to be away from paved areas because these areas are usually warmer due to the amount of energy absorbed and released. Thermometer shelters are used to protect the thermometer from sunlight, wind, and moisture that can affect its readings.*

    Students may not know what to write about how the thermometer helps with weather predictions. Some possible responses are: *By measuring the temperatures over many years, one can figure out the average temperatures for that location over a year, season, or month and use this value to make predictions about temperatures. By measuring the temperature and other factors of the weather, one could predict similar temperatures for similar conditions.*

Barometer: *The barometer measures air pressure. It can be placed inside or outside. Liquid barometers should be kept from wind and direct sunlight and needs more fluid added to it if any has evaporated. A change in pressure indicates a change in weather. High pressure usually results in sunny, clear skies. Low pressure usually means that rainy or stormy weather is coming.*

Anemometer: *An anemometer measures the speed of wind. It should be placed in the open or on the top of a building. The anemometer spins because air pushes it. Counting the number of turns it moves in a certain amount of time determines the speed of wind.*

Students may not know what to write about how the anemometer helps with weather predictions. Some possible responses are: *By measuring the wind speed, one might predict how quickly a warm front or cold front is moving in. By measuring the wind speed and other factors of the weather, one could predict similar weather for similar conditions.*

Wind Vane: *A wind vane measures the direction of the wind. It should be placed in the open or on top of a building. The wind vane usually has the directions, North, South, East, and West, indicated underneath an arrow that will point in the direction the wind is blowing. The arrow spins freely and will point in the direction of the wind.* Students may not know what to write about how the wind vane helps with weather predictions. Some possible responses are: *By measuring the wind direction, one might predict a warm front or cold front moving in by knowing its location. By measuring the wind direction and other factors of the weather, one could predict similar weather for similar conditions.*

3. Students' descriptions should include the information listed in Question 2.

NOTES

....

....

....

More to Learn

Global Warming

People have always watched weather patterns. Understanding these patterns helped ancient people know when to plant crops. It helped people who moved from place to place know when it was time to go to a new area. Understanding weather patterns also helps predict when snow can be expected and what the average temperature is going to be in July.

Meteorologists and other scientists have collected many years of weather data. When they look at these data carefully, they notice patterns. These patterns help them understand the types of weather, or climates, that can be expected in different places around the world.

climatologist: a scientist who studies the world's weather patterns.

global warming: the increase in the average surface temperature of Earth and in the average temperature of the oceans, and the prediction that this increase will continue.

greenhouse gases: gases like water vapor and carbon dioxide that trap the heat coming from Earth's surface.

All of this data has made it possible to understand the climate of different places in the world. Over the course of the last 50 years or so, scientists who study the world's climates, **climatologists**, have noticed that many of the world's climates are changing. The frozen tundra of the north is not as deeply frozen as it used to be. The ice caps are getting smaller. The average temperature of Earth is changing. It is increasing.

Scientists have spent many years analyzing the data. They have been watching trends and developing explanations of why the world's climates are changing. There have been many different explanations of these changes. However, there is only one way to explain the climate changes that includes all the new data. This explanation is called **global warming.**

Scientists have a theory. According to the theory, changes in Earth's atmosphere have been caused by an increase in several gases. These gases, including water vapor and carbon dioxide, trap heat that comes from Earth's surface. These gases are commonly called **greenhouse gases**. Normally, this trapped heat is what makes Earth habitable. If these gases did not trap the heat coming from Earth's surface, the heat would escape into space. Earth would be too cold to inhabit. However, human activities are putting more and more of these gases into the atmosphere. As the gases build up, more heat is being trapped than in the past. As a result, Earth's average temperature is increasing.

PF 188

Project-Based Inquiry Science

More to Learn: Global Warming

10 mins.

Students have a class discussion on global warming.

△ **Guide**

Have a class discussion on global warming using the information in the student text. Emphasize that scientists have carefully analyzed over 50 years of data and have found the world's climates are changing and the average temperatures of land and water are increasing. Point out some of the consequences of this: melting ice caps causing ecological problems, increasing of sea level, and more severe weather.

Discuss how greenhouse gases trap heat energy and do not allow it to escape Earth's atmosphere. Have students think of the temperature inside a car that has been sitting for hours in the Sun with the windows and doors closed, and a car sitting for hours in the Sun with the windows and doors open. The greenhouse gases trap the heat energy the same way the closed car traps it.

Emphasize that most greenhouse gases, such as water vapor and carbon dioxide, are not bad gases and are not directly toxic to plants and animals. These are not the only greenhouse gases put into the environment. The problem is these gases are in abundance because of human activities. The result is that the temperature of Earth is steadily increasing, causing severe weather and harm to ecosystems. Explain that measurements of carbon in ice cores taken from Antarctica show the amount of carbon did not change significantly from 1750 to 1850. It remained near 280 parts per million. Between 1850 and 2000, it increased to about 370 parts per million. Measurements of the atmosphere show a direct correlation between the amount of carbon in the atmosphere and the burning of fossil fuels (e.g. gasoline, oil, coal) causing an increase of about 25% in greenhouse gases between 1985 and 2005.

Consider discussing ways students could reduce greenhouse gases in their lives. Students may suggest unplugging devices that use transformers when not needed (e.g. cell phone adapters, printer adapters, etc), buying products made from biodegradable substances rather than plastics, recycling, etc.

META NOTES

Some other greenhouse gases are nitrous oxide, sulfur hexafluoride, hydrofluorocarbons, perfluorocarbons and chlorofluorocarbons.

Consider doing an internet search using keywords such as: global warming, green house gases. Select sources that are from universities, government, or reputable organizations.

NOTES

Assessment Options

Targeted Concepts, Skills, and Nature of Science	How do I know if students got it?
Weather moves in patterns that can be identified and tracked. Weather maps allow scientists to observe weather patterns and make predictions. Some factors that weather depends on are temperature, air pressure, wind direction, and wind speed.	**ASK:** What tools do scientists use to measure weather patterns and what do they measure? **LISTEN:** Students' responses should include that the rain gauge measures how much precipitation occurred, the thermometer shelter measures temperature, the barometer measures air pressure, the anemometer measures wind speed, and the wind vane measures the direction of the wind.
Trends in weather data show Earth's climate changing. Scientists believe these changes are caused by an increase in global warming due to an increase in greenhouse gases in the atmosphere.	**ASK:** What are greenhouse gases and what is global warming? **LISTEN:** Students should describe greenhouse gases as gases that trap heat energy, such as carbon dioxide, in the Earth's atmosphere. Students should describe global warming as the explanation that links the Earth's climate changes and increasing global temperatures to the build up or increase of greenhouse gases due to human activities.

Teacher Reflection Questions

- What difficulties did students have understanding what the instruments they built were for or how to use them?

- How did building and using the instruments help students' understanding?

- What difficulties did students have building or using the instruments?

NOTES

6.3 Explore

Why Does it Rain?

◀ *1 class period*

A class period is considered to be one 40 to 50 minute class.

Overview

Students observe a demonstration simulating the water cycle. The simulation provides a basis for students to build on as they read about and discuss the water cycle. Students are also introduced to the three states of water, preparing them for a deeper discussion in the next section.

Targeted Concepts, Skills, and Nature of Science	Performance Expectations
Scientists must keep clear, accurate, and descriptive records of what they do so they can share their work with others and consider what they did, why they did it, and what they want to do next.	Students should sketch the demonstration and record their observations to refer to later.
Scientists make claims (conclusions) based on evidence obtained (trends in data) from reliable investigations	Students should make claims based on their observations of the water cycle demonstration.
Energy from the Sun drives Earth's water cycle. Water moves between different physical states in a continuous cycle of evaporation, condensation, and precipitation.	Students should describe the water cycle as a cycle in which liquid water evaporates into a gas and goes into the atmosphere. As the water vapor rises, it cools and condenses to form liquid water drops and sometimes solid ice crystals. When these get too heavy for the air to support, they fall in the form of precipitation.

Materials	
1 per classroom	Glass jar with metal lid
	Hot water (to fill jar halfway)
	Ice cubes (to fill metal lid of jar)

Activity Setup and Preparation

Practice the demonstration prior to class. The water will need to be nearly boiling. Consider using an electric water kettle or a microwave to heat the water. The steps for the demonstration are described in the *Section 6.3 Implementation.*

Homework Options

Reflection

- **Science Content:** Describe what you observed in the demonstration. Explain how this models the water cycle. *(Students should describe how the hot water creates vapor in the jar like Earth's bodies of water evaporating and creating vapor in the atmosphere. The ice on the lid models the cold upper atmosphere and the water condensing on the lid models the water condensing in the upper atmosphere.)*

- **Science Content:** Why does it rain? *(Students should describe how water from Earth's surface evaporates into the atmosphere. When this water vapor rises, it cools down and condenses into a liquid or solid. When the droplets get too heavy to be held up by the air, they fall down to Earth as precipitation.)*

Preparation for 6.4

- **Science Content:** How do you think the Sun's energy drives the water cycle? *(The purpose of this question is to get students thinking about how the energy from the Sun affects the water cycle.)*

- **Science Content:** What are clouds? How do they form? What causes rain? *(The purpose of this question is to get students thinking about how the Sun affects the water cycle.)*

SECTION 6.3 IMPLEMENTATION

◀ *1 class period**

6.3 Explore

Why Does it Rain?

On the weather maps you were analyzing, there were several places where it was raining. Locations A, B, and C all had some rain during the three days shown on the maps. If the weather had been colder, perhaps in January, the rain might have been snow. Rain and snow, along with sleet and hail, are all different forms of precipitation. They each form in different ways. However, they are all made of water that falls from the sky. Think about how this happens as you watch a demonstration by your teacher.

Keep your work area dry. Clean up spills.

Demonstration

Observe a model of rain forming. Some very hot water will be placed in the bottom of a jar. A metal lid will be placed, upside down, on top of the jar. Ice cubes will then be added to the lid. If you look at the picture, you will see what your teacher will be doing. Observe what happens in the model. Record your observations and any ideas you have about what causes the changes you are seeing.

Reflect

Answer the following questions. Be prepared to share your answers with the class.

1. Draw a sketch of what happened in the model. On your sketch, label where it was hot and where it was cold.

2. Explain where the water on the bottom side of the lid came from.

3. Consider the jar with the ice cubes and hot water as a model of what happens when it rains. What do you think the hot water represents? What do you think the cold water represents? Make a diagram of what you observed.

○ **Engage**

Elicit students' ideas about precipitation and make connections to the previous section. Record students' ideas.

6.3 Explore

Why Does it Rain?

< 5 min.

Students observe a demonstration modeling rain to better understand the water cycle.

---

*A class period is considered to be one 40 to 50 minute class.

Demonstration

10 min.

Students observe a demonstration of water evaporating and condensing.

TEACHER TALK

❝Think about the weather maps you were working on in the previous section. There was rain in one location. What do you think caused it?

What do you know about precipitation? ❞

---

about how ~~~~ ppens as you watch a demonstration by your teacher.

Demonstration

Observe a model of rain forming. Some very hot water will be placed in the bottom of a jar. A metal lid will be placed, upside down, on top of the jar. Ice cubes will then be added to the lid. If you look at the picture, you will see what your teacher will be doing. Observe what happens in the model. Record your observations and any ideas you have about what causes the changes you are seeing.

Reflect

Answer the following questions. Be prepared to share your answers with the class.

1. Draw a sketch of what happened in the model. On your sketch, label where it was hot and where it was cold.

2. Explain where the water on the bottom side of the lid came from.

3. Consider the jar with the ice cubes and hot water as a model of what happens when it rains. What do you think the hot water represents? What do you think the cold water represents? Make a diagram of what you observed.

PF 189

PLANETARY FORECASTER

△ Guide

Let students know that you will demonstrate rain forming. Describe the demonstration for them and ask them to record their predictions of what will happen.

TEACHER TALK

❝This demonstration consists of a glass jar with very hot water in it, and a lid that will be upside down on top of the jar and filled with ice. Write down what you think will happen.❞

Emphasize to students to be careful not to touch the jar when they make their observations. The water is very hot.

To conduct the demonstration, pour boiling water in the jar until it is about half full, or heat it to boiling in a microwave. Place the jar with hot water on a stable surface and place the lid upside down over the jar. Place ice cubes in the lid. Ask students to describe what they see. Consider having groups take turns getting a closer look.

☐ Assess

Students should observe water condensing on the sides of the jar and dripping down. They should also observe water condensing on the lid and forming droplets that fall down into the jar. This may be difficult for students to see unless they bend down to look at the side of the lid facing the boiling water. Students should also observe the ice melting.

⬡ Get Going

Let students know they should work independently to answer the questions and a class discussion will follow and how much time they have.

△ Guide and Assess

Have a class discussion on students' responses.

1. Students should draw diagrams showing the model and label the water in the jar as hot and the ice on the top as cold.

2. Students should support their claims. Students may or may not realize that the water under the lid came from rising water vapor as the hot water changed to gas. As the hot water changes into gas vapor, it rises up to the lid and then cools against the cold lid. The cooling gas condenses (changes to a liquid) and collects on the cold lid until the liquid droplets becomes heavy enough to fall back into the jar as water drops.

3. Students' answers will vary. The hot water represents water on the surface of Earth that evaporates into the atmosphere. The atmosphere is represented by the air in the jar. The upper atmosphere is cold and is represented by the air under the cold lid. It is in the upper atmosphere where the water vapor condenses. When the water droplets get too massive for the air to support, they fall as rain.

Reflect

15 min.

The class has a discussion on students' observations and ideas about the demonstration.

The Water Cycle

10 min.

Students are introduced to the water cycle in a class discussion.

The Water Cycle

Water falls from the atmosphere to Earth as precipitation. Precipitation can be liquid or solid. It can take the form of rain, snow, sleet, or hail. Water falls from the sky and lands on Earth's surface. It may land in a river, lake, or ocean. It may also land on the ground. From there, it will eventually end up in a body of water.

How does the water that falls from the atmosphere get there? Water gets into the atmosphere through **evaporation**. Evaporation is the change of a substance from a liquid state into a gas. You already know that as a liquid heats up, its molecules move faster and faster. Some of the molecules gain enough speed to escape from the liquid into the air. When this air rises, it cools, and the water vapor **condenses**. **Condensation** is the change of a substance from a gas to a liquid state. The water vapor becomes liquid. When the water droplets get to be too heavy to be held up in the air, the water returns to Earth as precipitation. You saw this when you observed the model of rain forming.

evaporation: the change from a liquid to a gas.

condense: to change from a gas to a liquid.

condensation: the change from a gas to a liquid; also, the liquid that forms when a gas comes in contact with a cold surface and changes to a liquid state.

Did You Know?

Have you ever caught a snowflake in your glove or a raindrop in your hand? Every time you hold a snowflake or a raindrop, you are holding something that is over four billion years old! Scientists suggest that Earth is about four and a half billion years old, and water vapor has been present ever since. So how is it that you can hold such ancient water? The answer is in the water cycle.

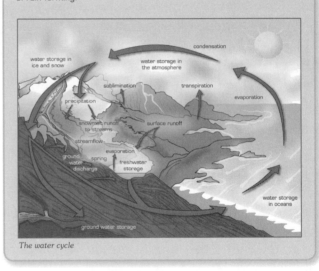

The water cycle

△ Guide

Have students read the segment on the water cycle and study the diagram. Use the information in the student text to have a class discussion introducing the water cycle. Emphasize that precipitation can be a solid or a liquid (snow, hail, sleet, rain). Discuss how water gets into the atmosphere by evaporation and is released after it condenses and reaches a mass that cannot be supported by the air.

6.3 Explore

The **water cycle** is the name given to the series of changes that water goes through in nature. A cycle is something that continuously repeats itself. Water continuously moves in a cycle between Earth's surface and the atmosphere, changing from a liquid to a gas and back again. Heat energy from the Sun powers this cycle. Look at the diagram of the water cycle, and find three sources that might supply water to the atmosphere.

The idea of a water cycle being powered by heat energy from the Sun is a really complicated idea. However, once you understand the parts, you might think the water cycle is awesome. You will come to understand how a snowflake could be coming from water that is over four billion years old.

water cycle:
the series of changes that water goes through in nature.

What's the Point?

In the demonstration model, you watched as water changed from a liquid to a gas and back to a liquid. You saw how the hot water in the jar evaporated, changing from a liquid to a gas. As the gas rose, the ice cubes cooled it. The gas that came in contact with the cold jar lid condensed into droplets of water that stuck to the jar lid. When the droplets on the lid became heavy enough, they fell back to the bottom of the jar.

You have seen a model of the water cycle, but you probably do not really understand why these things happen. The readings in the next section will help you better understand the process.

The mist in this valley is made up of water droplets suspended in the air.

Discuss the diagram with students. Ask students to identify and discuss the ways water gets into the atmosphere using the diagram. Ask students what transpiration is. Point it out in the diagram and explain it is when plants give off water. Let students know water also gets into the atmosphere by evaporating off of humans and animals.

Assessment Options

Targeted Concepts, Skills, and Nature of Science	How do I know if students got it?
Energy from the Sun drives Earth's water cycle. Water moves between different physical states in a continuous cycle of evaporation, condensation, and precipitation.	**ASK:** Describe the water cycle. **LISTEN:** Students should describe the water cycle as a cycle in which liquid water evaporates into a gas and goes into the atmosphere. As the water vapor rises, it cools and condenses to form liquid water drops and sometimes solid ice crystals. When these get too heavy for the air to support, they fall in the form of precipitation.

Teacher Reflection Questions

- What difficulties did students have with the water cycle?

- How did the demonstration help students understand the water cycle?

- What issues arose during the demonstration of the model water cycle? What would you do differently?

NOTES

6.4 Read

How Does the Sun's Energy Drive the Water Cycle?

◀ $1\frac{1}{2}$ *class periods*

A class period is considered to be one 40 to 50 minute class.

Overview

Students explain how the Sun's energy affects the water cycle. Students build on their knowledge of the water cycle and their observations from the previous section by considering the different states of matter. They read about and discuss the energy flow of atoms and molecules undergoing the melting and freezing processes, and are introduced to processes of deposition and sublimation. Students read about how water gets into the atmosphere due to absorption of the Sun's energy. They are introduced to the terms humidity and relative humidity, and consider how clouds are formed and are introduced to some cloud formations. Groups construct an explanation for how the water cycle is driven by the Sun's energy and present these to the class. After the class discusses the explanations, they update their *Project Board* with what they are learning and the evidence they have to support it.

Targeted Concepts, Skills, and Nature of Science	Performance Expectations
Scientists often work together and share their findings. Sharing findings makes new information available and helps scientists to refine their ideas and build on others' ideas. When another person's or group's idea is used, credit needs to be given.	Students should work in their groups to construct explanations about how the water cycle depends on the Sun's energy. Groups should share their ideas with the class and the class should update their *Project Board*.
Scientists must keep clear, accurate, and descriptive records of what they do so they can share their work with others and consider what they did, why they did it, and what they want to do next.	Students should use their records from previous sections to construct their explanation. The class should keep track of what they are learning and their questions using their *Project Board*.

Targeted Concepts, Skills, and Nature of Science	Performance Expectations
Explanations are claims supported by evidence, accepted ideas and facts.	Students should explain how the Sun's energy affects the water cycle and they should support their claims with observations from the demonstration and science knowledge from the information in the student text.
Energy from the Sun drives Earth's water cycle. Water moves between different physical states in a continuous cycle of evaporation, condensation, and precipitation.	Students should describe how the Sun's energy drives the water cycle.
Water changes state (solid, liquid, gas) by adding or removing heat energy.	Students should describe the three states of water (solid, liquid, and gas). They should describe how they change state by indicating when energy is needed and when it is released to change from one state to another.

Materials

1 per student	*Create Your Explanation* page *Project Board* page
1 per class	Class *Project Board*
1 per class (Optional, for demonstration)	2-L bottle Matches Warm water

NOTES

....

....

....

Activity Setup and Preparation

If you decide to do the cloud in a bottle demonstration, practice before as you may have to vary the number of squeezes to give the bottle or how long to compress the bottle before making the cloud.

To do the demonstration, fill a 2-L bottle 1/3 of the way with warm water. Warm water is needed for the water to evaporate into the air in the bottle. Light a match, let it burn for a few seconds, blow it out, and place the head of the match in the bottle for a few seconds to put a little smoke in the bottle. This is needed because the water droplets that form in clouds form on particles in the air such as dust or smoke. Next, quickly close the lid of the bottle without squeezing the bottle so the smoke and water stay in the bottle. Squeeze the bottle rapidly five to seven times, and then wait a few seconds. This helps to mix the water vapor, smoke, and air, and reduces the temperature of the air in the bottle. Squeeze the bottle, hold it for a few seconds, and quickly release. By holding the bottle for a few seconds, the compressed gas is allowed to transfer some of the energy it received to its surroundings. When you rapidly let go, air in the bottle expands and cools, transferring some of its energy in this expansion. As it cools, the water vapor in the bottle should condense around the smoke particles and fog should form.

Homework Options

Reflection

- **Science Content:** Give three examples of water you encounter in real life in gas form, liquid form, and solid form. Compare the energy of the water molecules in each example. *(Students should describe an example of liquid, solid, and gas water they see in weather or other settings. When comparing energy, students should describe gas as having the highest energy, then liquid, and solid having the least energy.)*

- **Science Content:** Describe the water cycle on an atomic level. *(Students should start to describe the water cycle when liquid water molecules change into a gas state after they have absorbed enough heat energy, and then rise with the air mass and cool. When they transfer enough of their energy to their surroundings, they condense into a liquid or solid state. When they become too heavy, they fall from the upper atmosphere in the form of snow, hail, sleet, or rain back to the ground. If the precipitation was a solid, it may transfer energy to its surroundings and go into the liquid state.)*

Preparation for 6.5

- **Science Content:** How are winds formed? *(The purpose of this is to elicit students' initial ideas and get them thinking about wind.)*

NOTES

....

....

....

....

....

....

....

....

....

....

....

....

....

....

....

....

SECTION 6.4 IMPLEMENTATION

6.4 Read

How Does the Sun's Energy Power the Water Cycle?

states of matter: the form of a substance; could be solid, liquid, or gas.

Water in the state of a liquid...

a solid...

The model your teacher showed you represented how water moves from a liquid on Earth to a gas in the air, and then back to a liquid falling from the atmosphere. In this section, you are going to find out how water can change from one form to another and back again—keeping the water cycle going for billions of years.

How Does Water Change State?

In the water cycle model, you saw water transform from liquid to gas and then transform back into liquid again. You were seeing water change states. Sometimes it was a liquid, and sometimes it was a gas. Scientists call these forms—liquid and gas—**states of matter**. Water moves through a continuous cycle by changing states over and over again. When liquids on Earth's surface are heated by the Sun, some of the liquid evaporates. They enter the atmosphere as a gas. In the atmosphere, the water molecules cool down again, causing them to condense. They eventually come back to Earth as rain (liquid) or snow or hail (solid).

Substances can exist in three states of matter—solid, liquid, or gas. By adding or removing heat energy, substances can change from one state to another. These changes are reversible. For example, when heat energy is added to water, it evaporates or changes to a gas. When heat energy is removed, the gas cools. It changes back into a liquid. If even more heat energy is removed, a substance becomes a solid. Water exists naturally on Earth in all three states. Whether it is a solid, liquid, or gas, it is still water.

Let's look at how substances change state. You read earlier that matter is made up of small particles called atoms and molecules. Molecules that do not have a lot of energy move very little, or simply vibrate. This is characteristic of a solid. The molecules in a solid are packed tightly together. This is why a solid can hold its shape.

and a gas (the water vapor leaving the clothes as they dry is invisible).

PF 192

Project-Based Inquiry Science

6.4 Read

How Does the Sun's Energy Drive the Water Cycle?

< 5 min.

Students are introduced to the concepts of the section.

⭕ Engage

Review the demonstration from the previous section and elicit students' ideas about how water (or any substance) changes state. Record students' ideas.

*A class period is considered to be one 40 to 50 minute class.

How Does Water Change State?

10 min.

Students have a class discussion on how water changes state.

TEACHER TALK

❝Remember the demonstration you observed when hot water in a jar evaporated and then condensed under the cold lid? That demonstration involved three states of matter: liquid, gas, and solid. Where were these three states of matter in the demonstration?

How do you think a substance like water changes state? What do you think happens to make it change from a liquid to a solid or a gas?❞

Have students look at the pictures in the student text of water in liquid, solid, and gas form. Ask them to think about the temperatures they would expect to encounter in each scene.

Water in the state of a liquid...

a solid...

and a gas (the water vapor leaving the clothes as they dry is invisible).

The model your teacher showed you represented how water moves from a liquid on Earth to a gas in the air, and then back to a liquid falling from the atmosphere. In this section, you are going to find out how water can change from one form to another and back again—keeping the water cycle going for billions of years.

How Does Water Change State?

In the water cycle model, you saw water transform from liquid to gas and then transform back into liquid again. You were seeing water change states. Sometimes it was a liquid, and sometimes it was a gas. Scientists call these forms—liquid and gas—**states of matter**. Water moves through a continuous cycle by changing states over and over again. When liquids on Earth's surface are heated by the Sun, some of the liquid evaporates. They enter the atmosphere as a gas. In the atmosphere, the water molecules cool down again, causing them to condense. They eventually come back to Earth as rain (liquid) or snow or hail (solid).

Substances can exist in three states of matter—solid, liquid, or gas. By adding or removing heat energy, substances can change from one state to another. These changes are reversible. For example, when heat energy is added to water, it evaporates or changes to a gas. When heat energy is removed, the gas cools. It changes back into a liquid. If even more heat energy is removed, a substance becomes a solid. Water exists naturally on Earth in all three states. Whether it is a solid, liquid, or gas, it is still water.

Let's look at how substances change state. You read earlier that matter is made up of small particles called atoms and molecules. Molecules that do not have a lot of energy move very little, or simply vibrate. This is characteristic of a solid. The molecules in a solid are packed tightly together. This is why a solid can hold its shape.

PF 192

Project-Based Inquiry Science

⬡ **Get Going**

Consider having students read independently and then discussing, or having them read aloud in groups or to the class.

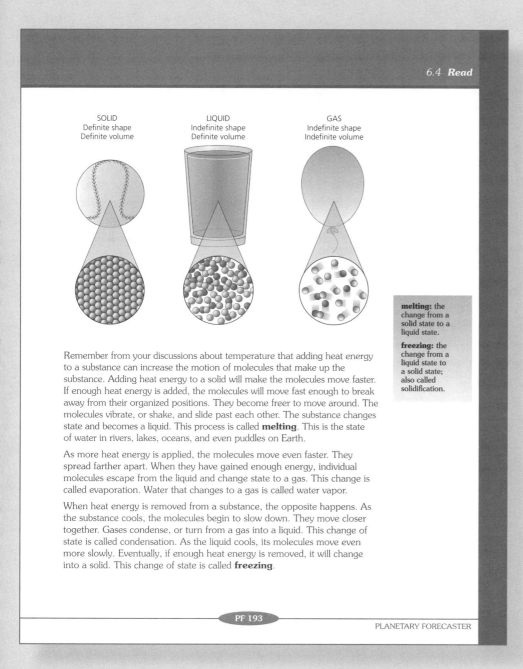

SOLID	LIQUID	GAS
Definite shape	Indefinite shape	Indefinite shape
Definite volume	Definite volume	Indefinite volume

melting: the change from a solid state to a liquid state.

freezing: the change from a liquid state to a solid state; also called solidification.

Remember from your discussions about temperature that adding heat energy to a substance can increase the motion of molecules that make up the substance. Adding heat energy to a solid will make the molecules move faster. If enough heat energy is added, the molecules will move fast enough to break away from their organized positions. They become freer to move around. The molecules vibrate, or shake, and slide past each other. The substance changes state and becomes a liquid. This process is called **melting**. This is the state of water in rivers, lakes, oceans, and even puddles on Earth.

As more heat energy is applied, the molecules move even faster. They spread farther apart. When they have gained enough energy, individual molecules escape from the liquid and change state to a gas. This change is called evaporation. Water that changes to a gas is called water vapor.

When heat energy is removed from a substance, the opposite happens. As the substance cools, the molecules begin to slow down. They move closer together. Gases condense, or turn from a gas into a liquid. This change of state is called condensation. As the liquid cools, its molecules move even more slowly. Eventually, if enough heat energy is removed, it will change into a solid. This change of state is called **freezing**.

PF 193

△ Guide

Have a discussion on how water changes state. Emphasize that the state of matter is dependent on how much energy the substance has. For liquid water to change to the gas form, it has to absorb more energy. For it to change to the solid form, it has to transfer energy to its surroundings.

Discuss the three states in terms of atomic particles. Let students know the molecules of water in the gas state are very energetic. They move a lot and are not closely spaced. Molecules of liquid water are closely spaced, but can slide past and around each other. They do not move as much as the molecules in water vapor and do not have as much energy. The molecules in solid water, or ice, are in an array. They are closely spaced and cannot move past or around each other. They are in a fixed position relative to each other, but they can still vibrate. The molecules in solid water has less energy than liquid water or water vapor.

Consider describing how the particles move using a model. Describe how a solid is like all the students sitting in their desks and holding hands. Everyone can move and wiggle slightly in their chairs, but they have to keep their hands together and stay in their seats. Their motion is limited. As energy is added, they can wiggle more in their chairs. When more energy is added, the substance goes into a liquid state. This is similar to having the students out of their seats. They can move around more, but they have to always hold hands on each side. They can exchange whom they are holding hands with and move from place to place, but each hand must be holding another students' hand. As energy is added, they move around more. When enough energy is added, they have enough motion to break free from holding hands. This is the like the gas phase when students are able to move around freely without holding hands and occasionally, but rarely, bumping into each other.

NOTES

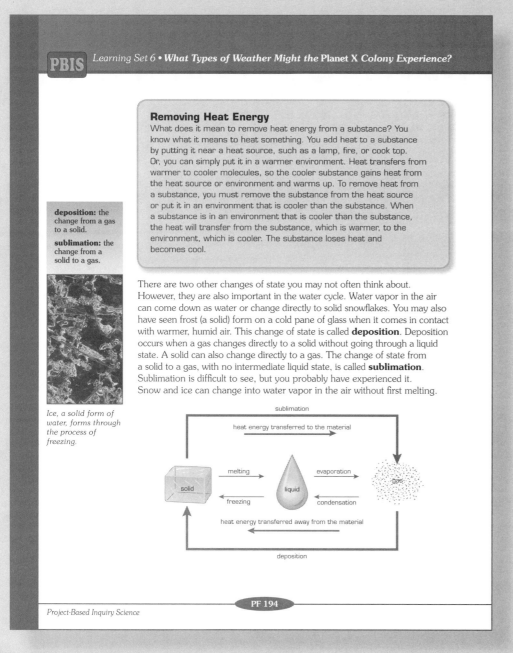

Removing Heat Energy
What does it mean to remove heat energy from a substance? You know what it means to heat something. You add heat to a substance by putting it near a heat source, such as a lamp, fire, or cook top. Or, you can simply put it in a warmer environment. Heat transfers from warmer to cooler molecules, so the cooler substance gains heat from the heat source or environment and warms up. To remove heat from a substance, you must remove the substance from the heat source or put it in an environment that is cooler than the substance. When a substance is in an environment that is cooler than the substance, the heat will transfer from the substance, which is warmer, to the environment, which is cooler. The substance loses heat and becomes cool.

deposition: the change from a gas to a solid.

sublimation: the change from a solid to a gas.

Ice, a solid form of water, forms through the process of freezing.

There are two other changes of state you may not often think about. However, they are also important in the water cycle. Water vapor in the air can come down as water or change directly to solid snowflakes. You may also have seen frost (a solid) form on a cold pane of glass when it comes in contact with warmer, humid air. This change of state is called **deposition**. Deposition occurs when a gas changes directly to a solid without going through a liquid state. A solid can also change directly to a gas. The change of state from a solid to a gas, with no intermediate liquid state, is called **sublimation**. Sublimation is difficult to see, but you probably have experienced it. Snow and ice can change into water vapor in the air without first melting.

△ Guide and Assess

Ask students what type of energy is being transferred for the substance to change from a solid to a liquid or a liquid to a gas. Students should realize heat energy is transferred. Ask students to describe how energy is transferred when a substance changes from a gas to a liquid or a liquid to a solid. Students should realize heat energy is transferred away from the substance to change it from a gas to a liquid, a gas to a solid, or a liquid to a solid. Heat energy is transferred to the substance when it changes from a solid to a liquid, a solid to a gas, or a liquid to a gas.

If needed, review what it means to remove heat energy. Emphasize heat energy is transferred from the substance to the surroundings. Energy is never created or destroyed, it is only transferred to or away from an object or substance.

△ Guide

Discuss deposition and sublimation with the class. Let students know when a solid changes directly to gas it is called sublimation. An example of this is dry ice. Let students know that a gas can change directly to a solid. It is called deposition.

NOTES

6.4 Read

How Does Water Get Into the Atmosphere?

When water evaporates from oceans, lakes, ponds, rivers, soil, and even plants and animals, the water vapor goes into the air. The molecules stay in the air and move with the air. Meteorologists call water vapor in the air **humidity**. In the summer, the amount of water in the air is higher than in winter, because warm air can hold more water than cold air.

When weather reports describe the amount of moisture in the air, they often give a percent. This describes the **relative humidity**. This percent describes the actual amount of water vapor in the air compared to what the air is capable of holding. Relative humidity affects how comfortable you are on a given day. If the relative humidity is low, you can feel cooler than the actual temperature. However, if the relative humidity is high, you feel much hotter and tend to sweat easily.

High humidity can make it very uncomfortable to be outside in the summer. Humans are most comfortable when the relative humidity is around 45%. When the relative humidity is 100%, the air has as much water vapor as it can hold. On a very hot day, when the relative humidity is near 100%, your perspiration will stay on your body. It will not evaporate, because the air is already so full of water it cannot hold any more.

humidity: water vapor in the air.

relative humidity: the actual amount of water vapor in the air compared to what the air can hold; usually shown as a percent.

The humidity can make a big difference in your comfort level on hot summer days.

PF 195

How Does Water Get into the Atmosphere?

5 min.

Students participate in a discussion about humidity.

⚠ Guide

Discuss humidity and relative humidity using the student text. Let students know humidity is a measure of how much water vapor is in the air and relative humidity is how much water is in the air compared to how much water the air can hold. When the relative humidity is high, less water can be held in the air. When the relative humidity is at 100%, the air cannot hold any more water. When this happens, perspiration cannot evaporate off the body to keep it cool. When the relative humidity is low, perspiration evaporates off the body and cools it as it absorbs energy to change state.

Remind students water vapor in the air rises with the air masses warmed by the land. As the air mass rises, energy is transferred to the surroundings and do work to move the surroundings out of the way.

NOTES

Stop and Think

1. Using what you now understand about the water cycle, make your own diagram showing how water moves from Earth's surface, into the atmosphere, and back again. Identify three sources on Earth's surface from which water can come.

2. Think about the model of the water cycle your teacher demonstrated. Use what you now know to describe what would have happened if the jar had been filled with cold water instead of hot.

Where Do Clouds Come From?

Temperatures are much lower higher up in the atmosphere than they are near Earth's surface. You saw this when you looked at the effects of elevation on temperature variations. When water vapor in the atmosphere rises, it begins to cool, and it condenses. Tiny droplets or ice crystals form. These droplets or ice crystals cluster together, forming clouds. Clouds form at different levels in the atmosphere and come in all sorts of sizes and shapes. Each type of cloud is associated with a different type of weather.

The pictures and captions on the next pages show you what the different types of clouds look like and the type of weather associated with each. As you read about each type of cloud, think about when you might have seen that type of cloud and the type of weather you experienced. Try to identify which types of clouds are probably at your location on the weather maps you analyzed earlier.

PF 196

Project-Based Inquiry Science

Stop and Think

10 min.

Students have a class discussion to assess their understanding of the water cycle.

○ Get Going

Let students know there will be a class discussion on their responses and how much time they have.

△ Guide and Assess

Using the information below, guide and assess students' understanding of the water cycle.

META NOTES

Consider adding a second part to the first question asking students where sources of water in your local area are that may evaporate into the air and where they think the water that precipitates originates.

1. Students should create a diagram of the water cycle that identifies at least three sources of liquid water on Earth's surface that goes into the atmosphere. Some examples are oceans, lakes, streams, ice, snow, and groundwater. It is important that students include the Sun to show how it can be a direct or indirect energy source that causes the evaporation of water from the surface into the atmosphere. Students should show precipitation and list the types of precipitation that may occur. They should show the cyclical nature of the water cycle in their diagrams. Use the diagram of the water cycle in *Section 6.3* in the student text to assess students' diagrams.

2. Students' responses should describe how cold water does not have as much energy as hot water and is unlikely to evaporate as quickly as the hot water. Because of this, students may not notice the effect. If the cold water was placed in the jar and ice cubes over the lid, some water may condense under the lid, but this water would be from water vapor that was already present in the air, not water vapor that evaporated from the cold water in the jar.

Where Do Clouds Come From?

Temperatures are much lower higher up in the atmosphere than they are near Earth's surface. You saw this when you looked at the effects of elevation on temperature variations. When water vapor in the atmosphere rises, it begins to cool, and it condenses. Tiny droplets or ice crystals form. These droplets or ice crystals cluster together, forming clouds. Clouds form at different levels in the atmosphere and come in all sorts of sizes and shapes. Each type of cloud is associated with a different type of weather.

The pictures and captions on the next pages show you what the different types of clouds look like and the type of weather associated with each. As you read about each type of cloud, think about when you might have seen that type of cloud and the type of weather you experienced. Try to identify which types of clouds are probably at your location on the weather maps you analyzed earlier.

PF 196

Project-Based Inquiry Science

Where Do Clouds Come From?

5 min.

Students participate in a class discussion on clouds.

△ Guide

Discuss cloud formation with the class and review the images of different cloud types using the student text.

Many students may incorrectly believe clouds are made up of water vapor. Emphasize to students clouds are actually made of tiny drops of liquid water or ice crystals that form as the water vapor within air masses rise and cool.

6.4 Read

Cumulus
*Base below 2000 m (about 6600 ft) —
Clouds are white and fluffy with flat bottoms;
they indicate fair weather.*

Cumulonimbus
*Base below 2000 m (about 6600 ft) —
Towering billows of puffy clouds with dark,
flat bottoms, they often produce
thunderstorms, and sometimes hail, strong
winds, or tornadoes.*

Stratus
*Base below 2000 m (about 6600 ft) —
Smooth gray clouds covering the whole sky,
they often indicate rain or drizzle.
At ground level, they form fog.*

Nimbostratus
*Base below 2000 m (about 6600 ft) —
Thick, dark gray clouds, often with a
ragged base, they usually bring rain or snow.*

PF 197

PLANETARY FORECASTER

The droplets are so small they are suspended in the air. Remind students when water vapor condenses to liquid form, or as deposition occurs, heat energy is transferred from the water vapor to the surrounding air mass. This warming of the air causes the surrounding air to rise and clouds are observed puffing upwards, with level or flat bottoms (e.g. the cumulus and cumulonimbus clouds). As more water condenses or deposits in the form of liquid or ice, these droplets or crystals become heavier. When they are too heavy to be supported by the air below them, they fall.

Altocumulus
Base between 2000-6000 m (about 6600-20,700 ft) — Roll-like puffy, patchy clouds grouped in large sheets, on a hot, humid day they may signal thunderstorms.

Altostratus
Base between 2000-6000 m (about 6600-20,700 ft) — Uniformly gray or bluish-white layers covering most of sky, they often indicate storms with continuous rain or snow.

Cirrus
Base above 6000 m (about 20,700 ft) — Wispy and feathery, composed of ice crystals, they are seen in fair weather, but may indicate incoming rain or snow.

Cirrocumulus
Base above 6000 m (about 20,700 ft) — Puffy and patchy, forming wave-like patterns, they usually indicate fair but cold weather.

PF 198

Project-Based Inquiry Science

Consider having students look out the window and identify the types of clouds they see.

At this point, you may choose to show the students a cloud demonstration. Use the directions and explanation from the *Activity Setup and Preparation* found in the introduction of this section to show the class.

Explain

You have seen how the Sun's energy powers the water cycle and affects precipitation. With your group, explain a part of the water cycle that depends on the Sun's energy. Take a few minutes to think about the evidence you have from the demonstration and the reading. Think about what happens to molecules when they are heated, and how this can make a substance change state. Make sure your explanation connects together a claim, evidence, and science knowledge. Use a *Create Your Explanation* page to guide you as you create your explanation.

Communicate

Share Your Explanation

When everyone is finished, you will share your explanation with the class. As each group shares their explanation, make a record of it. You might also create a poster for the classroom that has the full set of explanations on it. Then you will have the complete story of the water cycle and how it relates to precipitation.

Update the *Project Board*

In this section, you explored about the water cycle and how precipitation, evaporation, and condensation are all parts of it. Return to the *Project Board* and add your understanding of these ideas to the *What are we learning?* column. Make sure to include a description of how the Sun's energy powers the water cycle. Put your evidence, either from your model of the water cycle or your reading, in the *What is our evidence?* column. You may also have new questions you want to think about. Now is a good time to add those to the *Project Board*.

What's the Point?

The water cycle moves all the water on Earth. It is a constant cycle of evaporation, condensation, and precipitation. Energy from the Sun begins the process with evaporation and heats up water found on Earth's surface. This energy causes the water molecules to move faster. As they move faster, water molecules move into the atmosphere. As you read earlier, air at higher levels of the atmosphere is cooler. This means that as water molecules move higher in the atmosphere, water molecules cool. This causes the vibrations to slow and the water condenses. The water droplets cluster together into clouds. When they get heavy, the drops fall to Earth as rain, snow, sleet, or hail. This is called precipitation.

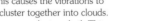

PLANETARY FORECASTER

Get Going

Let students know each group should construct an explanation for how a part of the water cycle depends on the Sun's energy. Students should also describe the water cycle. Let them know each group will be presenting their explanation to the class. Have students use a *Create Your Explanation* page. Emphasize they should back up their claims with evidence from their observations and science knowledge.

Explain

10 min.

Groups construct explanations of how a part of the water cycle depends on the Sun's energy.

Guide and Assess

Monitor students' progress. Check to see if each group member is contributing. Groups' explanations should describe how the Sun's energy is needed to warm and evaporate water on Earth's surface. Students should provide evidence in the form of personal observation, data from the demonstration, and information from the reading.

Communicate

15 min.

Students share their group explanations and have a class discussion.

science knowledge. Use a *Create Your Explanation* page to guide you as you create your explanation.

Communicate

Share Your Explanation

When everyone is finished, you will share your explanation with the class. As each group shares their explanation, make a record of it. You might also create a poster for the classroom that has the full set of explanations on it. Then you will have the complete story of the water cycle and how it relates to precipitation.

Update the *Project Board*

△ Guide

Let students know each group will be presenting their description of the water cycle and their explanation of how the Sun's energy affects a part of the water cycle.

Have each group present their explanations. Encourage the class to ask questions of the presenting group. Consider having the class pick out the claim, evidence, and science knowledge in each explanation presented.

After each group presents, have a discussion on the similarities and differences between explanations. Consider recording the similarities and differences, and constructing a class explanation when all groups have presented. Consider having groups work together to create a classroom poster that combines their work.

◇ Evaluate

Use the following example explanation to evaluate students:

The Sun's energy drives the water cycle by causing the water on Earth's surface to evaporate. The water on Earth's surface consists of water in oceans, lakes, streams, snow, glaciers, and groundwater. When water on Earth's surface absorbs energy from the Sun, it warms and can change into gas becoming water vapor in the atmosphere. As the air warms from energy transferred to it from the ground (land and water that was warmed by the Sun), it rises and the water vapor in the air rises, too. As the air rises, it transfers energy to its surroundings and does work on its surroundings as it pushes its surroundings out of the way. The water vapor in the air cools, transferring its energy to its surroundings. As it continues to transfer energy to the air mass it begins to condense into a liquid or solid state, forming water droplets or ice crystals on particles in the air. These water droplets and/or ice crystals are suspended in the air, supported by the air so they do not fall, to create clouds. When the droplets or crystals become too heavy for the air to support, they fall to Earth's surface in the form of precipitation (snow, hail, sleet, rain) and collect on Earth's surface in groundwater, lakes, streams, oceans, etc. The cycle repeats itself as the water on Earth's surface absorbs Earth's energy.

have the complete story of the water cycle and how it relates to precipitation.

Update the *Project Board*

In this section, you explored about the water cycle and how precipitation, evaporation, and condensation are all parts of it. Return to the *Project Board* and add your understanding of these ideas to the *What are we learning?* column. Make sure to include a description of how the Sun's energy powers the water cycle. Put your evidence, either from your model of the water cycle or your reading, in the *What is our evidence?* column. You may also have new questions you want to think about. Now is a good time to add those to the *Project Board*.

Update the Project Board
10 min.

The class updates their Project Boards.

△ Guide

Remind students the class *Project Board* is used to organize all their ideas, questions, and information. Let them know the new information they know about weather needs to be added to the *Project Board*. Focus on the third and fourth columns. Ask students what claims they can make about weather to put in Column 3 of their *Project Board* and what evidence they have for these claims to put in Column 4 of their *Project Board*.

◇ Evaluate

Students should have the following information on their *Project Board*. This information may be spread across many claims, or combined into one claim. The wording may be different; however the main ideas should be present.

Column 3 (claim): Scientists measure many factors such as the temperature, amount of precipitation, humidity, wind speed and direction, and air pressure that affect or describe weather. Small air pressure differences we do not notice have large affects on weather.

Column 4 (evidence): We analyzed three consecutive days of weather maps that showed the trends of changing air pressure changing the weather. Increasing air pressure changed the rainy weather to clear. We read about and built different measuring devices. The student text states that high pressure usually results in weather with sunny, clear skies and low pressure indicates rain or stormy weather may occur soon. (Students should also include any data they took.)

Column 3 (claim): Precipitation in our weather is due to the water cycle. The Sun's energy drives the water cycle.

Column 4 (evidence): The Sun's energy drives the water cycle by causing water on Earth's surface to evaporate. The water on Earth's surface consists of water in oceans, lakes, streams, snow, glaciers, and groundwater.

When water on Earth's surface absorbs energy from the Sun, it warms. When it absorbs enough energy from the Sun it can change into the gas state, becoming water vapor in the atmosphere. As the air is warmed by energy from the ground (land and water that was warmed by the Sun) it rises, and the water vapor in the air rises, too. As the air rises, it transfers energy to its surroundings and does work on its surroundings as it pushes its surroundings out of the way. The water vapor in the air also cools, transferring its energy to its surroundings. As it continues to transfer energy to the air mass it begins to condense into a liquid or solid state, forming water droplets or ice crystals on particles in the air. These water droplets and/or ice crystals are suspended and supported by the air so they do not fall and form clouds. When the droplets or crystals become too heavy for the air to support, they fall to Earth's surface in the form of precipitation (snow, hail, sleet, rain) and are collected on Earth's surface in groundwater, lakes, streams, oceans, etc. This is the cycle which repeats itself as the water on Earth's surface absorbs Earth's energy.

△ Guide

Ask students if they have any questions to investigate to add to Column 2 or things they think they know to include in Column 1. Students should have some questions they would like to investigate about weather.

- *What causes wind?*

- *How does wind affect weather?*

- *Are Earth's winds caused by Earth's rotation?*

- *What causes severe weather such as hurricanes or tornados?*

Assessment Options

Targeted Concepts, Skills, and Nature of Science	How do I know if students got it?
Energy from the Sun drives Earth's water cycle. Water moves between different physical states in a continuous cycle of evaporation, condensation, and precipitation.	**ASK:** How does the Sun's energy drive the water cycle? **LISTEN:** Students should describe how the Sun's energy causes the water on Earth's surface to evaporate, rise, condense, and fall back to Earth in the form of precipitation (snow, sleet, hail, rain). The process then repeats itself.

Targeted Concepts, Skills, and Nature of Science	How do I know if students got it?
Water changes state (solid, liquid, gas) by adding or removing heat energy.	**ASK:** Describe the three states of water (gas, liquid, solid) and how energy is transferred to or from one state to another.
	LISTEN: Students should describe how molecules in solid water (ice) are defined in a structure free to vibrate (wiggle) around a fixed location. The molecules in water (liquid) are free to vibrate and slide past, over, and around each other and are very close together. Water vapor (gas) is made of molecules that can vibrate and move around without being near another molecule. The gas state has more energy than the liquid state, which has more energy than the solid state. For a solid to change to a liquid or gas and for a liquid to change to a gas, it must absorb energy or have energy transferred to it. For a liquid to change to a solid and for a gas to change to a liquid or solid, it must release energy or transfer energy to its surroundings.

Teacher Reflection Questions

- What was helpful in guiding students' understanding about how a substance changes state and the role the Sun plays in the water cycle?

- What evidence do you have that students are using the *Project Board?* Do you think students would have added questions to the *Project Board* without prompting?

- How did you manage the various reading levels or language abilities in your classroom?

NOTES

6.5 Read

How Does the Sun's Energy Affect Wind?

◀ *1 class period*

A class period is considered to be one 40 to 50 minute class.

Overview

Students explore the processes that create wind and Earth's wind patterns. Students read how wind is caused by movement of air from higher to lower pressures and how the Sun's energy plays a large role. They discuss local winds close to Earth's surface caused by land and water differences in a region and how these can set up sea and land breezes. They discuss global winds that occur due to the different intensities of sunlight shining on Earth's surface due to its shape and tilt. Students are introduced to Earth's major global wind patterns such as the trade winds, prevailing easterlies, prevailing westerlies, and polar easterlies.

Targeted Concepts, Skills, and Nature of Science	Performance Expectations
Scientists often work together and share their findings. Sharing findings makes new information available and helps scientists to refine their ideas and build on others' ideas. When another person's or group's idea is used, credit needs to be given.	The class should discuss how local and global winds compare and the how the Sun's energy affects winds, and then update their *Project Board*.
Scientists must keep clear, accurate, and descriptive records of what they do so they can share their work with others and consider what they did, why they did it, and what they want to do next.	Students should keep records to refer to later when they make predictions about weather on *Planet X*.
Wind results from the Sun's energy heating Earth. Solar energy heats air molecules and creates areas of high and low pressure. Wind is created as air molecules move from high to low pressure areas. This is affected greatly by landforms and water on a local scale.	Students should discuss and describe how the Sun's energy warms the Earth's surface and atmosphere, and causes high and low pressure air masses in the atmosphere, which cause winds locally and globally.

Materials	
1 per class	Class *Project Board*
1 per student	*Project Board* page
1 per classroom (optional)	Balloon

Homework Options

Reflection

- **Science Content:** What causes wind? How does the Sun's energy affect wind? *(Students' responses should state wind is caused by high pressure air masses moving toward low-pressure air masses. The Sun warms the air, but direct warming of the air is not significant. The Sun warms the land and water, which warms the air above it. The warming of the air above the surface causes these air masses to increase in temperature and pressure and rise as it moves toward lower-pressure regions. As it rises and expands, it pushes the surrounding air out of the way and transfers energy to it. The cooler air masses get pushed out of the way and move downward toward the surface where they are warmed.)*

- **Science Content:** What is the difference between local and global winds? *(Students should describe local winds being affected by the local terrain and local heating of land and water masses. Global winds are caused by differences in global heating and cooling and occur primarily between the warm air near the Equator rising and the cool air from the poles moving in.)*

Preparation for 6.6

- **Science Content:** What do you think causes changes in the weather? *(The purpose of this is to elicit students' initial ideas and to see how students put together the ideas they have been discussing.)*

SECTION 6.5 IMPLEMENTATION

6.5 Read

How Does the Sun's Energy Affect Wind?

Imagine for a moment that you have just blown up a balloon. Instead of tying it, you pinch it closed with your fingers. The air pressure is higher inside the balloon than outside. All the air molecules are crowded together inside the walls of the balloon. Meanwhile, outside the balloon, the air molecules are free to spread apart. The pressure is lower. Now, what do you think will happen when you let go of the balloon? All of the air inside the balloon, where the pressure is higher, is going to rush out, moving toward where the pressure is lower. If you put your hand by the balloon, you can feel the air moving.

Wind is the movement of air from areas of higher pressure to areas of lower pressure. Consider what makes air pressure different from one place to another. You probably will not be surprised to learn that the Sun's energy plays a big role in changing air pressure.

wind: the movement of air from areas of higher pressure to areas of lower pressure

Thinking about what you already know will help you get started.

*   Molecules in warmer air move more quickly than molecules in cooler air. This means that the molecules in warmer air tend to have more space between them than the molecules in cooler air. When there are fewer molecules in a space, the space exerts less pressure on the space below it. Air molecules are farther apart in warm air than in cool air, so warm air has less pressure than cooler air. This means that air will tend to move from cooler areas, with higher pressure, to warmer areas, with lower pressure.

*   When molecules in a space are farther apart, the space is less dense than a space where molecules are closer together. The molecules in warmer air are farther away from one another than the molecules in

PF 200

Project-Based Inquiry Science

6.5 Read

How Does the Sun's Energy Affect Wind?

5 min.

Students participate in a discussion reviewing what affects air masses and introduces local and global winds.

⬡ Get Going

Consider having students read the segment and then discussing it as a class. Students could read independently, in pairs, in groups, or aloud to the class.

○ Engage

Describe blowing up a balloon or demonstrate it to the students. Ask what is happening to the air inside and outside of the balloon. Record their responses.

Ask students what it would feel like at the end of the balloon if you released some air. Ask students what would happen if you let go of the balloon. If you are doing the demonstration, do both of these things, first release some air on a few students' hands and have them describe it. Then, release the balloon into the air.

Discuss what happened when the balloon was being blown up. The molecules of air in the balloon were getting closer because they did not have many places to go. To push out the sides of the balloon, the molecules had to be under higher pressure. Describe how the balloon expanded and pushed the surrounding air out of the way. Discuss how the air released felt like wind because it was under high pressure and was moving things out of the way as it was expanding. When the balloon was let go, it moved around the room because the air pushed out propelled the balloon forward.

Emphasize that the example of the balloon is an example of air moving from a higher pressure to a lower pressure.

△ Guide

Review with students what they know about air masses moving from higher to lower pressure by recording their ideas and discussing each bulleted point in the student text. Ask guiding questions such as those listed below.

Ask students if they see the connection between the Sun's energy and the

TEACHER TALK

"How is the movement of molecules in the air different in warm air versus cool air?

How does the temperature and movement of molecules in the air affect air pressure?

Why is air denser closer to Earth's surface?

What warms the air and what happens to it after it warms?**"**

movement of air or wind. Emphasize that warm air close to the surface rises and the cooler, less dense air moves in to replace it. Introduce the terms local wind and global wind. Describe local winds as winds near the surface of the Earth affected by local land and water differences and land forms. Describe how global winds occur due to the warmer temperatures at the Equator. The air at the Equator rises and moves toward the poles, and the colder, denser air from the poles sinks and moves toward the Equator.

cooler air. Warm air is less dense than cool air. When they are free to move, substances that are less dense rise above substances that are more dense. So, warm air will rise over cooler air.

- Air that is lower in the atmosphere is warmer than air that is higher in the atmosphere. This is because the air closer to Earth's surface is heated by the surface.

With those reminders, you can now begin to understand how the Sun's energy affects winds. Warm air close to Earth rises. Cooler, denser air moves in to replace it, producing an area of high pressure. As this air is warmed by Earth's surface, it rises. Near Earth's surface the movement of air produces winds that blow over short distances. These are called **local winds**. At higher altitudes and on a much larger scale, temperature differences generate movements of air between Earth's poles, where air is colder, and the Equator, where air is warmer. These are called **global winds**. You will read about both kinds.

global winds: winds that blow at high altitudes over long distances.

local winds: winds that blow at low altitudes over short distances.

Hot air balloonists rely on heaters to make sure the air inside the balloon remains warm while in flight. What do you think they do when they want to come down?

Local Winds

While investigating temperature, you saw that land and water heat up and cool down at different rates. This has an effect on local winds. During the day, land heats up more quickly than water. This means the air above land is warmer. Therefore, it is less dense than the air above water. Cooler water temperatures make the air above water cooler and denser. This sets up a pressure difference. Warm air over the land rises and is replaced by the cooler air from over the water.

PF 201

PLANETARY FORECASTER

Local Winds

5 min.

Students have a discussion on local winds.

△ Guide

Consider assigning a group to facilitate a class discussion on this segment.

Describe how land and water absorb and release heat energy at different rates, and how this affects the temperature of the air above. Using the images in the student text, emphasize that during the day the land is warmer than water because water must absorb more energy to change its temperature. The air above the land during the day rises and is replaced by cooler air over the water. This causes sea breezes. Throughout the night, the water is warmer than the land and the air above the water rises. The air over the land flows over the water in land breezes.

Global Winds

5 min.

Students have a discussion on global winds.

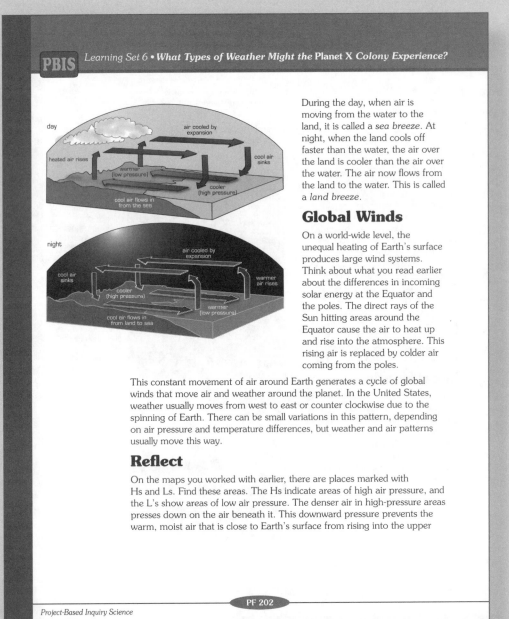

During the day, when air is moving from the water to the land, it is called a *sea breeze*. At night, when the land cools off faster than the water, the air over the land is cooler than the air over the water. The air now flows from the land to the water. This is called a *land breeze*.

Global Winds

On a world-wide level, the unequal heating of Earth's surface produces large wind systems. Think about what you read earlier about the differences in incoming solar energy at the Equator and the poles. The direct rays of the Sun hitting areas around the Equator cause the air to heat up and rise into the atmosphere. This rising air is replaced by colder air coming from the poles.

This constant movement of air around Earth generates a cycle of global winds that move air and weather around the planet. In the United States, weather usually moves from west to east or counter clockwise due to the spinning of Earth. There can be small variations in this pattern, depending on air pressure and temperature differences, but weather and air patterns usually move this way.

Reflect

On the maps you worked with earlier, there are places marked with Hs and Ls. Find these areas. The Hs indicate areas of high air pressure, and the L's show areas of low air pressure. The denser air in high-pressure areas presses down on the air beneath it. This downward pressure prevents the warm, moist air that is close to Earth's surface from rising into the upper

PF 202

Project-Based Inquiry Science

△ Guide

Consider assigning a group to facilitate the class discussion on this segment. Discuss how globally more of the Sun's energy is absorbed by the land and water near the Equator than at the poles due to the shape and tilt of the Earth. This difference in absorption of the Sun's energy sets up differences in warming and cooling of air masses by the Equator and the poles. There is a general trend of air masses rising by the Equator and being replaced by air masses coming from the poles.

Describe how in the United States weather usually moves from west to east, but variations can occur due to local patterns in air pressure.

6.5 **Read**

atmosphere. Without this warm, moist air in the upper atmosphere, clouds do not form. This is why high-pressure systems usually bring clear and sunny days. Check your maps and see if this trend is accurate for the Hs on the maps.

Air in low-pressure areas (marked with Ls) does not press down on the air below as much as air in high-pressure areas. This means the warm, moist air close to Earth's surface can rise into the upper atmosphere. If the air contains enough moisture, clouds will form. So, low-pressure areas can bring damp, wet weather. Check and see if this trend is accurate for the Ls in the maps.

Local and Global Winds Are Part of the Same System

Winds happen when air moves from areas of higher pressure to areas of lower pressure. Wind strength is determined by two factors. The first factor is the difference in pressure between the two air systems. If there is only a little difference in pressure between two areas, the winds will be calm. The greater the difference in air pressure, the stronger the wind. The second factor is the distance between the area of higher pressure and the area of lower pressure. When areas close to each other have big differences in pressure, the winds are strong.

The movement of air between high-pressure and low-pressure areas is a cycle. The Sun heats Earth's surface. As air moves near Earth's surface, it is heated. Since warmer air is less dense, it rises up into the atmosphere. As it moves higher into the atmosphere, it cools, becomes denser, and starts to sink. Once near the ground, the air warms again. You can see these cycles play out over and over again all around the planet. You can see that there are many of these cycles. Even on the maps, you notice several high-and low-pressure areas. Each system works in the same way.

Stop and Think

1. How are local and global winds alike? How are they different?

2. The Sun's energy heats land and water at different rates. This generates local winds near large bodies of water. Draw a diagram to show how land breezes near water develop. Show the areas of higher and lower pressure on your diagram.

PF 203

PLANETARY FORECASTER

Reflect
10 min.

Students participate in a class discussion of groups' analysis of the weather maps from Section 6.1.

⬡ Get Going

Have groups revisit the three days of weather maps in *Section 6.1* to review the trends in high and low pressure air masses. Let the class know how much time they have and a discussion will follow.

△ Guide and Assess

Have groups present their results. Record any similarities and differences in the results and discuss them. Students should observe high pressure systems usually bring clear, sunny days, and do not allow the warm, moist air to rise. Low pressure areas cause cloud formation, and/or damp and wet weather.

From the maps, students may note that Location A decreased in humidity and seems to have a low pressure above it moving eastward and a high pressure to the southeast moving westward. Location B has a high pressure air mass moving by and is increasing in humidity. Location C has a low pressure nearby for the first two days. High humidity exists for both days and it is raining the on first day. On the third day, no highs or lows are indicated for Location C and the humidity dropped. At Location D, there are high pressure air masses nearby. The barometer is steady and the weather is fairly constant.

Local and Global Winds Are Part of the Same System

5 min.

Students have a class discussion on wind strength and wind cycles.

enough m............ads will form. So, low-pres......as can bring damp, wet weather. Check and see if this trend is accurate for the Ls in the maps.

Local and Global Winds Are Part of the Same System

Winds happen when air moves from areas of higher pressure to areas of lower pressure. Wind strength is determined by two factors. The first factor is the difference in pressure between the two air systems. If there is only a little difference in pressure between two areas, the winds will be calm. The greater the difference in air pressure, the stronger the wind. The second factor is the distance between the area of higher pressure and the area of lower pressure. When areas close to each other have big differences in pressure, the winds are strong.

The movement of air between high-pressure and low-pressure areas is a cycle. The Sun heats Earth's surface. As air moves near Earth's surface, it is heated. Since warmer air is less dense, it rises up into the atmosphere. As it moves higher into the atmosphere, it cools, becomes denser, and starts to sink. Once near the ground, the air warms again. You can see these cycles play out over and over again all around the planet. You can see that there are many of these cycles. Even on the maps, you notice several high-and low-pressure areas. Each system works in the same way.

Stop and Think

○ **Engage**

Ask students what affects the strength of the wind and record students' ideas.

△ **Guide**

Discuss how the strength of wind depends on the difference in pressure between interacting air masses. Emphasize that the greater the difference in pressure there is, the greater the wind speed will be.

Discuss wind cycles. Use the information in the student text and the illustrations of sea and land breezes to guide students. Emphasize how air is warmed by the surface, expands, rises, and becomes less dense. Cool, denser air replaces the rising warmed air, and the process repeats itself.

Discuss the similarities and differences between local and global winds. Describe how local and global winds are caused by differences in air pressure due to warming air masses by the Earth's land and water. Remind students that Earth's land and water are warmed by incoming sunlight and the land and water transfer heat energy to the air as it cools.

Point out the major difference between global and local winds is caused by the large and small scale difference of incoming solar radiation and absorption of the Sun's radiation. Emphasize that locally the land and water differences play a big role in the amount of absorbed energy from the Sun and the amount of energy re-radiated from the land and water to warm the air. Globally, the planet's shape and tilt play a large role in the amount of incoming solar energy reradiated to warm the atmosphere, and causes air masses to move due to pressure differences.

low-pressure areas. Each system works in the same way.

Stop and Think

1. How are local and global winds alike? How are they different?

2. The Sun's energy heats land and water at different rates. This generates local winds near large bodies of water. Draw a diagram to show how land breezes near water develop. Show the areas of higher and lower pressure on your diagram.

Stop and Think

10 min.

Students have a class discussion on their responses.

⬡ Get Going

Let students know they should answer the questions with their group members and a class discussion will follow.

△ Guide and Assess

Have a class discussion on groups' responses. Use the information below to guide and assess students.

1. Students' responses should describe how local and global winds are caused by differences in air pressure due to the warming of air masses by Earth's land and water. Students should describe the differences caused by large and small scale differences of incoming solar radiation and absorption of the Sun's radiation. Locally, the land and water differences play a big role in the amount of absorbed energy from the Sun and the amount of energy reradiated to warm the air. Globally, the planet's shape and tilt play a large role in the amount of incoming solar energy that is reradiated to warm the atmosphere.

2. Students should draw a diagram similar to the night diagram shown in the student text.

Update the Project Board

5 min.

Students participate in a class discussion and update their Project Board.

Update the *Project Board*

Winds are a very important part of the process of moving weather. You have read a lot about winds in this section. Add this new information to the *Project Board*. Remember to include details that will help describe this information and how it relates to the *Big Challenge*. The *Project Board* is probably full of ideas now. This would be a good time to read over the ideas you have recorded in the past and see if there are ways you might want to update those ideas by using any new information you now have.

What's the Point?

The processes that produce wind are both simple and complex. The large global patterns that are easy to notice stay the same from month to month and year to year. The smaller, local patterns are more complicated. This makes weather prediction, knowing how the patterns are going to work, difficult.

Winds come from the Sun's energy heating Earth. On a local scale, the different rates of heating for land and water can make a big difference in

wind. Land and sea breezes are produced because land and water are heated by the Sun at different rates and cool at different rates. Global winds are produced as warm, moist air near the Equator rises up, into the atmosphere. This rising air generates an area of low pressure near the Equator, all around the globe.

As this warm, moist air rises and spreads out, away from the Equator, it starts to cool and becomes denser. Eventually, the denser air starts to sink back down toward Earth's surface. This produces large zones of high-pressure areas. Global winds are set in motion as air moves from these high-pressure zones to low-pressure zones. This cycle happens over and over again. When these large systems run into each other, winds result. When air moves from a higher-pressure area to a lower-pressure area, wind is produced.

△ Guide

Ask the class what information they would like to add to Columns 3 (*What are we learning?*) and 4 (*What is our evidence?*) of their *Project Board*.

Edit the claim and supporting evidence and science knowledge until the class agrees upon the wording, then record it on the class *Project Board* and have students record it on their own *Project Board* pages.

◇ Evaluate

The class should include that winds are caused by differences in air pressure due to the warming of air by Earth's land and water. The winds' strength increases with increasing air pressure. Students should describe how local winds are caused by the differences in how land and water absorb the Sun's energy and then transfer heat energy to the atmosphere. Students should describe how global winds are caused by the incoming solar radiation due to shape and tilt of the planet. It should also be noted that wind patterns are cyclical.

NOTES

More to Learn: Earth's Major Wind Patterns

5 min.

Students have a discussion on global wind patterns.

More to Learn

Earth's Major Wind Patterns

As warm, moist air from the Equator rises into the atmosphere, it spreads out to the north and south. As it moves away from the Equator, it begins to cool. By the time it reaches about 30° north and south latitudes, it has become cool enough and dense enough to begin sinking. This produces an area of high pressure. Some of the air moves back toward the Equator to be reheated and start the circulation again.

This steady movement of air forms a belt of winds known as the *trade winds*. Early European sailors relied on the trade winds as they traveled trade routes to and from the New World.

Some of the blowing air from the Equator does not return. Some of the air continues on from 30° north and south latitude toward the poles. In the Northern Hemisphere, this band of air curves to the right due to Earth's rotation. In the Southern Hemisphere, it curves to the left. This makes it appear that, in both hemispheres, these winds blow from west to east. Therefore, they are called the *prevailing westerlies*.

You know what happens to the incoming solar energy at the poles. The Sun's rays strike at such an angle that the energy is spread over a very large area. This results in extremely cold air. Cold air is denser and can hold less moisture. The cold, dry air sets up an area of very high pressure. Air moves from these high-pressure areas toward lower-pressure areas around 60° north and south latitudes. These bands of air curve to the west due to the Earth's rotation. This makes them appear to blow from east to west. They are called *polar easterlies*.

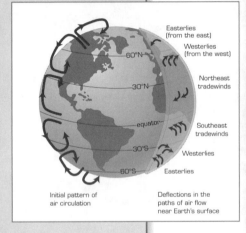

Initial pattern of air circulation

Deflections in the paths of air flow near Earth's surface

△ Guide

Discuss global wind patterns using the information in the student text. Emphasize how trade winds are formed by rising air masses from the Equator that sink at around 30°N and 30°S; not all the air rising from the Equator sinks at this latitude. Point out some of this air mass continues northward and southward to the Poles. Discuss how the prevailing westerlies move from west to east in the Northern and Southern Hemispheres from 30° to 60° due to Earth's rotation. Discuss how the polar easterlies arise from cold, high-pressure air from the poles moving downward toward the 60° latitudes and appear to be moving from east to west due to Earth's rotation.

Consider asking students if they want to add any of this information to their *Project Board*.

Assessment Options

Targeted Concepts, Skills, and Nature of Science	How do I know if students got it?
Wind results from the Sun's energy heating Earth. Solar energy heats air molecules and creates areas of high and low pressure. Wind is created as air molecules move from high to low pressure areas. This is affected greatly by landforms and water on a local scale.	**ASK:** What causes wind and how is the Sun's energy involved? **LISTEN:** Students should describe how the Sun's energy warms the Earth's surface, and how the Earth's surface then warms the atmosphere. The warming of the atmosphere causes high and low pressure air masses in the atmosphere, which cause winds both locally and globally.

Teacher Reflection Questions

- Which idea about wind was most difficult for students to understand and how did you guide their understanding? What would you do next time?

- How did the questions in the student text help students to connect the information about winds with the information presented earlier in this *Learning Set?*

- How could you or how did you get students to actively participate in class discussions?

NOTES

SECTION 6.6 INTRODUCTION

6.6 Explain

What Causes Weather Changes?

◀ $1\frac{1}{2}$ *class periods*

A class period is considered to be one 40 to 50 minute class.

Overview

Students explain changes in weather. Students read about and discuss warm and cold fronts and what occurs when these fronts collide. Students revisit the weather maps from *Section 6.1* and explain changes in weather. Groups present their explanations to the class and the class discusses the trends and the information that help students identify or predict weather changes. The class updates the *Project Board* and reads about storms and severe weather.

Targeted Concepts, Skills, and Nature of Science	Performance Expectations
Scientists often work together and share their findings. Sharing findings makes new information available and helps scientists to refine their ideas and build on others' ideas. When another person's or group's idea is used, credit needs to be given.	Students should work in groups to explain weather changes and to find patterns in weather changes and share their results with the class. The class should work together to find patterns in weather changes and update their *Project Boards*.
Scientists must keep clear, accurate, and descriptive records of what they do so they can share their work with others and consider what they did, why they did it, and what they want to do next.	Students should refer back to their explanations from *Section 6.1* of weather changes and revise these based on the information presented in this *Learning Set*.
Graphs, maps, and tables are an effective way to analyze and communicate results of scientific investigation.	Students should use weather maps to analyze and explain weather changes.
Explanations are claims supported by evidence, accepted ideas and facts.	Students should construct explanations of weather changes over a three-day period based on information provided in weather maps.
Temperatures around the Earth's surface vary widely, but can be predicted somewhat by location and season.	Students should describe how surface temperatures vary based on factors such as pressure changes.

PLANETARY FORECASTER

Targeted Concepts, Skills, and Nature of Science	Performance Expectations
Changes in weather are caused when air fronts of different temperatures interact with each other. The different pressures of the fronts cause air masses to move and create precipitation and other forms of weather. Special conditions are needed to develop storms, tornados, and hurricanes.	Students should describe how air fronts cause changes in weather and how storms can form.

Materials	
1 per student	*Create Your Explanation* page *Project Board* page
1 per class	Class *Project Board*

Homework Options

Reflection

- **Science Content:** Describe what happens at a cold front and a warm front. *(Students should describe how warm fronts occur where warm air masses meet cooler air masses. The warm air rises up over the cooler air mass because it is less dense and clouds form as water vapor condenses. Precipitation may occur. The cooler air moves under the warm air pushing it up and the temperature falls. When a cold front moves faster than a warm front, an occluded front may occur where the cold front overtakes the warm front. A stationary front occurs when a cold and warm front meet and no movement occurs. This can bring cloudiness and rain for several days.)*

Preparation for **Back to the Big Challenge**

- **Science Content:** What do you think the weather is like at the location you suggested for a human colony on *Planet X?* For the location on *Planet X* that should not be colonized, what do you think the weather is like? *(The purpose of this question is for students to think about how they will apply what they now know to predict weather patterns on* Planet X.*)*

SECTION 6.6 IMPLEMENTATION

◀ $1\frac{1}{2}$ *class periods**

6.6 Explain

What Causes Weather Changes?

At the beginning of the *Learning Set*, you investigated the weather at one location on a weather map. You may have noticed symbols, like those in the pictures below, that were part of the weather map. These symbols show **fronts**. The blue symbols are cold fronts and the red symbols are warm fronts. In this section, you will learn more about different fronts, why they form, and the kinds of weather they produce. You will use that information to explain weather changes on your maps.

> **front:** the area where two air masses collide.

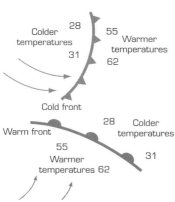

Warm and cold fronts form at the borders of very large areas of air that have similar temperature, pressure, and humidity throughout. These areas of air are called air masses. When two different air masses meet, they do not blend together. Instead, they hit each other hard. The warm air and cold air slam into each other. The area where two air masses collide is called a front. Look at the two fronts at location C on the maps you worked on earlier. What type of weather occurred where the two fronts collided?

Warm fronts occur when a particularly warm air mass meets a cooler air mass. The warm air rises up and over the cold mass because it is less dense. The warm air rises into the upper atmosphere where temperatures are cooler. It cools, and the water condenses. This forms clouds and precipitation. Usually, this weather lasts from 12 to 24 hours. It is followed by a period of hot and humid weather. Look back at the location where there is a warm front on the map. Look at the temperatures before the warm front and after the warm front moved through. Notice how much the temperature rose.

PF 206

Project-Based Inquiry Science

6.6 Explain

What Causes Weather Changes?

5 min.

Students participate in a class discussion of air fronts.

○ Engage

Let students know air fronts are represented on weather maps using red lines with semi-circles to show the direction the cold air mass is moving and blue lines with triangles to show the direction warm air masses are moving. Ask students what they think happens when a cold/warm air meets warm/cold air. Record students' ideas.

*A class period is considered to be one 40 to 50 minute class.

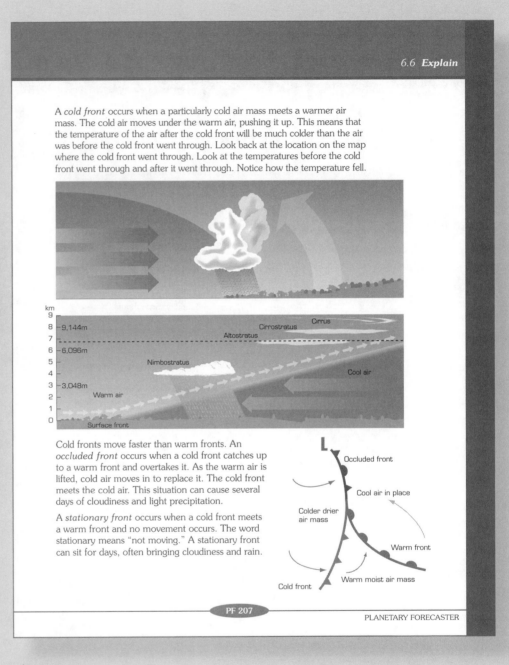

6.6 Explain

A *cold front* occurs when a particularly cold air mass meets a warmer air mass. The cold air moves under the warm air, pushing it up. This means that the temperature of the air after the cold front will be much colder than the air was before the cold front went through. Look back at the location on the map where the cold front went through. Look at the temperatures before the cold front went through and after it went through. Notice how the temperature fell.

Cold fronts move faster than warm fronts. An *occluded front* occurs when a cold front catches up to a warm front and overtakes it. As the warm air is lifted, cold air moves in to replace it. The cold front meets the cold air. This situation can cause several days of cloudiness and light precipitation.

A *stationary front* occurs when a cold front meets a warm front and no movement occurs. The word stationary means "not moving." A stationary front can sit for days, often bringing cloudiness and rain.

PF 207

PLANETARY FORECASTER

META NOTES

Students often misinterpret the nature of warm and cold fronts because of the type of graphic used. Although the fronts are shown as lines, the lines actually only represent the leading edge of the front. The air in the front can take several different shapes and depths behind the front line.

△ Guide

Discuss cold fronts, warm fronts, occluded fronts, and stationary fronts using the information in the student text.

Consider having students read and present the information.

Emphasize to students that all fronts are boundaries between masses of air with different densities, usually caused by temperature differences. Describe how the red and blue lines drawn to indicate a front show the leading edge of the front and a front can have different shapes and depths.

Emphasize that cold air masses are denser than warm air masses that are expanding, so the warmer air moves up over the colder air and the colder air moves in under the warmer air pushing it up. When a warm front moves through, usually the temperatures in the location increase for 12 to 24 hours. When a cold front moves through, the temperatures decrease.

Point out how warm and cold fronts collide in different ways. If a cold front moves faster than a warm front heading in the same direction, the area where they collide is called an occluded front. The warm air still rises and the cold air helps to push it up, and several days of cloudiness and precipitation can occur. A stationary front occurs when a cold front collides head on with a warm front and the two fronts do not move. This can bring cloudiness and rain for days.

Remind students that winds are caused by differences in air pressure. The greater the differences in air pressure, the stronger the winds.

NOTES

Explain

15 min.

Groups analyze and explain the weather maps from Section 6.1 with new science knowledge.

Explain

Your group was given the challenge of investigating several weather maps at the beginning of the *Learning Set*. You have a lot of information now about the reasons for the weather at your location. Return to the maps, the weather data for your assigned location, and your initial descriptions of what you thought would happen. Discuss the following questions with your group and prepare to present the answers to the rest of the class. Much of what you will be doing in answering these questions is creating explanations. Use *Create Your Explanation* pages to help you keep track of claims you are making and the evidence and science knowledge that support them.

Location A

1. Use the map key. Describe in detail each of the symbols that are shown at location A.

2. How do the high and low temperatures change over the course of the three days? Explain why the temperatures changed.

3. Now you know that the blue line represents a cold front. What happens to the air pressure and temperature readings as the cold front moves through? Why does that happen? Explain.

4. In what direction does the blue line move near location A? Compare this direction to other cold fronts on the map.

Location B

1. Use the map key. What are the symbols at location B? Label each map symbol at this location on your copy of the map.

2. Why do you think the air pressure changed? Explain.

3. Why do you think the high and low temperatures changed over the course of the three days? Explain.

4. Using the maps, determine the direction the weather moves near location B.

Location C

1. Use the map key. There is both a cold front and a warm front near location C. What happens when the two fronts collide? What type of weather should that bring?

△ Guide

Let students know there are four different locations and each group will analyze weather conditions for one location. Groups will share their results with the class and the class will look for trends in weather patterns across the locations.

Let students know they should only answer the questions and construct explanations for the location they were previously assigned.

△ Guide and Assess

Monitor students' progress and guide them if needed. Note areas to bring up during the class discussion. Use the information below to guide and assess students.

Location A

1. Students should describe a cold front moving through between Day 1 and Day 2 indicated by the blue line with triangles showing it moving from the northwest to the southeast and low pressure indicated on the map.

2. Students' responses should state the high temperature drops seven degrees from Day 1 to Day 2, and increases two degrees from Day 2 to Day 3. The drop in temperature between Day 2 and Day 1 occurs as the cold front with low pressure air is moving through. After the cold front passes through, the temperatures increase. As the cold front passed through and low pressure air was in the region, the humidity dropped from 62% to 56% to 50%.

3. Students' responses should include that as the cold front passed between Day 1 and Day 2, the temperatures dropped and the air pressure increased slightly. After it passed, the temperatures started to increase and air pressure increased slightly.

4. Students should describe the movement of the fronts. The cold front moved from the northwest to the southeast on the first day and continued in that direction the second and third day. Another cold front on Day 1 appeared to be going in a similar direction, but was much farther south of location A. Two warm fronts were indicated on the maps. One on the East Coast was moving in a northeasterly direction. Another on the west coast was moving to the east and north.

Location B

1. Students should note the high pressure on Day 1. For Day 2, students should indicate a warm front moving in from the southwest and high pressure to the southeast of Location B. For Day 3, students should describe how the warm front is closer and high pressure to the northwest of Location B.

2. Students should indicate that the air pressure decreased by 0.24 on Day 2 and by 0.09 from Day 2 to Day 3. The pressure dropped as the high pressure air mass passed. The drop in air

pressure indicates other weather on the way and a warm front moving in from the south and a cold front moving in from the west.

3. Students should describe the temperature changes and indicate a relationship between these and the high pressure air moving through. The high temperature increases one degree from Day 1 to Day 2, and increases two degrees from Day 2 to Day 3. The low temperature decreased four degrees from Day 1 to Day 2 and increased one degree from Day 2 to Day 3. The low temperature increased two degrees from Day 1 to Day 2 and decreased eight degrees from Day 2 to Day 3. These changes were most likely caused by the warm air front moving in from the south and likely causing the increase in humidity as well.

4. Students should indicate there are two trends in weather movement. The high pressure air and cold fronts generally move from the northwest toward the southeast (predominantly east). From the south, warm weather moves northward over Location B.

Location C

1. Students should describe the rain shown in green, the warm front headed to the northeast, and the cold front moving to the southeast, which nearly intersect under the rain area to the left of Location C. Because the fronts are next to each other on the map for Day 1, the cold front could occlude the warm front. Storms or precipitation often occur when a cold front overtakes, or occludes, a warm front.

2. Students should describe the high temperature increase of nine degrees between Day 1 and Day 2, and two degrees between Day 2 and Day 3. The temperature increases as the warm front passes by.

3. Students should support their claim with reasons. Students may suggest the wind speed and direction changed because weather was driven by the incoming cold front from the northwest, the low-pressure air mass, and the outgoing warm front from the southwest. The wind speed picked up after the warm front passed and a low pressure system was set up as the cold front moved in. The cold front has a high-pressure air mass that pushes the warmer air out of the way, increasing the wind speed. Winds are caused by differences in air pressure. The greater the difference in air pressure there is, the stronger the winds will be.

4. Students should describe the direction of the weather indicated by the three maps. On Day 1, the warm front moved toward the northeast and the cold front moved to the East. The weather patterns seem to be from the west to the east. The winds are from the southwest, indicating the direction of movement from high to low pressure.

NOTES

2. Explain what causes the temperature to change at location C.

3. Why do you think the wind speed and direction changed over the course of three days? Explain.

4. Using the maps, determine the direction the weather moves near location C.

Location D

1. Briefly describe the weather on each day. Try to include as many details as possible.

2. You looked at the weather for each day. What changes do you see in temperature, wind direction, or air pressure that might indicate changes in the weather? Explain your answer using data and science knowledge.

3. On which day does the weather begin to change? Where is the symbol on that day?

4. Using the maps, determine the direction the weather moves near location D.

Communicate

Share your answers and explanations with the class. Discuss the weather maps and your explanations of what is happening in each location. Answer these questions together.

1. How difficult is it to identify changes in the weather based on the symbols on the map?

2. What other information might you like to have that would make it easier to identify or predict weather changes?

3. Imagine that a warm front is heading toward your city. What do you think the weather will be like as the front moves through? What will the temperature, precipitation, and wind speed and direction be like? Do you think it will rain?

4. Imagine that a cold front is coming. What do you think will happen to the weather?

PF 209

PLANETARY FORECASTER

Location D

1. Day 1 was windy and there were two high-pressure air masses, one to the northeast and one to the northwest. The temperature ranged from 77 degrees to 60 degrees. The wind came from the northwest. The air pressure was 30.10 and steady. The humidity was 72%. On Day 2, there was high-pressure to the southeast. The high temperature was 82 degrees and the low temperature was 57 degrees. The winds were from the northwest and the air

pressure was 29.65 and rising. The humidity increased to 73%. On Day 3, the high pressure remained to the southeast of Location D, the temperature range was between 77 and 55 degrees, the wind was from the west, the air pressure was 30.12 and steady, and the humidity was 70%.

2. Students should describe the high-pressure areas to the northwest and northeast of Location D on Day 1, and to the southeast on Days 2 and 3. Students should state it was windy on Day 1. The winds were caused by differences in air pressures, high pressure air was to the North of Location D, and the winds came from the northwest and it was only windy on the first day. High pressure air pushing toward low pressure air caused winds. For Day 2 and Day 3, the pressure systems did not change.

3. Students should indicate that there is not much change in weather. It was windy on Day 1 and there were two high-pressure areas nearby (to the northeast and northwest), but it was not windy after the high pressure system moved to the southeast and stayed there over Days 2 and 3.

4. There is not a lot of information to determine the direction of the weather. The wind is from the northwest to the southeast, which follows the cold front and the high-pressure area moving south, and the moving the wind is to the west.

NOTES

....

....

....

....

....

....

....

Communicate

20 min.

Groups present their results to the class, and then have a class discussion to find trends in weather patterns.

4. Using the maps, determine the direction the weather moves near location D.

Communicate

Share your answers and explanations with the class. Discuss the weather maps and your explanations of what is happening in each location. Answer these questions together.

1. How difficult is it to identify changes in the weather based on the symbols on the map?

2. What other information might you like to have that would make it easier to identify or predict weather changes?

3. Imagine that a warm front is heading toward your city. What do you think the weather will be like as the front moves through? What will the temperature, precipitation, and wind speed and direction be like? Do you think it will rain?

4. Imagine that a cold front is coming. What do you think will happen to the weather?

PF 209

PLANETARY FORECASTER

△ Guide

Let students know that each group will be presenting their results and they will need to answer all the questions for their location during their presentations. Point out that the class will answer the four questions listed in this segment after all groups have presented. Emphasize to the class that the audience should ask questions as needed to help clarify responses, gain understanding, and explore ideas.

△ Guide and Assess

Have each group present, making sure the groups that analyzed the same location present back-to-back. After each presentation, ask students what trends they found in the weather data over three days. Encourage the class to ask questions. Use the information for each location in the previous segment to help guide and assess the discussion.

After all groups of a given location have presented, have a discussion on any differences the groups found. After all groups have presented, have a class discussion on the trends in weather patterns and have the class answer the four questions listed in this segment.

Use the information below to help guide the discussion.

1. Students should provide examples and reasons why they think it is easy or difficult to identify changes in weather based on the symbols on the maps.

2. Students should provide reasons and examples if possible of how the extra information would help them make it easier to predict weather changes.

3. Students should provide reasons to support their predictions. Students should note that when a warm front moves in the temperatures increase, the humidity increases, precipitation is likely, and the winds should pick up. The humidity increases because the warmer temperatures cause more water to be evaporated into the air. As the warm air rises above the cooler air, the water vapor condenses and produces clouds and often precipitation. The winds usually form from the direction of the higher pressure air to lower pressure air. The cold air has higher pressure, so the winds should come from the colder air toward the warmer air, but the warmer air moving forward will affect the wind patterns and cause a stationary front. Students should indicate that as the warm air moves in, it often results in a stationary front because it is less dense than the cold air. Stationary fronts can sit for several days, often bringing cloudiness and precipitation before the warm front overtakes the cold front and pushes it out. When this occurs warmer, drier air then moves in.

4. Students should provide reasons to support their predictions. As a cold front is moving in, it pushes the warmer air up and out of the way causing clouds to form, precipitation, and storms. After the front passes, air should be cooler and drier. The winds usually form from the direction of the higher pressure air to lower pressure air. The winds should generally be from the cold front toward the warm front. If the warmer air does not contain a lot of water vapor, then the cold front can bring in dryer (less humid) air.

> **META NOTES**
>
> As students try to find trends in weather patterns across locations they should have formed questions. These questions should be included in the class *Project Board*.

Update the Project Board

10 min.

The class updates the Project Board.

Update the *Project Board*

It is time to update the *Project Board* one last time before returning to address the *Big Challenge*. Record on the *Project Board* what you now know about warm and cold fronts and severe weather. Look at the *What do we think we know?* column, and see if there are some things you listed there that you can now restate more accurately in the *What are we learning?* column. Look at the *What do we need to investigate?* column. You may know answers to some of those questions that you can put into the *What are we learning?* column. Don't forget to add evidence to the *Project Board* each time you record something in the *What are we learning?* column. Describe, too, how this information can be important to solving the Big Challenge.

Weather maps like this one help meteorologists describe the weather and help people plan their activities.

What's the Point?

Warm and cold fronts have important effects on the weather in an area. You have looked at the maps several times now and have gained a lot from the information that can be found on one set of maps. You will see these types of maps often in weather reports and will be able to understand the predictions you hear now that you understand the symbols on them.

PF 210

Project-Based Inquiry Science

△ Guide

Ask students what claims they can make about weather patterns that are supported by evidence and science knowledge. Record this information and let students know that this information should be included in Column 3 (*What are we learning?*) and Column 4 (*What is our evidence?*) on their *Project Board*. Edit ideas with the class and then record them on the class *Project Board*. Remind students to update their *Project Board* pages.

◇ Evaluate

Make sure students include the following information.

Column 3 (claim): Winds are caused by differences in pressure. Air flows from high pressure to low pressure.

Column 4 (evidence): High pressure air expands upward, pushing its surroundings out of the way. It pushes upward because the air above is less dense and therefore easier to push out of the way then the air below it. Warmer air tends to rise, and cooler air will replace the warmer air. Students may add information about sea and/or land breezes, high and low pressure areas, cold and warm fronts.

Column 3 (claim): Precipitation occurs after water vapor condenses in rising air masses and gets too heavy for the air to support. Students may have made this claim already within the claims concerning the water cycle.

Column 4 (evidence): When the Sun warms the land and water, some water evaporates into the air. When land and water warm the air above, some water goes into the gas state and water vapor is suspended in the air. As the warmed air rises, the water vapor condenses into a liquid or solid state. As the mass of the condensed water increases, it eventually gets too heavy for the air to support and precipitation occurs.

Column 3 (claim): Most storms are caused at fronts (where warm/cold air meets cold/warm air). High pressure systems tend to bring drier, sunny weather and low pressure systems tend to bring clouds and precipitation.

Column 4 (evidence): When the Sun warms the land and water, some water evaporates into the air. When land and water warm the air above it, some water goes into the gas state and water vapor is suspended in the air. As the warmed air rises, the water vapor condenses into a liquid or solid state. As the mass of the condensed water increases, it eventually gets too heavy for the air to support and precipitation occurs.

△ Guide

Remind students they will need to use this information to predict the weather for the locations on *Planet X* that they suggested will be good and will be bad places to build a colony.

More to Learn: Storms

25 min.

The class discusses the impact of storms.

More to Learn

Storms

You probably noticed that location C on the maps is having some severe weather. The winds are whipping, the rain is falling, and the temperatures are dropping. Sometimes, very severe weather can hit different parts of the country. Location C includes the area around New Orleans, Louisiana. In August 2005, one type of severe weather, a hurricane, hit this area. It was one of the costliest and deadliest hurricanes in United States history. The storm's winds reached 190 km (120 mi) from the storm's center. Wind speeds were as high as 210 km/h (130 mph). By the time it was over, an estimated 1836 people lost their lives. Damages were estimated at $81.2 billion. This storm had tremendous social, economic, and political effects on the country.

For a hurricane to develop, the ocean waters must be at least 81°F. Warm, moist air begins to rise very quickly, forming a low-pressure area. As you discovered when reading about winds, air moves from areas of high pressure to areas of low pressure. The low-pressure area formed by the rising warm air produces conditions for cooler air to rush in. Typically, a ring of thunderstorms is formed. These were the exact conditions for a hurricane that were present in August 2005.

Rainstorms, Thunderstorms, and Tornados
You know that rainstorms and high winds can occur when two different fronts collide. When a warm front meets a cold front, rainstorms or snowstorms can result. In the summer, the rain can fall for several

PF 211

PLANETARY FORECASTER

⬡ Get Going

Consider having students read independently, in groups, or aloud to the class before discussing the information in the student text.

△ Guide

Emphasize the importance of understanding and predicting severe weather and its impact on social, environmental, and economical situations. Discuss Hurricane Katrina which is presented in the student text and the conditions

days. Sometimes, flash-flood alerts are issued by the weather service. In the winter, heavy snowfalls can result in dangerous travel conditions and the closing of many schools and businesses.

Thunderstorms are heavy rainstorms with lightning and thunder. They usually develop in warm air that is just in front of a cold front. The moving cold air pushes the warm air up very rapidly. Cumulonimbus clouds are formed. As more warm air rises, it makes the developing cumulonimbus cloud grow larger and taller. The rising air is called an updraft. Eventually, the cloud can no longer contain all the water droplets and ice crystals. Heavy rain or hail falls to Earth's surface. As the rains fall, it causes air to rush downward in downdrafts. As air is rushing up and down, the water droplets and ice crystals bounce off each other. This creates static electrical charges. Clouds, like batteries, have a positive end at the top and a negative end toward the bottom.

PF 212

Project-Based Inquiry Science

Rainstorms, Thunderstorms, and Tornadoes
5 min.

Students discuss types of severe weather

for hurricanes. Describe the importance of being able to predict storms and their severity in advance so people can prepare for them and evacuate if needed.

○ Engage
Ask students what types of severe weather they know of and if they have any firsthand experiences of these. Record the types of severe weather and allow students to share their stories with the class.

More to Learn

When enough charge builds up, it is released as lightning. The sound associated with lightning is thunder.

Lightning bolts can travel from cloud to cloud. They can also travel from a cloud to the ground. Lightning can even travel from the ground to a cloud! Although a storm may be local, lightning can travel great distances before striking the ground. These are just a few reasons lightning can be very dangerous.

Sometimes, very violent thunderstorms result in tornadoes. Tornadoes are a type of cyclone. A cyclone is an area of low pressure that contains warm, rising air. As cooler air moves in to take the place of the rising warm air, the air begins to spin. This may occur even before the thunderstorm develops as air gets caught between two layers of air coming in from opposite directions. This starts the air spinning in a horizontal direction. The updrafts associated with thunderstorms tilt this spinning column of air from horizontal to vertical. Under the right conditions, a very strong tornado can develop within minutes. As the air goes into a spin, it lowers the pressure even more. This causes more air to move in, feeding the force of the tornado. The characteristic funnel-shaped cloud develops and eventually touches ground.

Tornadoes usually last only a few minutes, but these can be the most destructive minutes in anyone's life. Winds inside the funnel can reach speeds of 300 miles per hour and are capable of picking up incredibly large objects, including automobiles and even houses. The average speed of the tornado as it moves across the ground is around 30 miles per hour, but it can move at speeds of up to 70 miles per hour. As a tornado moves, it can change direction very quickly and very unpredictably.

Tornadoes occur in many parts of the world. They are very common in three parts of the United States—the Great Plains, the Mississippi Valley, and Florida. Because they rely on big differences in air masses, they occur most frequently in the spring and summer.

tornado: a type of cyclone; a vertical spinning column of air.

cyclone: an area of low pressure that contains warm rising air. As cooler air moves in, the air begins to spin.

Stop and Think

1. Describe the sequence of events as a thunderstorm develops.

2. Describe one experience you have had with severe weather. Were there high winds, lots of precipitation, or thunder and lightning?

△ Guide

Let the class know severe weather occurs when warm and cold fronts meet, causing precipitation, possible high winds, floods, electrical storms, and tornadoes.

Discuss how flooding often occurs in dry areas, such as the southwest, because the dry ground does not absorb water well and the runoff that occurs usually gains tremendous volumes and speeds.

Discuss how thunderstorms occur when a fast moving cold front overtakes a slow moving warm front pushing the warm air rapidly upward, forming cumulonimbus clouds, precipitation, updrafts and down drafts, which charge the clouds and cause electrical storms.

Discuss tornadoes and where they commonly occur due to big differences in pressures of air masses.

◯ Get Going

Have students answer the questions independently. Let the class know that a discussion will follow and how much time they have.

△ Guide and Assess

Have a class discussion on students' responses.

1. Students' responses should describe how thunderstorms typically occur as a cold front moves in and pushes warm air upward. As the warm air moves upward, it forms a cumulonimbus cloud that continues to grow as the water condenses and pushes the warm air up. When the cloud has grown too large to hold the water droplets, a heavy rain begins to fall and the storm develops.

2. Students should describe an experience they had with severe weather. Encourage them to include descriptions of the wind, humidity, temperature changes, how the sky appeared, the type of precipitation (if any), the time of year, and where the weather occurred.

Stop and Think

10 min.

Students participate in a class discussion of their responses.

NOTES

....

....

....

....

....

....

Assessment Options

Targeted Concepts, Skills, and Nature of Science	How do I know if students got it?
Changes in weather are caused when air fronts of different temperatures interact with each other. The different pressures of the fronts cause air masses to move and create precipitation and other forms of weather. Special conditions are needed to develop storms, tornados, and hurricanes.	**ASK:** What causes changes in weather and what conditions are needed for storms to develop? **LISTEN:** Students should describe how air fronts cause changes in weather. Students should describe how storms form where cold and warm fronts meet and if there is a big difference in the air pressure a severe storm can develop.

Teacher Reflection Questions

- What difficulties did students have explaining what caused changes in weather based on the information in the weather maps?

- How did the questions in the *Communicate* segment help the class identify trends in weather patterns?

- Describe any management issues that arose during the class and how you dealt with them. What would you do differently?

NOTES

....

....

....

....

Back to the Big Challenge

Which Regions of a Newly Discovered Planet Have Surface Temperatures Appropriate for a Human Colony?

◀ $1\frac{1}{2}$ *class period*

A class period is considered to be one 40 to 50 minute class.

Overview

Students apply what they know about weather to predict weather patterns for *Planet X*. Students select two locations near the equator on *Planet X* and two locations far from the equator and groups predict the weather patterns, including seasonal patterns and severe weather that might occur. Students share their predictions with the class and discuss the science concepts that support their weather predictions. From the class's predictions and discussion, students gain a good basis for making predictions of weather patterns for the recommended locations for and against building a colony on *Planet X*.

Targeted Concepts, Skills, and Nature of Science	Performance Expectations
Scientists often work together and share their findings. Sharing findings makes new information available and helps scientists to refine their ideas and build on others' ideas. When another person's or group's idea is used, credit needs to be given.	Students should work with their group members to make predictions of the weather patterns of six locations on *Planet X*, including their two recommended locations. Students should share their predictions with the class.
Scientists must keep clear, accurate, and descriptive records of what they do so they can share their work with others and consider what they did, why they did it, and what they want to do next.	Students should refer to their records from this *Learning Set*, as well as records from previous *Learning Sets*, and create new records explaining their weather predictions for various locations on *Planet X*.

Targeted Concepts, Skills, and Nature of Science	Performance Expectations
Explanations are claims supported by evidence, accepted ideas and facts. • Temperatures around the Earth's surface vary widely, but can be predicted somewhat by location and season. • Energy from the Sun drives Earth's water cycle. Water moves between different physical states in a continuous cycle of evaporation, condensation, and precipitation. • Water changes state (solid, liquid, gas) by adding or removing heat energy. • Wind results from the Sun's energy heating Earth. Solar energy heats air molecules and creates areas of high and low pressure. Wind is created as air molecules move from high to low pressure areas. This is affected greatly by landforms and water on a local scale. • Changes in weather are caused when air fronts of different temperatures interact with each other. The different pressures of the fronts cause air masses to move and create precipitation and other forms of weather. Special conditions are needed to develop storms, tornados, and hurricanes.	Students should create explanations for the claims they make about weather conditions on *Planet X*. Their explanations should include the application of the ideas listed.

NOTES

....

....

....

....

....

636

Materials	
1 per group	Computer with *My World* software Presentation materials
1 per student	Blank map of *Planet X* *Solution Briefing Notes* page
2 per student	*Create Your Explanation* page
1 per class	Class *Project Board*

Homework Options

Reflection

- **Science Content:** : What weather information is important in predicting weather patterns? *(Students should explain how information such as temperature, air pressure, wind direction, wind speed, and precipitation amounts are used to predict weather.)*

Preparation for Address the Big Challenge II

- **Science Process:** What will you need to complete the challenge? *(The purpose of this is to help students organize the information they will need to complete their recommendations to the CSA.)*

NOTES

....

....

....

....

....

NOTES

◀ $1\frac{1}{2}$ *class period**

Learning Set 6

Back to the Big Challenge

Which regions of a newly discovered planet have surface temperatures appropriate for a human colony?

The letter from the Cooperative Space Agency asked you to describe the weather that might be expected on *Planet X* at the locations you recommended for colonization. If they know the weather patterns, colonists will be able to prepare for bad weather. You will use what you have discovered about weather patterns to report to the CSA the weather that colonists might find at the *Planet X* location you are recommending.

Get Started

In your groups, look again at your assigned locations on the weather maps. Locations A, B, C, and D will not exist on *Planet X*. However, locations like them will. Rather than thinking about specific locations, such as A, B, C, and D as exact spots in the United States, think about the characteristics of each place that affect the weather. With your group, write a description of the weather patterns at each of these locations.

Location A: Far away. . .

Location B: Far away. . .

Location C: Near the Equator. . .

Location D: Near the Equator. . .

Consider the following questions in your weather description:

- What severe weather conditions are likely at this location?
- Would you want to live there?
- Would you live there all year long or only during some seasons?
- Are there some seasons when you would need to be especially careful because of severe weather?

PF 214

Project-Based Inquiry Science

Learning Set 6

Back to the Big Challenge

< 5 min.

Students are introduced to the section.

△ Guide

Display the class *Project Board* and review their entries. Discuss what it has meant for the *Big Challenge*. Make sure to focus on their entries about weather.

Let students know they will be predicting weather for various locations on *Planet X*, locations near and far from the equator in each hemisphere, as well as the locations they recommended previously to the *CSA*. Remind them the locations they recommended previously consisted of one location to avoid and one location they thought would be a good place to build a colony.

*A class period is considered to be one 40 to 50 minute class.

Get Started

20 min.

Students create predictions and explanations for weather patterns on Planet X.

Which regions of a newly discovered planet have surface temperatures appropriate for a human colony?

The letter from the Cooperative Space Agency asked you to describe the weather that might be expected on *Planet X* at the locations you recommended for colonization. If they know the weather patterns, colonists will be able to prepare for bad weather. You will use what you have discovered about weather patterns to report to the CSA the weather that colonists might find at the *Planet X* location you are recommending.

Get Started

In your groups, look again at your assigned locations on the weather maps. Locations A, B, C, and D will not exist on *Planet X*. However, locations like them will. Rather than thinking about specific locations, such as A, B, C, and D as exact spots in the United States, think about the characteristics of each place that affect the weather. With your group, write a description of the weather patterns at each of these locations.

   Location A: Far away. . .

   Location B: Far away. . .

   Location C: Near the Equator. . .

   Location D: Near the Equator. . .

Consider the following questions in your weather description:

* What severe weather conditions are likely at this location?

* Would you want to live there?

* Would you live there all year long or only during some seasons?

* Are there some seasons when you would need to be especially careful because of severe weather?

PF 214

Project-Based Inquiry Science

△ Guide

Let students know they will be predicting weather patterns for *Planet X* by having each group make predictions for four different locations on *Planet X* and sharing their results. Point out that each group will select two locations near the equator and two locations far from the equator of *Planet X* (one of each in the northern hemisphere and one of each in the southern hemisphere). Let students know they should label the locations they select on a blank map of *Planet X*, as well as the two locations they recommended previously. Each group should address all the bulleted questions in the student text and make a claim of the weather for each location supported by evidence and science knowledge. Let students know that each group will be creating a poster of their results and presenting it to the class.

⬡ Get Going

Distribute *Create Your Explanation* pages and blank maps of *Planet X,* and let groups know how much time they have.

Guide and Assess

Monitor students' progress. Check that they have selected two locations in the northern and southern hemispheres. Groups should be addressing all the bulleted questions and completing a *Create Your Explanation* page to support the claims they make about the weather in each location.

NOTES

Communicate Your Solution: *Solution Briefing*

20 min.

The class discusses groups' presentations of predictions and explanations.

- What else do you. . . .
- Are there ways to . . . .

Use the *Create Your Explanation* pages to refine this description as your claim. Record the evidence and science knowledge that support them. With your group, make a poster that describes the weather patterns at your assigned location. Be sure to include supporting science concepts from this *Learning Set*. You will be using these descriptions and supporting evidence to compare these locations to *Planet X* locations.

Communicate Your Solution

Solution Briefing

After everyone has finished making their posters, display them with the poster your group made at the beginning of this *Learning Set*. Check to see if you have described everything you saw on your map at the beginning. Each group will present their ideas to the class in a *Solution Briefing*. Your *Solution Briefing* should focus on these things:

- Present a description of the weather patterns likely at this location.
- Tell others how the science concepts and knowledge you used support your weather-pattern description.

As you listen, it will be important to carefully look at each poster. You will be using this information to predict weather patterns at the *Planet X* colony locations you are recommending. You should ask questions about the science concepts and knowledge used to support the weather-pattern description.

Recommend

In *Learning Set 5*, you selected *Planet X* locations that might be appropriate for a human colony. Use the weather-pattern descriptions just presented to describe the predicted weather patterns at the *Planet X* locations you are recommending.

Explain

Use a *Create Your Explanation* page to refine your description as a claim and record the evidence and science knowledge that support them. Write a brief letter to the colonists describing the weather they might experience and your recommended preparations or provisions.

△ Guide

Let students know they will be displaying their posters around the room for everyone to view and then presenting their predictions and explanations to the class.

Remind the students the goal of a *Solution Briefing* is for everyone to hear how other students approached the problem and to see how a variety of solutions might work. Emphasize that after listening to all the solutions, the class will discuss the weather on *Planet X* and come to some agreement on what they think the weather might be like on *Planet X*.

Let students know where to display their posters and have groups visit each poster for about one minute or so. Emphasize to students they should begin preparing questions for each poster. Let them know if they are not answered during the groups' presentation, then they should ask questions to the group.

☐ Assess

Decide features of each poster that should be discussed during class discussion and prepare questions you may have for each group.

△ Guide and Assess

Have each group present their predictions and explanations to the class. Remind students to take notes during each presentation using their *Solution Briefing Notes* page. Have a class discussion on each presentation. Discuss the similarities and differences in weather predictions between presentations. Spend time comparing locations in close proximity to each other.

Locations near water may show land and sea breezes. These locations may have more severe storms or more rainfall during spring and fall when water and land temperatures change. Locations with warm air masses moving north or south from the equator and colder air masses moving west may have more rain and storms.

After all groups have presented, have a discussion on the similarities and differences between predictions and explanations. Ask students if they think any of the predictions or explanations should be revised. Allow time for students to revise their predictions or explanations.

△ Guide

Remind students that in *Learning Set 5* they made recommendations to the *CSA* for one location they thought would be a good place to create a colony and one location they thought would be a bad place to create a colony. Let groups know they should make predictions about the weather patterns for these two locations.

◯ Get Going

Let students know how much time they have and let them begin.

Guide and Assess

Monitor students. If students are having difficulty, try to have them match up similar locations between their recommended selections and similar locations on *Planet X* or on Earth.

Recommend
10 min.

Students apply weather predictions to the locations they recommended to the CSA.

Explain

10 min.

Groups construct explanations to support their weather predictions.

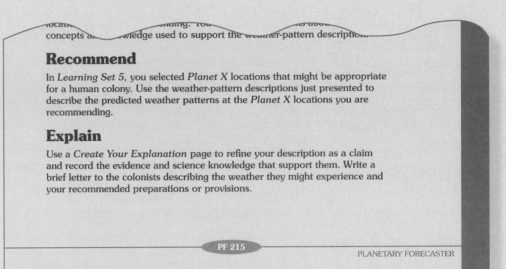

concepts a... ...wledge used to support the weather-pattern description...

Recommend

In *Learning Set 5*, you selected *Planet X* locations that might be appropriate for a human colony. Use the weather-pattern descriptions just presented to describe the predicted weather patterns at the *Planet X* locations you are recommending.

Explain

Use a *Create Your Explanation* page to refine your description as a claim and record the evidence and science knowledge that support them. Write a brief letter to the colonists describing the weather they might experience and your recommended preparations or provisions.

PF 215

PLANETARY FORECASTER

△ Guide

Let groups know they should construct explanations to support the claims of their weather predictions and revise their previous claims for their recommended locations. Emphasize that groups should also write a letter to the colonists describing the weather they might experience along with the group's recommendation of what to bring to prepare.

Describe to students what they should explain and what should be in the letter to the colonists that they should write.

TEACHER TALK

"You should write your explanation using a *Create Your Explanation* page to help support your claims about the weather patterns for the locations you recommended. Include any information about severe or extreme weather as well. You will need to write a letter to the colonists describing the type of weather you expect them to experience along with your recommendations of what preparations or provisions they will need."

What's the Point?

You have just explored factors that cause weather. From that information, you have written a description of what you predict the weather patterns to be like at the *Planet X* locations you are recommending. Now you have all the recommendations and supporting evidence to share with the CSA and your classmates.

NOTES

Address the Big Challenge II: Final Recommendations

Which Regions of a Newly Discovered Planet Have Surface Temperatures Appropriate for a Human Colony?

◀ *1 class period*

A class period is considered to be one 40 to 50 minute class.

Overview

Students prepare their final recommendations for a location on *Planet X* to colonize. After each group presents their recommendations and their explanations of how each factor affects surface temperature and weather conditions, students select two or three locations they think are best to build a colony on.

Targeted Concepts, Skills, and Nature of Science	Performance Expectations
Scientists often work together and share their findings. Sharing findings makes new information available and helps scientists to refine their ideas and build on others' ideas. When another person's or group's idea is used, credit needs to be given.	Students should work with their group members to make their final recommendations. Groups should present their recommendations to the class and students should select two or three locations they think are best to colonize.
Scientists must keep clear, accurate, and descriptive records of what they do so they can share their work with others and consider what they did, why they did it, and what they want to do next.	Students should use their previous records to prepare their final recommendations to the *CSA*. Students should prepare a presentation of their records to share with the class.
Graphs, maps, and tables are an effective way to analyze and communicate results of scientific investigation.	Students should use and/or prepare maps, tables, and graphs to present their recommendations to the class.

647

Targeted Concepts, Skills, and Nature of Science	Performance Expectations
Explanations are claims supported by evidence, accepted ideas and fact. • The intensity of light on an object depends on its shape and the angle it strikes the object at. As the curvature of the object's surface increases, the angle at which the light strikes increases and the intensity of light on the object decreases. • The average amount of solar energy that strikes Earth's surface over a year is highest near the Equator and the intensity of the solar energy that strikes the surface decreases as you move farther away from the Equator, whether you are moving north or south. • Earth makes one complete rotation every day about its axis that is tilted with respect to the Sun. It takes a year for the planet to revolve around the Sun. • Earth's tilted axis causes differences in how solar energy strikes its surface as it moves in an orbit around the Sun. • Seasons experienced on Earth are caused by its rotation on a tilted axis. The tilt causes either the Northern or Southern Hemisphere to have more direct sunlight and an increase in the exposure time to the Sun, creating summer conditions. The other hemisphere receives less direct sunlight and less exposure time to the Sun and experiences winter. • Different substances (such as soil and water) transfer heat energy at different rates and require different amounts of energy to raise their temperatures. The amount of energy needed to raise the temperature of a substance is described by its specific heat capacity.	Students should construct explanations of how the four factors affect surface temperatures, and weather conditions, which support their recommendations for a location to be used as a colony site and a location that should not be used as a colony site. Students' explanations and recommendations should contain the application of ideas in the Unit.

Targeted Concepts, Skills, and Nature of Science	Performance Expectations
Explanations are claims supported by evidence, accepted ideas and fact. • The atmosphere is made up of molecules. The density and pressure of air decreases with increasing elevation. • Surface temperature changes with changes in elevation and air pressure. As elevation increases, the air pressure and temperature decrease. As the pressure increases the temperature increases. • When an air mass is warmed, it pushes the surrounding air out of the way, rises, expands, and cools in the process. Cooler air masses take its place as it rises, and then they are warmed and rise. This is one way that heat is transferred through the atmosphere by convection. • Temperatures around the Earth's surface vary widely, but can be predicted somewhat by location and season. • Energy from the Sun drives Earth's water cycle. Water moves between different physical states in a continuous cycle of evaporation, condensation, and precipitation. • Water changes state (solid, liquid, gas) by adding or removing heat energy. • Wind results from the Sun's energy heating Earth. Solar energy heats the molecules of air and creates areas of high and low pressure. Wind is created as air molecules move from high to low-pressure areas. This is affected greatly by landforms and water on a local scale. • Changes in weather are caused when air fronts of different temperatures interact with each other. The different pressures of the fronts cause air masses to move and create precipitation and other forms of weather. Special conditions are needed to develop storms, tornadoes, and hurricanes.	Students should construct explanations of how the four factors affect surface temperatures, and weather conditions, which support their recommendations for a location to be used as a colony site and a location that should not be used as a colony site. Students' explanations and recommendations should contain the application of ideas in the Unit.

649

Materials	
1 per group	Computer with *My World* software and printer
	Blank copies of *Planet X* map
	Presentation materials
1 per class	Class *Project Board*

Activity Setup and Preparation

Have all materials and computers ready and available for students to use. Consider how you will have students print out final shape, tilt, land/water differences, and elevation habitability maps and weather maps ahead of time, or have this information available on the computers.

Decide how you will have students present their final recommendations. Students could project maps using a computer projection system or by projecting printed maps. Students could also create presentation boards.

Homework Options

Reflection

- **Science Content:** What surprised you when you were studying the four factors *(shape, tilt, land and water differences, and elevation)* and why? *(The purpose of this question is to have students reflect on what they learned.)*

- **Science Process:** What other factors do you think might affect surface temperatures? Select one of the factors you listed and describe how you could determine how it affects surface temperatures? *(Students should describe how they would design an experiment and observe a relationship between the factor they selected and the surface temperature.)*

Address the Big Challenge II:
Final Recommendations

Which Regions of a Newly Discovered Planet Have Surface Temperatures Appropriate for a Human Colony?

You have discovered how elevation, land and water differences, tilt, and shape affect surface temperatures at different locations on Earth. You have selected *Planet X* locations that would be appropriate for a human colony and predicted possible weather patterns for that location.

This challenge has given you the opportunity to investigate a natural phenomenon using the same steps a scientist might use. You asked questions and gathered information to answer them. Class discussions around the *Project Board* helped you identify things you know and new questions to explore. The *Project Board* has also helped you keep track of your progress. You should have all the information you need to now prepare and share final recommendations.

TO: Scientific Research Team
FROM: The Cooperative Space Agency
SUBJECT: Request for Final Recommendation

Several colonization teams are in training to prepare for this exciting mission. The CSA would like to provide them with information about expected surface temperatures on *Planet X* and the colony locations you are recommending.

Prepare a report that summarizes what you have found out about the factors that affect surface temperature on *Planet X*. Be sure to include supporting data and maps that can be used to inform the colonization teams.

Explain why your group thinks the areas you selected have appropriate surface temperatures for the colony. This information will help the team plan and prepare. The report should also include a description of possible weather patterns at each of these locations.

The CSA is confident that your *Planet X* colony location recommendations will be well received. You used what you discovered about the surface temperature factors to guide your recommendations. The CSA would also like your assistance in narrowing the list of recommended colony locations.

Thank you for your efforts in conducting this critical investigation for this mission. We look forward to receiving your final report and recommendations.

PF 217

PLANETARY FORECASTER

Address the Big Challenge II: Final Recommendations

Which Regions of a Newly Discovered Planet Have Surface Temperatures Appropriate for a Human Colony?

< 5 min.

Review what students have completed and introduce the section.

META NOTES

The *Project Board* should contain all the information necessary for completing the challenge.

△ Guide

Display the class *Project Board* and review with the class what they have done so far. Emphasize the four factors they studied (shape, tilt, land and water differences, and elevation) and how they affect surface temperatures. Consider having students briefly summarize these. Review the factors that affect weather and consider having students summarize these. Then have the class read the bulletin from the *CSA*.

Communicate Your Solution:

Solution Showcase

30 min.

Students prepare and present their final recommendations.

Communicate Your Solution

Solution Showcase

It is time to organize and present your final recommendations for the locations of the new colony on *Planet X*. Each group may organize its presentation differently, but it must include all of the following:

• A title, such as "Colonization Recommendation for *Planet X*"

• A statement of your group's final explanation for each factor–shape, tilt, land and water differences, and elevation.

• For each factor, you must include the temperature prediction map you made and any other evidence you choose. Be sure to explain how and why each factor affects surface temperatures.

• A blank map of the new planet, with habitable and non-habitable locations marked, that you prepared in *Learning Set 5*.

• Explanations for why your group thinks the areas you selected are habitable or non-habitable. Match each explanation with the location on the map using symbols, numbers, or arrows.

• Descriptions you created in *Learning Set 6* of the weather patterns colonists might expect at each of the recommended locations.

When each group has completed its work for the presentation, you will share your recommendations and explanations with the class as other groups make their presentations, observe and listen carefully. Think about how their recommendations are similar to or different from yours. Think about whether there is evidence that would have strengthened your own recommendations.

As you participate in the *Solution Showcase*, you will be both audience and presenter. Be prepared to answer, and also ask other groups, the following questions:

• Do you think your group made a convincing argument? Why or why not?

• What else could you have included in your presentation to make your recommendation more convincing?

PF 218

Project-Based Inquiry Science

△ Guide

Let students know what is expected in their final recommendations using the information in the student text. Emphasize that students should have previously completed each of the first set of six bulleted items listed in the student text, but they may revise or update the information if they want to.

Emphasize they should be prepared to answer the five bulleted questions listed in the lower section.

- How did the locations of habitable areas selected by your group compare to others? Why do you think there were differences? If there were differences, did the other groups make convincing arguments for why their locations may be better?

- How did the locations of non-habitable areas selected by your group compare to others? Why do you think there were differences? If there were differences, did the other groups make convincing arguments for why the locations they identified were non-habitable?

- How did your descriptions of the weather patterns compare with others?

Recommend

You have now heard several recommendations for appropriate locations for the colony on *Planet X*. As a class, select a short list (two or three) locations that would be highly recommended to the CSA. This will help the CSA narrow their list of possible colonization locations.

PF 219

PLANETARY FORECASTER

◯ Get Going

Let students have the materials they need and let them know how much time they have to prepare their presentations.

☐ Assess

Check that students have all the items from the bulleted list in the student text. Most of these items they have already completed in the *Address the Big Challenge I* and during the *Back to the Big Challenge* in the previous section. Ask groups if they have made any revisions from their previous presentations.

△ Guide and Assess

Have a class discussion after each group presents. Encourage the class to ask questions and check if the class is able to answer the bulleted questions listed for the presenting group.

During discussions, compare groups' results.

Check students' explanations of the four factors using the information in *Address the Big Challenge I*. Check students' explanations for the claims made on the weather predictions they made for the locations they recommended for and against building a colony using the information in the previous *Back to the Big Challenge*.

Each group should be able to justify why one area is more suitable for habitation than another based on temperature data. However, the students may also be able to support their choices based on personal preferences or other needs besides temperature. For example, one landmass has much more gently sloping land available while another has a lake with fresh water. There is not one correct answer. Certainly, some areas should jump out at you as either reasonable or unreasonable.

Recommend

10 min.

The class selects two or three locations they feel are best for a colony.

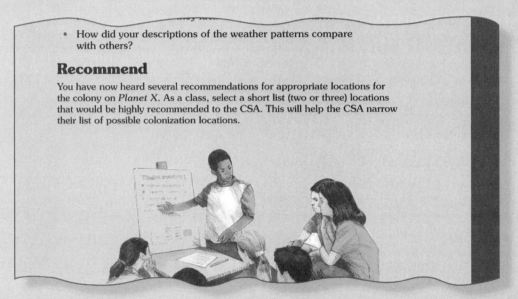

- How did your descriptions of the weather patterns compare with others?

Recommend

You have now heard several recommendations for appropriate locations for the colony on *Planet X*. As a class, select a short list (two or three) locations that would be highly recommended to the CSA. This will help the CSA narrow their list of possible colonization locations.

△ Guide

Let students know they should work as a class to select the top two or three locations for a colony of all the locations that were presented, and explain why they feel these locations are best. As a class, these locations should be suggested to the *CSA*.

Teacher Reflection Questions

- What misconceptions did your students seem to still hold at the end of the curriculum? How did you address those misconceptions?

- Did students see the value in the selecting two to three locations as a class to recommend to the *CSA?*

- What issues arose with the preparation of the presentations? What ideas do you have for next time?

NOTES

META NOTES

In completing this project, students will have gone through several processes that scientists go through when presented with a new discovery or novel problem to solve. A common approach is to compare a new problem to similar problems with existing solutions. Scientists may piece together bits of other solutions to create a new and improved solution. As the students did here, scientists compare their different solutions to a shared problem with their peers and evaluate which solutions are the best and are based on the most solid evidence.

NOTES

Planetary Forecaster Blackline Masters

Project Board

Name: _____ Date: _____

Position of flashlight	Shining on the ball		Shining on the box	
	Distance from top to bottom of the light beam	Brightness of the light beam	Distance from top to bottom of the light beam	Brightness of the light beam
at centerline				
below centerline				
close to bottom				
above centerline				
close to top				

Name: _____ Date: _____

Angle	Brightness of light (less bright or brighter than the previous angle)	Area covered by light (squares)		
		Full squares	Full and partial squares	Average
90°	Initial point of reference			
110°				
130°				
150°				

Name: _____ Date: _____

	Incoming Solar Energy
Latitude	Amount of incoming solar energy (units/m²)
80°N	
60°N	
40°N	
20°N	
0 (Equator)	
20°S	
40°S	
60°S	
80°S	

Change in Incoming Solar Energy				
More direct solar energy (units/m²)	minus	Less direct solar energy (units/m²)	equals	Difference in the amount of solar energy (units/m²)
60°N _____		80°N:_____		
40°N: _____		60°N: _____		
20°N: _____		40°N:_____		
0°: _____		20°N:_____		
0°: _____		20°S : _____		
20°S : _____		40°S : _____		
40°S : _____		60°S : _____		
60°S : _____		80°S : _____		

Create Your Explanation

2.3.1 / 2.5.1
3.2.2 / 4.3.1
4.5.2 / ABCI.1
6.4.1 / 6.BBC.1

Name: _____ **Date:** _____

Use this page to explain the lesson of your recent investigations.

Write a brief summary of the results from your investigation. You will use this summary to help you write your Explanation.

Claim – a statement of what you understand or a conclusion that you have reached from an investigation or a set of investigations.

Evidence – data collected during investigations and trends in that data.

Science knowledge – knowledge about how things work. You may have learned this through reading, talking to an expert, discussion, or other experiences.

Write your Explanation using the *Claim*, *Evidence,* and *Science knowledge*.

Name: _____ Date: _____

Month	Latitudes receiving most direct solar energy	Latitudes receiving least direct solar energy	Latitudes receiving no solar energy at all	Latitudes receiving 24 hours of solar energy
December				
March				
June				
September				

Monthly Temperature Data

Name: _____ Date: _____

Location	Jan.	Feb.	Mar.	Apr.	May	June	July	Aug.	Sep.	Oct.	Nov.	Dec.
Peary Land, Greenland (81°N, 36°W) *polar*												
Helsinki, Finland (60°N, 24°E) *mid-latitude north*												
Atlanta, GA, USA (33°N, 84°W) *mid-latitude north*												
Quito, Ecuador (0°, 78°W) *tropic*												
Darwin, Australia (14°S, 131°E) *tropic*												
Buenos Aires, Argentina (34°S, 58°W) *mid-latitude south*												
Sydney, Australia (34°S, 150°E) *mid-latitude south*												
Mount Seeling, Antarctica (82°S, 104°E) *polar*												

Temperature Range Data

Name: _____ Date: _____

Location	High temperature	Month	Low temperature	Month	Yearly temperature change (high-low)
Peary Land, Greenland (81°N, 36°W) *polar*					
Helsinki, Finland (60°N, 24°E) *mid-latitude north*					
Atlanta, GA, USA (33°N, 84°W) *mid-latitude north*					
Quito, Ecuador (0°, 78°W) *tropic*					
Darwin, Australia (14°S, 131°E) *tropic*					
Buenos Aires, Argentina (34°S, 58°W) *mid-latitude south*					
Sydney, Australia (34°S, 150°E) *mid-latitude south*					
Mount Seeling, Antarctica (82°S, 104°E) *polar*					

Name: _____ Date: _____

Predictions: _____

_____

_____

	Time (minutes)	Sand temperature (degrees C)	Water temperature (degrees C)
	Start		
Heat source on (heating)	3		
	6		
	9		
	12		
Heat source off (cooling)	3		
	6		
	9		
	12		

Use the information in the table to complete the graph. Use one color for the sand data points and a different color for the water data points.

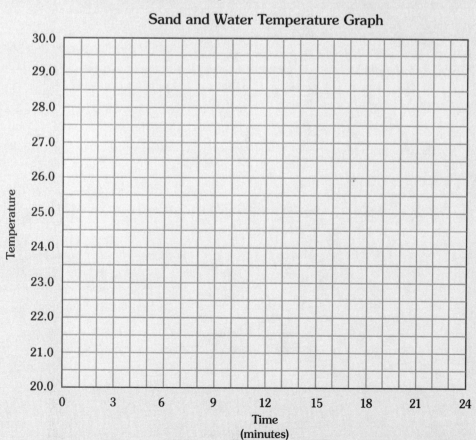

Sand and Water Temperature Graph

Name: _____ Date: _____

Northern Hemisphere Temperatures on January Map (season: _____)

	Overall average (°F)	Land (°F)	Water (°F)	Land difference (=land-average) (°F)	Water difference (=water-average) (°F)
mid-latitudes (30°N-60°N)					
tropics (0°-30°N)					

Southern Hemisphere Temperatures on January Map (season: _____)

	Overall average (°F)	Land (°F)	Water (°F)	Land difference (=land-average) (°F)	Water difference (=water-average) (°F)
mid-latitudes (30°S-60°S)					
tropics (0°-30°S)					

Name: _____ **Date:** _____

January		
Latitude band	**Land difference (land – average)**	**Water difference (water – average)**
30°N — 60°N (winter)		
0° — 30°N (winter)		
0° — 30°S (summer)		
30°S — 60°S (summer)		

July		
Latitude band	**Land difference (land – average)**	**Water difference (water – average)**
30°N — 60°N (summer)		
0° — 30°N (summer)		
0° — 30°S (winter)		
30°S — 60°S (winter)		

Solution-Briefing Notes

Name: _____ Date: _____

Recommendations	How I think the recommendations will work	Changes to recommendations	Science ideas I should use

Name: _____ Date: _____

Record the elevation and temperature data to the nearest whole unit. The last column will be used in a later investigation.

Cell	Latitude (degrees)	Longitude (degrees)	Elevation (meters)	Temperature (°F)	
1					
2					
3					
4					
5					
6					

Graph the relationship between temperature and elevation.

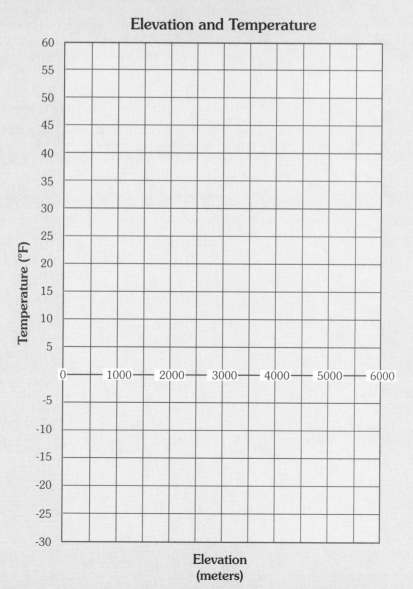

Elevation and Temperature

Name: _____ Date: _____

Find the average temperature for every 1000 m in elevation change.

Elevation (m)	Average temperature (°F)	Temperature change (°F)
0		
1000		
2000		
3000		
4000		
5000		
6000		
Average temperature change per 1000 m		

Calculate the average change in temperature per 1000 m change in elevation.

If you travel _____ above sea level	The temperature changes by:
1500 m	
2500 m	
3500 m	
4500 m	
5500 m	

Name: _____   **Date:** _____

	Squeezability	Mass	Temperature
High Pressure			
Low Pressure			
Change in Pressure			

Name: _____ Date: _____

Factor	Explanation of effect on temperature
Shape	
Tilt	
Land/water	
Elevation	

Project Board

Name: _____ Date: _____

What do we think we know?	**What do we need to investigate?**	**What are we learning?**	**What is our evidence?**	**What does it mean for the challenge or question?**

84 Business Park Drive, Armonk, NY 10504
Phone (914) 273-2233 Fax (914) 273-2227
www.its-about-time.com

Publishing Team

President
Tom Laster

Director of Product Development
Barbara Zahm, Ph.D

Creative Director
John Nordland

Managing Editor
Maureen Grassi

Production/Studio Manager
Robert Schwalb

Project Development Editor
Ruta Demery

Production
Sean Campbell

Project Manager
Sarah V. Gruber

Illustrator
Dennis Falcon

Assistant Editors, Student Edition
Gail Foreman
Susan Gibian
Nomi Schwartz

Technical Art/Photo Research
Sean Campbell
Michael Hortens
Marie Killoran

Assistant Editors, Teacher's Planning Guide
Kelly Crowley
Edward Denecke
Heide M. Doss
Jake Gillis

Equipment Kit Developers
Dana Turner
Joseph DeMarco

Safety and Content Reviewers
Edward Robeck
Barbara Speziale

NOTES

NOTES

NOTES

NOTES

NOTES

NOTES

NOTES

NOTES

NOTES

NOTES

NOTES

NOTES